PEARSON

Investigating
SCIENCE *AND*
TECHNOLOGY

8

PEARSON

Investigating
SCIENCE AND
TECHNOLOGY

8

Senior Author

Lionel Sandner
Science Education Consultant and Writer
formerly Lead Coordinator, Pan-Canadian Science Project

Authors

Nora Alexander
Rosebank Road Public School
Durham District School Board

Mike Carlin
Vice-Principal
Walter Scott Public School
York Region District School Board

Glen Fatkin
North Surrey Secondary School
Surrey School District, BC

Doug Herridge
Greensborough Public School
York Region District School Board

Michael Lattner
Special Assignment Teacher
Algonquin and Lakeshore Catholic District School Board

Catherine Little
Program Coordinator
Science, Environmental and Ecological Studies
Toronto District School Board

Jim Walsh
Instructor, Science and Technology
Faculty of Education, University of Ottawa

Sandy M. Wohl
Instructor, Curriculum Studies
Faculty of Education, University of British Columbia

Contributing Authors

Jay Ingram
Science Journalist
Daily Planet
Discovery Channel Canada

Sandra Mirabelli
Academic Consultant, Literacy, Grades 4–8
Dufferin-Peel Catholic District School Board

Senior Technology Consultant

Josef Martha
Science Education Consultant and Writer
formerly Northern Gateway Public Schools, AB

PEARSON

PEARSON

ISBN-13: 978-0-13-208049-1
ISBN-10: 0-13-208049-4

Printed and bound in Canada

PROJECT MANAGER: Yvonne Van Ruskenveld (Edvantage Press)

DEVELOPMENTAL EDITORS: Nancy Andraos, Tricia Armstrong, Janis Barr, Susan Girvan, Georgina Montgomery, Rosemary Tanner

CONTRIBUTING WRITERS: Erin Khelouiati, Ken Peck

COPY EDITORS: Moira Calder, Louise Oborne

PROOFREADERS: Jennifer Hedges, Christine McPhee, Kari Magnuson

INDEXER: Jennifer Hedges

PRODUCTION COORDINATORS: Sharlene Ross, Shonelle Ramserran

SENIOR MANUFACTURING COORDINATOR: Jane Schell

DESIGN: Alex Li

COMPOSITION: Carolyn E. Sebestyen

ILLUSTRATORS: Kevin Cheng, David Cheung, Crowle Art Group, Jeff Dixon, Jane Whitney

PHOTO RESEARCHER: Terri Rothman

PUBLISHER: Reid McAlpine

MANAGING EDITOR: Cecilia Chan

RESEARCH AND COMMUNICATION MANAGER: Deborah Nelson

This book was printed using paper containing recycled fibre content.

Acknowledgements

Consultants and Reviewers

Program

Marietta (Mars) Bloch
Director, Education Services
Let's Talk Science

Assessment

Derek Totten
Curriculum Consultant
York Region District School Board

Literacy

Sandra Mirabelli
Academic Consultant, Literacy, Grades 4 - 8
Dufferin-Peel Catholic District School Board

Catherine Costello
Education Consultant
formerly Curriculum Coordinator, Literacy
York Region District School Board

Environmental Education

Jane Forbes
Instructor, Science and Technology
Ontario Institute for Studies in Education, University of Toronto

Aboriginal Education

Darin Corbiere
Consultant, Aboriginal Education
Toronto District School Board

Differentiated Instruction

Karen Hume
Student Success Leader
Durham District School Board

Numeracy

Sue Continelli
Grapeview Public School
District School Board of Niagara

Character Education

Dennis Caron
St. Maurice Catholic School
Toronto Catholic District School Board

Leda Ostafichuk
Josyf Cardinal Slipyj Catholic Elementary School
Toronto Catholic District School Board

Mirella Sanwalka
Curriculum Consultant
Science K-12, Environment
York Region District School Board

Raymond Wiersma
Lord Elgin Public School
Thames Valley District School Board

Combined Grades

Maureen Sims
St. Timothy Catholic School
Toronto Catholic District School Board

ELL/ESL

Jane E. Sims
Education Consultant
formerly Sir Sandford Fleming Academy
Toronto District School Board

Maureen Sims
St. Timothy Catholic School
Toronto Catholic District School Board

Safety

Peter Bloch
Northern Secondary School
Toronto District School Board

Expert Reviewers

Ingrid Bajewsky
Nipissing University

Randy Dumont
McMaster University

Marina Milner-Bolotin
Ryerson University

Dr. Nagina Parmar
Hospital for Sick Children (Toronto)

Unit Reviewers

Marietta Alibranti
Bayview Middle School
Toronto District School Board

Chris Atkinson
Math/Science/Technology Consultant
Catholic District School Board of Eastern Ontario

Angela Cule
Highview Public School
Hamilton-Wentworth District School Board

Acknowledgements

Jodie Hancox-Meyer
Doon Public School
Waterloo Region District School Board

Terry Jay
Assikinack Public School
Simcoe County District School Board

Kristina Kernohan
Applecroft Public School
Durham District School Board

Jessica Kotsopoulos
Yorkhill Elementary School
York Region District School Board

Heather A. Mace
Featherston Drive Public School
Ottawa-Carleton District School Board

Audra Morgan
Donview Middle School
Toronto District School Board

Brian Murrant
Regent Park Public School
Simcoe County District School Board

Jette Powrie
Orchard Park Public School
Halton District School Board

Rebecca Ridler
Prince of Wales Public School
Simcoe County District School Board

Allan Savage
Joseph Howe Senior Public School
Toronto District School Board

Jeffrey Schaeffer
Blue Willow Public School
York Region District School Board

Robert Stronach
Annette Street Public School
Toronto District School Board

Casey Wilson
W.G. Davis Senior Public School
Peel District School Board

Susan Wilson
St. Rita Catholic Elementary School
Dufferin-Peel Catholic District School Board

Field-Test Teachers

Chris Atkinson
St. Francis Xavier Catholic School
Catholic District School Board of Eastern Ontario

Jody Bonner-Vickers
J.W. Walker School
Rainy River District School Board

Anne Bradley
St. James the Greater Catholic School
Catholic District School Board of Eastern Ontario

Helen Brown
Gordon B. Attersley Public School
Durham District School Board

Patricia Cava
Sacred Heart High School
Ottawa Catholic District School Board

Brenda Collins
St. Jude Catholic School
London Catholic District School Board

Chris di Tomasso
Sacred Heart Catholic School
Catholic District School Board of Eastern Ontario

Jessica Egelnick
Royal Orchard Middle School
Peel District School Board

Jody Ferdinand
A.J. Charbonneau Public School
Renfrew County District School Board

Heidi Ferguson
Our Lady of Sorrows Catholic School
Renfrew County Catholic District School Board

Alison Fernandes
St. Sebastian Catholic Elementary School
Dufferin-Peel Catholic District School Board

Andy Forgrave
Harmony Public School
Hastings and Prince Edward District School Board

Donna Forward
Sacred Heart Intermediate School
Ottawa Catholic District School Board

David Gillespie
Roland Michener Public School
Durham District School Board

Daniel Green
Ruth Thompson Middle School
Peel District School Board

Jocelyn Harrison
Dixon Grove Junior Middle School
Toronto District School Board

Pat Hogan
St. Francis de Sales Catholic School
Catholic District School Board of Eastern Ontario

Bill Hrynkiw
Nottingham Public School
Durham District School Board

Nizam Hussain
Military Trail Public School
Toronto District School Board

Colleen Hutcheson
Glashan Public School
Ottawa-Carleton District School Board

Terry Jay
Assikinack Public School
Simcoe County District School Board

Matt Johnston
Birch Cliff Public School
Toronto District School Board

Kristi Johnston Bates
St. Michael Catholic High School
Catholic District School Board of Eastern Ontario

Tom Karrow
Wellesley Public School
Waterloo Region District School Board

Kristina Kernohan
Applecroft Public School
Durham District School Board

Irene Kicak
Glenview Senior Public School
Toronto District School Board

Heather Lanning
General Crerar Public School
Toronto District School Board

Jeff Laucke
Rosedale Public School
Lambton Kent District School Board

Nicholas Lemire
Humberwood Downs Junior Middle Academy
Toronto District School Board

Tait Luste
Glenhaven Senior Public School
Peel District School Board

Hugh MacLean
Centennial Public School
Waterloo Region District School Board

Marjory Masson
Earl Beatty Junior and Senior Public School
Toronto District School Board

Irene McCuaig
Lakewood School
Keewatin-Patricia District School Board

Mary Sue McIntyre
Monsignor Michael O'Leary School
Simcoe Muskoka Catholic District School Board

Brian Murrant
Victoria Harbour Elementary School
Simcoe County District School Board

Tom Rhind
Lakewood School
Keewatin-Patricia District School Board

Rebecca Ridler
Prince of Wales Public School
Simcoe County District School Board

Phil Sanders
Northdale Central Public School
Thames Valley District School Board

Rey Sandre
St. Mark Catholic School
Toronto Catholic District School Board

Ryan Seale
Sacred Heart Catholic School
Catholic District School Board of Eastern Ontario

John Starratt
Monsignor Michael O'Leary School
Simcoe Muskoka Catholic District School Board

Corinna Taverna-Rossi
Kateri Tekakwitha Catholic Elementary School
York Catholic District School Board

Stacy van Boxtel
St. Andrew's School
Renfrew County Catholic District School Board

Cathy Viscount
Stanley Park Public School
Waterloo Region District School Board

Janice Whiton
Kateri Tekakwitha Catholic Elementary School
York Catholic District School Board

Raymond Wiersma
Chippewa Public School
Thames Valley District School Board

Craig Winslow
St. Martin School
Niagara Catholic District School Board

Students

The authors and Pearson Education Canada would like to thank all the students who participated in focus groups and field tests during the development of this book.

Acknowledgements

Prepublication Reviewers

Lisa Ackman
Highview Public School
Renfrew County District School Board

Ann-Marie Babineau
D.A. Moodie Public School
Ottawa-Carleton District School Board

Savita Balagopal
Sir John A. Macdonald Middle School
Peel District School Board

Vijaya Balchandani
North Kipling Junior Middle School
Toronto District School Board

Swarnaly Banerjee-Modi
Tomken Road Middle School
Peel District School Board

Janet Bartolini
Humber Valley Village Junior School
Toronto District School Board

Martin Beswick
Princess Margaret Public School
District School Board of Niagara

Shivani Bhagria
Huttonville Public School
Peel District School Board

Marlene Bilkey
Roberta Bondar Public School
Peel District School Board

Tracy Bridgen
Westdale Park Public School
Limestone District School Board

Melissa Brownlow
Earnscliffe Senior Public School
Peel District School Board

Mahlon Bryanton
Beachburg Public School
Renfrew County District School Board

Sukwinder Buall
Elia Middle School
Toronto District School Board

Shayne Campbell
King George Public School
Upper Grand District School Board

Patricia Cava
Sacred Heart High School
Ottawa Catholic School Board

Lenny Chiro
Amesbury Middle School
Toronto District School Board

Michele Chomniak
Abbey Lane Public School
Halton District School Board

Brenda Collins
St. Jude School
London District Catholic School Board

Craig Corbett
Rolling Meadows Public School
Halton District School Board

Rosalie Cross
Blossom Park Public School
Ottawa-Carleton District School Board

Mary Cuylle
Hillcrest Public School
Peel District School Board

Kara Dalgleish
Bellmore Elementary School
Hamilton-Wentworth District School Board

Brett Davis
Queen Elizabeth Public School
Hastings and Prince Edward District School Board

Ian Dawson
Roberta Bondar Public School
Peel District School Board

Veronica Deignan
St. Elizabeth Catholic School
Waterloo Catholic District School Board

Sonia DiCola Kopichanski
Our Lady of Lourdes School
London District Catholic School Board

Nadine Dodds Cormack
W.H. Day Elementary School
Simcoe County District School Board

Seana Donohue
Notre Dame High School
Ottawa Catholic School Board

Kristy Duncan
Lockview Public School
District School Board of Niagara

Sam Falzone
R.J. Lang Elementary & Middle School
Toronto District School Board

Julia Farewell
Camilla Road Senior Public School
Peel District School Board

Jodi Ferdinand
A.J. Charbonneau Public School
Renfrew County District School Board

Heidi Ferguson
Our Lady of Sorrows
Renfrew County Catholic District School Board

Ian Fischer
St. Joseph High School
Ottawa Catholic School

Erika Fleming Gillespie
St. Andrews Public School
Waterloo Regional District School Board

Kim Foley
Perth Road Public School
Limestone District School Board

Donna Forward
Sacred Heart High School
Ottawa Catholic School Board

Michael Frankfort
Thornhill Woods Public School
York Region District School Board

Jeff Fraser
Roberta Bondar Public School
Peel District School Board

Jennifer Freelandt
Immaculata High School
Ottawa Catholic School Board

Lorraine Ganesh
Fairwind Senior Public School
Peel District School Board

Sarah Garrett
King George Public School
Upper Grand District School Board

Krista Gauthier
Rockwood School
Renfrew County District School Board

Fraser Gill
McCrimmon Middle School
Peel District School Board

Mike Glazier
London District Catholic School Board

Kevin Goode
Minesing Central Public School
Simcoe County District School Board

Shaunna Goode
Mount Royal Public School
Peel District School Board

Rob Green
Treeline Public School
Peel District School Board

Akaran Guyadin
The Elms Junior Middle School
Toronto District School Board

Deb Hearn
McCrimmon Middle School
Peel District School Board

Tara Hewitt
Agnes Hodge Public School
Grand Erie District School Board

Marc Hodgkinson
Lorn Avenue Public School
Thames Valley District School Board

Bryan Honsinger
Carleton Public School
District School Board of Niagara

Colleen Hutcheson
Glashan Public School
Ottawa-Carleton District School Board

Wayne Isaac
St. Andrews Public School
Waterloo Regional District School Board

Krista Jarvie
Huttonville Public School
Peel District School Board

Brent Johnston
W.T. Townsend Public School
Waterloo Region District School Board

Kristi Johnston-Bates
St. Michael High School
Catholic District School Board of Eastern Ontario

Darayus Kanga
Hilltop Middle School
Toronto District School Board

Tom Karrow
Wellesley Public School
Waterloo Regional District School Board

Adam Kelly
Greenbank Public School
Ottawa-Carleton District School Board

Gita Khanna
Fisherville Junior High School
Toronto District School Board

Deb Kiekens
Earling Public School
Thames Valley District School Board

Amy Kilty Schwandt
Oxbow Public School
Thames Valley District School Board

Dr. Jean Kisoon-Singh
Mount Royal Public School
Peel District School Board

ix

Brenda Kusmenko
Fairwind Senior Public School
Peel District School Board

Helen Laferriere
Monsignor J.E. Ronan School
Simcoe Muskoka Catholic District School Board

Marilyn Lajeunesse
Monsignor William Gleason Catholic School
Waterloo District School Board

Jean-Benoit Lanca
Immaculata High School
Ottawa Catholic School Board

Chris Lanis
John English Junior Middle School
Toronto District School Board

Bill Legate
Beavercrest Community School
Bluewater District School Board

Natalie Leitch
J.D. Hogarth Public School
Upper Grand District School Board

Andrew Leslie
Hillcrest Public School
Simcoe County District School Board

Steve Logue
Cheyne Middle School
Peel District School Board

Lara Loseto
Walter Scott Public School
York Region District School Board

Andrew Lovatt
St. Thomas Aquinas High School
Catholic District School Board of Eastern Ontario

Heather Mace
Featherstone Drive Public School
Ottawa-Carleton District School Board

Jenn MacKinnon
St. Agnes Catholic School
Waterloo Catholic District School Board

Tracey MacMillian
Herman Street Public School
Renfrew County District School Board

Art MacNeil
McCrimmon Middle School
Peel District School Board

Sean Matheson
Highland Junior High School
Toronto District School Board

Elizabeth Mayock
Harry J. Clarke Public School
Hastings and Prince Edward District School Board

Monica McArthur-Joseph
Erin Centre Middle School
Peel District School Board

Rob McBeth
Baden Public School
Waterloo Region District School Board

Cara McCrae
Centennial Central Public School
Thames Valley District School Board

Diana McFarland-Mundy
Queen Elizabeth Public School
Ottawa-Carleton District School Board

Dave McGaghran
Ryerson Public School
Grand Erie District School Board

Mark McKinley
James Strath Public School
Kawartha Pine Ridge District School Board

Chris McKinnon
St. Timothy Catholic School
Waterloo Catholic District School Board

Hugh Mclean
Centennial Public School
Waterloo Regional District School Board

Manish Mehta
Lisgar Middle School
Peel District School Board

Paul Menicanin
Winona Public School
Hamilton-Wentworth District School Board

Cindi Mitchell
Armadale Public School
York Region District School Board

Yvan Moise
St. Paul High School
Ottawa Catholic School Board

Ginny Monaghan
Bristol Road Middle School
Peel District School Board

Luis Morgadinho
Sir John A. Macdonald Middle School
Peel District School Board

Frank Muller
Bristol Road Middle School
Peel District School Board

Katie Muller
Gateway Public School
Upper Grand District School Board

Trevor Ormerod
Elementary Instructional Resource Teacher
Peel District School Board

Johanna Pastma
Caistor Central Public School
District School Board of Niagara

Steacy Petersen
Kortright Public School
Upper Grand District School Board

Jennifer Phillips
Humberwood Downs Junior Middle Academy
Toronto District School Board

Elizabeth Piwowar
Sir John A. Macdonald Middle School
Peel District School Board

Julie Podesta
Hillcrest Public School
Thames Valley District School Board

Georgina Purchase
Jack Donahue Public School
Ottawa-Carleton District School Board

Rena Ro
Sunny View Middle School
Peel District School Board

Lisa Rome
Hawthorn Public School
Peel District School Board

Michaeline Rowberry
Bristol Road Middle School
Peel District School Board

Ernie Salac
James Strath Public School
Kawartha Pine Ridge District School Board

Shirley Saunders
Hawthorn Public School
Peel District School Board

Tamara Sayers-Pringle
Harry J. Clarke Public School
Hastings and Prince Edward District School Board

Ericka Schroeder
St. Clemens Catholic School
Waterloo Catholic District School Board

Manny Sciberras
John McCrae Public School
York Region District School Board

Clare Shannon
Egremont Community School
Bluewater District School Board

David Shulman
German Mills Public School
York Region District School Board

Denise Stansfield
Sir John A. Macdonald Middle School
Peel District School Board

Trevor Starkes
Ruth Thompson Middle School
Peel District School Board

Corrina Strong
Lisgar Middle School
Peel District School Board

Enzo Tignanelli
St. Luke Catholic School
Waterloo Catholic District School Board

John Tovey
Nobleton Sr. Public School
York Region District School Board

Brandon Tse
Lisgar Middle School
Peel District School Board

Cathy Viscount
Stanley Park Public School
Waterloo Regional District School Board

Dana Wallace
Sir Winston Churchill Public School
Ottawa-Carleton District School Board

Greg Watson
Port Weller Public School
District School Board of Niagara

Corey Wells
Baxter Central Public School
Simcoe County District School Board

Deborah Weston
Lisgar Middle School
Peel District School Board

Lisa Weston Tourigny
Sir Arthur Carty School
London District Catholic School Board

Annie White
Bennetto Elementary School
Hamilton-Wentworth District School Board

Michelle Willson
Courtland Public School
Grand Erie District School Board

Sandy Wilson
Hillcrest Public School
Thames Valley District School Board

Contents

Contents

Contents

Contents

Contents

Contents

Science and Technology Safety Procedures

You will be doing many activities in this book.

When doing an activity, it is very important that you follow the safety rules below. Your teacher may have safety instructions to add to this list. As you read the rules, discuss with a partner or note why each one is an example of common-sense safety.

Before You Begin

1. Read and make sure you understand the instructions in the text or in any handouts your teacher may provide. Follow your teacher's direction always. Never change or start an activity without approval.

2. Watch for "Caution" notes. These notes will tell you how to take extra care as you work through the activity. Make sure you understand what the cautions mean.

3. Learn to recognize the warning symbols for hazardous materials shown in Toolkit 1, pages 367–368.

4. Keep your work area uncluttered and organized.

5. Know the location of fire extinguishers and other safety equipment.

6. Always wear safety goggles and any other safety clothing as requested by your teacher or this book.

7. If you have long or loose hair, tie it back. Roll up long shirt sleeves.

8. Inform your teacher if you have any allergies or medical conditions, or anything else that might affect your work in the science classroom.

During the Activity

9. Report any safety concerns you have or hazards you see (such as spills) to your teacher.

10. Don't eat, drink, or chew gum in your science classroom.

11. Never taste anything in science class.

12. Never smell any substance directly. Instead, gently wave your hand over it to bring its vapours toward your nose, as shown in the photo below.

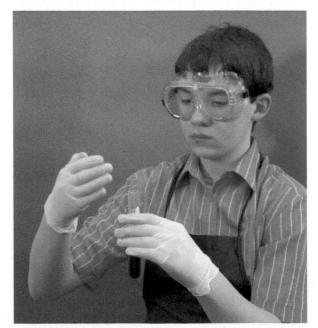

Smell an odour by wafting it toward you.

13. Handle all glassware carefully. If you see cracked or broken glass, ask your teacher how to dispose of it properly.

14. Handle knives and other sharp objects with care. Always cut away from yourself, and never point a sharp object at another person.

15. Heat solids and liquids only in open heat-resistant glass containers and test tubes. Use tongs or protective gloves to pick up hot objects.

16. When you heat test tubes, make sure that the open end is pointing away from you and anyone else in the room. The photo below shows the correct way to do this.

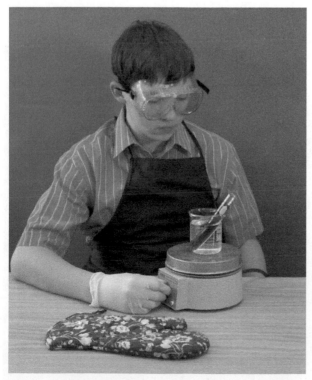

Make sure the open end of the test tube is pointing away from you when you heat it.

17. When heating a substance, make sure the container does not boil dry.

18. If any part of your body comes in contact with a chemical, wash the area immediately and thoroughly with water. If you get anything in your eyes, do not touch them. Wash them immediately and continuously with water for 15 minutes. Inform your teacher.

19. Keep water or wet hands away from electrical outlets or sockets.

20. Use tools safely when cutting, joining, or drilling. Make sure you know how to use any tools properly.

21. Use special care when you are near objects in motion, gears and pulleys, and elevated objects.

22. Make sure equipment is placed safely so that people will not knock it over or trip over it. Report any damaged equipment to your teacher immediately.

23. Treat all living things with respect. Follow your teacher's instructions when working with living things in the classroom or on a field trip.

When You Finish the Activity

24. Make sure you close the containers of chemicals immediately after you use them.

25. Follow your teacher's instructions to safely dispose of all waste materials.

Wear the proper safety equipment when doing science activities.

26. Always wash your hands well with soap, preferably liquid soap, after handling chemicals or other materials. Always wash your hands after touching plants, soil, or any animals and their cages or containers.

27. When you have finished an experiment, clean all the equipment before putting it away. Be careful with hot plates and equipment that have been heated as they may take a long time to cool down.

Learning Checkpoint

Safety Skills

The picture shows a science class performing a science activity. Unfortunately, some of the students are not following proper safety procedures. Work with a partner to identify and list the problem actions. Then suggest a better, safer way to perform each action. After you have finished, share your observations with the class.

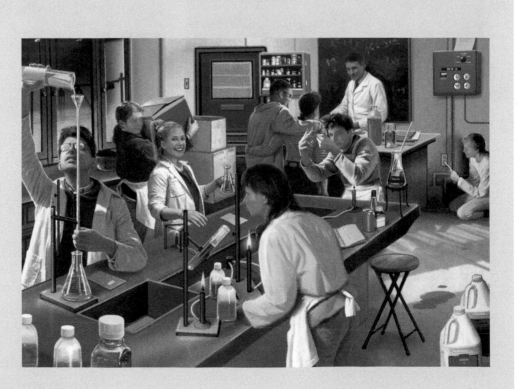

Exploring Your Textbook

Investigating Science and Technology 8

Discover how to use your *Investigating Science and Technology 8* book. Explore the different parts of your textbook by finding the answers to the following questions.

Discover

1. What are the four units you will study in *Investigating Science and Technology 8*?

2. How many chapters are there in Unit A? Each chapter is divided into parts. What are these parts called? How many are there in Chapter 3?

3. Find examples of two different types of reading activities. Where will you find each one?

Learn

1. Where can you find a summary of what you will learn in each section?

2. Find a Words Matter margin feature from Chapter 9 that describes what SCUBA means. What can you learn about in a Words Matter margin feature?

3. When would you use a Learning Checkpoint?

Explore

1. Find the Unit Overview for Unit B. What Big Ideas will you learn as you explore this unit?

2. At the beginning of each chapter you can find a list of key terms. How many key terms are there in Chapter 5? Where can you go to find the meanings of these terms?

3. Find a Take it Further margin feature in Chapter 7 that describes plasma. Where can you go to explore this topic in more detail?

4. For some of the Inquiry Activities, there are symbols at the top of the Materials & Equipment list. Find and sketch three of these symbols and describe what they mean. Can you find a place in your textbook where all of the symbols are explained?

Analyze

1. Look at the Getting Ready to Read feature at the beginning of Unit A. What does it suggest you do to help you read the unit? Find an example of another Getting Ready to Read feature in your textbook.

2. When would you use the Toolkits located at the back of the book? Find an activity that refers you to Toolkit 2.

3. Find an example of a Before Reading Activity at the beginning of a chapter. How could this activity help you to understand the chapter better?

4. Look at the headings for a Chapter Review and a Unit Review. Which headings occur in both reviews? Which headings occur in only one review?

Cindy Klassen's gold-medal efforts are a result of all her cells, tissues, and organs working together at peak efficiency.

Unit Overview

Fundamental Concepts

In Science and Technology for grades 7 and 8, six fundamental concepts occur throughout. This unit addresses the following two:

- Systems and Interactions
- Structure and Function

Big Ideas

As you work through this unit, you will develop a deeper understanding of the following big ideas:

- Cells are the basis of life.
- Cells organize into tissues, tissues into organs, organs into organ systems, and organ systems into organisms.
- Healthy cells contribute to healthy organisms.
- Systems are interdependent.

Overall Expectations

By the end of this unit, you will be expected to:

1. assess the impact of cell biology on individuals, society, and the environment

2. investigate functions and processes of plant and animal cells

3. demonstrate an understanding of the basic structure and function of plant and animal cells and cell processes

Exploring

Mosquitoes feed on the blood of animals. They bite birds, cats, dogs, people, and other animals in their hunt for food to ensure their survival.

When you get a mosquito bite, you may get an itchy red bump where you were bitten. If you live in a country near the equator, you may develop malaria after the bite. If you live in North America, you may develop West Nile virus. If you get sick, you may have a fever or you may ache all over. We now know what is happening to our bodies during all these events. However, until doctors and scientists were able to examine human cells, they had no idea what was causing illnesses.

This unit is about cells, the tiny units that make up human tissues and organs. You will use a microscope to observe the basic structures of plant and animal cells. You will find out how cells function and interact and learn about processes inside cells. You will also assess the impact of technologies that change cellular structures and processes.

Mysterious Deaths

In 1999, there were reports in the northeastern United States of unusually high numbers of dead birds. Similar reports were released in southern Ontario in 2001.

Microbiologists, who study cells, examined the bird carcasses to find out what was happening. They studied blood and tissue samples under their microscopes, and they were able to see a virus in the birds' blood cells. They compared the virus they saw to other known viruses in North America and around the world. Modern technologies such as advanced microscopes, technologies for viewing cells, and electronic communication helped them identify the West Nile virus.

By 2002, people were diagnosed with the virus, and scientists were working to find out how they had become infected. While birds carried the virus, they were unlikely to pass it to humans unless people handled an infected bird carcass. Mosquitoes, which dine on both birds and humans and transfer saliva in the process, were identified as the organisms that transmitted the virus.

Before the development of the microscope and the study of cells, this illness would have been a mystery. People could avoid the carcasses of birds to protect themselves, but it would have taken much longer to realize that mosquitoes were the link.

Twenty percent of people infected with the virus will have a mild fever, a rash, and a headache. Two percent will have much more severe symptoms and, on rare occasions, they will die. The rest of those infected will experience no symptoms at all.

Canadian communities now protect themselves by monitoring mosquito populations, thanks to the knowledge gained from studies of cells under a microscope.

West Nile virus has killed crows, blue jays, chickadees, and robins. By 2007, over 150 bird species were identified as carriers of the virus.

Pools of standing water are ideal places for mosquitoes to lay their eggs.

...MORE TO EXPLORE

One Big Cell

Not all cells are microscopic. You have probably seen this cell in your kitchen at home. It is too big to view with a microscope.

Purpose

To examine a basic structure of a cell.

Procedure

1. Read the following description of an egg.

   The photograph here shows the contents of a single cell. It is a specialized cell for the reproduction of a chicken. The yellow part, called the yolk, is a food source for the developing chicken. The clear, milky part, called albumin, is mostly protein.

   These structures were in a protective covering made up of a hard, outer shell filled with tiny holes and two layers of thin, flexible membrane that also has tiny holes. The shell and the membranes allow air into the egg.

2. Answer the questions as a class.

Questions

1. Do you think the contents of the egg could survive without the protective coating?

2. Most cells are tiny. Do you think they have a protective coating? Explain your reasoning.

This chicken egg is a single cell.

Using an Insecticide

One of the ways to control the spread of the West Nile virus is to use insecticides to kill the mosquitoes. This can be done in a variety of ways. Spraying from the air will kill mature adults, or chemicals can be used earlier in the season to kill the eggs and larvae before they mature.

Consider This

As a class, answer the following questions.

1. What would be the impact on society if insecticides eliminated West Nile virus?

2. What would happen in the environment if mosquitoes were eliminated through the use of insecticides?

UNIT A

Contents

Unit Task

The health of any organism — including you — depends on healthy cells. You are going to learn about cells, including their structure and how they function. Cells are the basic unit of life that few people understand. Your task will be to find an entertaining way to tell people about cells and their importance.

Essential Question

What should people know about their cells?

Getting Ready to Read

Thinking Literacy

Anticipation Guide

The statements in an anticipation guide can help you make sense of information by activating your prior knowledge. Before reading this unit, read each statement in the anticipation guide provided. Circle "Agree" or "Disagree" to indicate your position on each statement. You will revisit the statements in this anticipation guide when you have finished reading the unit to see whether your opinion has changed based on what you have learned.

Red blood cells carry oxygen to all parts of the body. White blood cells destroy infections. Before the microscope was developed scientists did not understand the function of blood and blood cells.

In this chapter, you will:

- explain why cells are considered to be the basic units of life
- identify key organelles in plant and animal cells and explain their functions
- distinguish between the processes of diffusion and osmosis

Skills You Will Use

In this chapter, you will:

- demonstrate the proper care and use of a microscope

Why This Is Important

Organisms are composed of cells. Healthy organisms have healthy cells. In order to ensure good health, it is essential to know more about cells, what they are made of, and how they function.

Before Reading

Thinking Literacy

Skimming and Scanning Text Features
Different reading tasks require different reading styles. "Skimming," or quickly looking across each line of text, gives an idea of the subject matter and if it will be useful. Skim the headings in chapter 1. Will it help you prepare microscope slides?

To find a specific word or piece of information, "scanning" by looking down or diagonally across the page will be more useful. Scan chapter 1 for new vocabulary words.

Key Terms

- cell theory
- eyepiece
- organelle
- selective permeability
- diffusion
- membrane
- osmosis
- stage

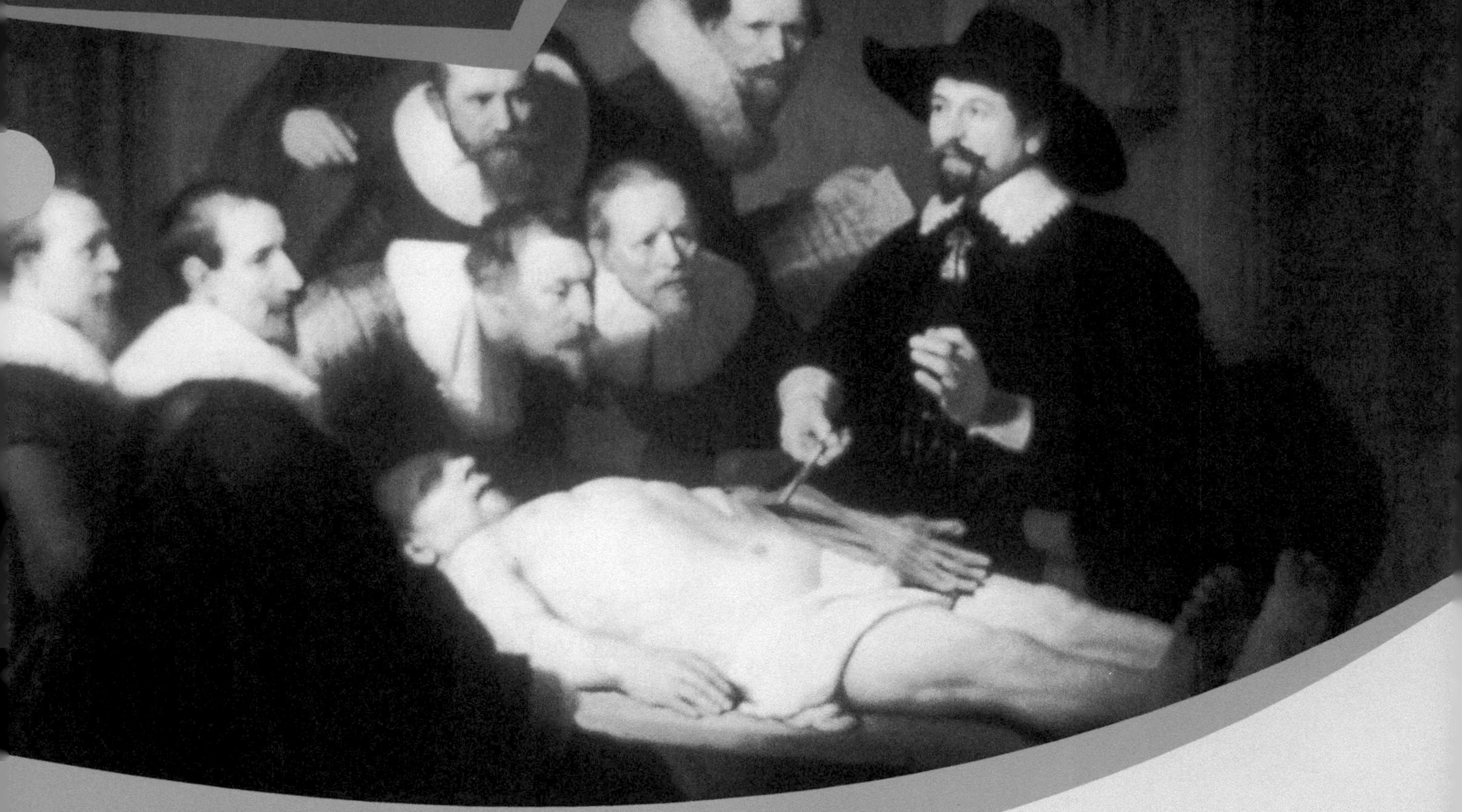

Figure 1.1 This painting, which shows an early anatomy lesson, was painted in 1632. In the Netherlands, in those days, one dissection each year was a public one, and spectators could pay a fee to watch the proceedings.

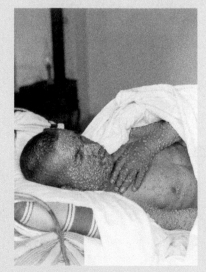

Figure 1.2 Smallpox was once a deadly disease that killed millions of people. After the microscope was developed, doctors were able to find out what was causing the disease and find a way to control it.

Living things need a suitable habitat that supplies their basic needs for oxygen, food, and water. They convert energy with these resources and carry out a variety of activities. Early doctors and scientists could only guess at how living things carried out these activities. They studied whole plants and animals, including humans, in an effort to find out. They were very curious about how living things worked. They also needed to know how organisms like the human body worked in order to treat diseases and injuries (Figure 1.2).

As early scientists continued their inquiries, they began to cut dead organisms into smaller parts in an effort to see what was inside. They looked at organ systems and individual organs such as hearts and lungs. They looked at muscles and brain tissue (Figure 1.1). Scientists began to develop new ideas about how living things worked, but until the first microscopes were built, they had no way of seeing the smallest unit of living things: the **cell**. The cell is the basic structural unit of an organism and the building block of life.

Microscopes gave scientists their first glimpses of cells. As microscopes improved, scientists saw that cells are made up of tiny structures. They now know that these structures cannot work independently. Cell structures must work as part of the cell unit to carry out activities.

The chicken egg cell you examined in Activity A1 was big, and ostrich eggs are even bigger, but most cells are incredibly small. Most are much smaller than 0.5 mm, which is about the size of the period at the end of this sentence. This is why microscope technology is essential for the study of cells.

Figure 1.3 There are a number of living and non-living things in this scene.

Defining Living Things

In grade 7 you learned that biotic elements — living things — need oxygen, food, water, energy, and a suitable habitat. You can expand this explanation by listing common characteristics of all forms of life.

Purpose

To develop definitions of living and non-living things

Procedure

1. With a partner, create a T-chart with the headings "Living" and "Non-living."

2. Together, think about things that are living, and list the characteristics or features that these things have. For example, you might say that living things grow.

3. List characteristics or features of non-living things on the other side of your T-chart.

4. With scissors, cut your chart in half. One partner will take the living list, and the other will take the non-living list.

5. Each partner will form a group with two other classmates who have the same half of the chart.

6. As a group, write a definition of a living or non-living thing.

7. As a class, combine group definitions of living and non-living things, and create a generally accepted definition of each.

Questions

8. The method used by you and your classmates to define a living thing is similar to the method used by scientists. They also created and collected ideas, and then discussed and edited them until they had an acceptable definition. Despite this, a simple definition of life does not exist in the scientific community. Not every scientist is happy with the accepted definition. Is there a portion of your class definition that you think could be explained better? How?

9. What do you think a scientist would need to do if he or she disagreed with a generally accepted definition?

Here is a summary of what you will learn in this section:

- Living things are made of cells.
- Scientists knew very little about cells before the microscope was developed.
- Cell theory is a way to describe the nature of cells.

Living things are all shapes and sizes. They can be plants or animals. They can live in a variety of habitats — from the tops of mountains to deep in the ocean. They have common basic needs, and they are all made up of cells.

In order to study these living things, scientists needed to be able to see them more clearly. There are written references to the use of some type of magnifier almost 2000 years ago. However, technological advances in both glass making and the grinding of lenses were required before magnification could be improved. Lenses for eyeglasses became available around the end of the 13th century. Lens makers became more skilled at grinding lenses as the demand for eyeglasses increased.

The earliest microscope was a tube with a single lens at one end and a plate for the object at the other. The magnification was 10 times the actual size of the object.

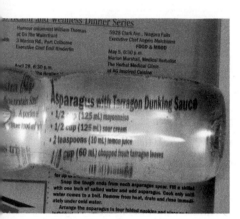

Figure 1.4 You can make a simple magnifier with a water-filled bottle.

A4 *Starting Point*

Skills Ⓐ Ⓒ

Make Your Own Magnifier

When light passes through a curved surface, it bends slightly. As a result, the image we see of the object beyond the curved surface seems larger than the actual object. This knowledge enabled people to magnify small objects. You can experiment to make your own magnifier.

1. Place a large drop of water on a microscope slide. Move the slide carefully to view the writing on a piece of newspaper.

2. Place a large drop of water on a clear overhead sheet. Move the sheet carefully over a piece of newspaper to view the writing on it.

3. Fill a test tube with water, and fit a stopper in it. Turn it sideways, and read through the test tube.

4. Fill a clear plastic bottle with water, and secure the cap. Turn it sideways, and read through the water-filled bottle (Figure 1.4).

Microscopes and Cell Theory

Since most cells are too small to see with the unaided eye, the existence and structure of cells remained unknown until the late 1600s. It was Antony van Leeuwenhoek (1632–1723) who built what is thought to be the first successful light microscope (Figure 1.5). Van Leeuwenhoek had taught himself how to grind and polish lenses in order to make his own magnifiers. Eventually, he made tiny lenses that could magnify an object up to 270 times. With this tool and a lot of curiosity, he uncovered the mysteries of the microscopic world. He was the first person to see bacteria cells, yeast cells, and blood cells. He also observed the variety of life in a drop of pond water.

The Basic Ideas of Cell Theory

The scientists who came after van Leeuwenhoek used increasingly effective microscopes. Over time, their discoveries led to the following key ideas of the **cell theory**.

1. The cell is the basic unit of life. In other words, the cell is the smallest living organism that shows the characteristics of living things.

2. An organism can be as simple as one cell (unicellular), like a paramecium, or it can be made up of trillions of cells (multicellular), like an elephant.

3. All cells are created from existing cells through a process called **cell division** by which a cell divides into two new cells.

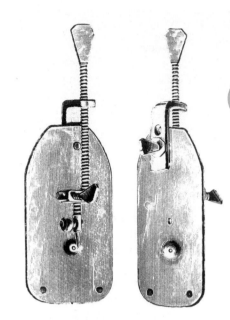

Figure 1.5 Antony van Leeuwenhoek built one of the first successful light microscopes.

A5 *During Reading*

Thinking
Literacy

Reading like a Writer

Textbook writers include a variety of text features to help the reader navigate the text more easily. As you read pages 13 and 14, record any scientific vocabulary you encounter. Compare the different ways scientific vocabulary is presented on these pages. Why might the writer have chosen different ways to highlight these specialized words? How does the "Words Matter" feature help you with the scientific vocabulary presented on these pages? What other text features do textbooks contain that help readers make sense of specialized vocabulary?

The Compound Light Microscope

A **compound light microscope** uses light focussed through several different lenses to form a magnified image of a specimen. A modern compound microscope, like the one shown in Figure 1.6 below, is a delicate and expensive instrument and needs to be handled with care.

Eyepiece or ocular lens This is the lens that magnifies the specimen, usually by 10 times (10x). This is the lens you look into.

Coarse adjustment knob This knob moves the stage up or down to focus on the specimen. This is the first knob you use to focus on a specimen.

Fine adjustment knob Use this lens to sharpen an image under low and medium power. It is the only adjustment knob needed with the high-power lens.

Revolving nosepiece This is where the objective lenses are mounted. Rotate the lens to select low-, medium-, or high-power lenses.

Objective lenses There are three lenses that magnify the specimen: low-power (4x), medium-power (10x) and high-power (40x). Keep the lenses free of dirt and fingerprints.

Stage This is where you place a slide for observation. Always keep the stage dry.

Stage clips These are used to hold a slide in position on the stage.

Diaphragm This has different-sized holes that let different amounts of light pass through the specimen on the stage.

Lamp The lamp supplies the light that passes through the specimen on the stage. Microscopes that do not have a lamp may have a mirror to collect and direct light.

10 Arm The arm holds the tube in place and is used to carry the microscope.

11 Base This provides a stable platform for the microscope. Always set it on a flat, dry, uncluttered surface.

12 Tube The tube separates the ocular lens from the objective lenses at a distance calculated for proper magnification.

13 Condenser lens This lens is under the stage. It helps focus light onto the specimen on top of the stage.

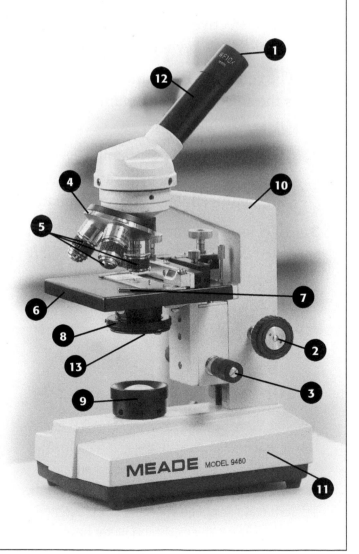

Figure 1.6 This compound light microscope is typical of the ones found in many science classrooms.

Care and Use of a Microscope

When used correctly, microscopes are powerful scientific tools. They are also expensive and delicate. Refer to Toolkit 9 before you follow the steps below to use them safely and effectively.

Purpose

To use a microscope correctly and follow safe laboratory procedures

Materials & Equipment

- compound light microscope
- lens paper
- prepared microscope slides

Procedure

1. Make sure you have a clear, clean, dry, flat work surface for the microscope. If the microscope has a plug, position the microscope so that it is close to the outlet.

2. Use two hands to carry the instrument — one hand on the base and the other on the arm.

3. Use lens paper to clean the lenses. *Never* touch the lenses with your fingers.

4. Rotate the revolving nosepiece until the low-power lens clicks into place.

5. View the microscope from the side. Turn the coarse adjustment knob until the low-power lens is about 1 cm from the stage. It will stop at the correct position. Do not force it.

6. Look through the ocular lens. Adjust the diaphragm until it is as bright as possible.

7. Place a prepared slide on the stage, and secure it with the stage clips. Check to make sure the object on the slide is centred over the hole in the stage.

8. Look through the ocular lens.

9. Slowly turn the coarse adjustment knob to bring the object into focus. The image should be very clear. If it is not, use the fine adjustment knob to make the image sharper.

10. Without adjusting the focus, rotate the revolving nosepiece until the medium-power lens clicks into place.

11. Use the fine adjustment knob to sharpen the image.

12. View an object and at the same time move the slide left, then right, then up, and then down. Describe what happens to the image.

Questions

13. Refer to Drawing Hints in Toolkit 9 to help you draw and label the images you see under the microscope. Draw sketches of two of the specimens you viewed. How are they the same? How are they different?

Figure 1.7 The coarse adjustment knob moves the stage up or down.

Figure 1.8 The fine adjustment knob brings the object into sharper focus.

Key Concept Review

1. In your own words, restate the three key ideas about cell theory.

2. Create a chart listing the names of the parts of a microscope on the left-hand side and the functions of each part on the right-hand side. Your chart should have 13 rows.

3. In your own words, define a compound light microscope.

Connect Your Understanding

4. Your classmate is viewing a sample using high power and is about to refocus using the coarse adjustment knob. What would you recommend your classmate do and why?

Practise Your Skills

5. Write up the procedure for bringing a microscope from the storage area to your work space and setting it up.

6. The student in the photo below is using a microscope safely. Name three things she is doing correctly.

For more questions, go to ScienceSource.

A7   *Thinking about Science, Technology, and Society*   STSE

The Importance of Technology in Science

Most technologies are developed to answer a specific need, but they often lead to more questions, more studies, and whole new areas of knowledge. This is the case with the use of lenses to create microscopes.

What to Do

1. Compare the difference in the detail you observed while viewing the microscope slide with your unaided eye and viewing the slide under the microscope.

Consider This

With a classmate or as a whole class, discuss these questions.

2. Do you think it would have been possible to know that living things are made of cells if microscopes had not been developed? Explain your thinking.

3. Do you think that scientific discoveries always require the invention of new technologies? Explain your reasoning.

Here is a summary of what you will learn in this section:

- Plant and animal cell structures are called organelles.
- Plant and animal cells perform some similar functions, such as converting energy and getting rid of wastes.
- Plant cells perform a unique function, which is using energy from the sun to convert carbon dioxide and water into food.

When you first learned to classify living things, the easiest ones to classify were likely the members of the plant kingdom and the members of the animal kingdom. Think of the main differences between plants and animals that you observed and that helped you decide which category the organism belonged to. Scientists decide which is which by dividing organisms into those that can make their own food (plants) (Figure 1.9) and those that must consume other living things in order to get the nutrients they need (animals).

This difference between plants and animals is reflected in the structure of their cells. Plant and animal cells have some similar specialized parts that do the same job. Plant cells also have some unique parts that allow them to transform the Sun's energy into food in the form of sugars.

Figure 1.9 Plants have cells with special parts that enable them to use energy from the Sun to produce food.

A8 *Starting Point*

Skills **A** **C**

What is the magnification?

The size of a red blood cell is about 0.007 mm. A liver cell is about 0.02 mm. The point of a ballpoint pen is about 0.2 mm. The head of a pin is about 1 mm.

What to Do

1. List which of the above items you could see with your unaided eyes.

2. Compare the actual size of a red blood cell with the image shown in Figure 1.10. Estimate how many times it has been magnified.

Consider This

3. When you are looking at a magnified image, is it important to know the magnification? Explain your answer.

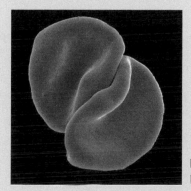

Figure 1.10 Red blood cells

Parts of Plant and Animal Cells

All plant and animal cells contain a jelly-like material called **cytoplasm** in which the parts of a cell float. To keep the cytoplasm together, cells possess a thin covering called a **cell membrane**. The cell membrane acts like a security guard, allowing only certain materials in or out. Floating in the cytoplasm are structures (parts) called organelles. **Organelles** are tiny parts within the cell that have special functions that help the cell survive, grow, and reproduce. Most organelles are contained inside a **membrane** of their own. Organelle membranes keep different parts of the cell separate from one another.

Plant Cells

Figures 1.11 and 1.12 show various organelles and structures typical of plant cells.

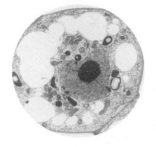

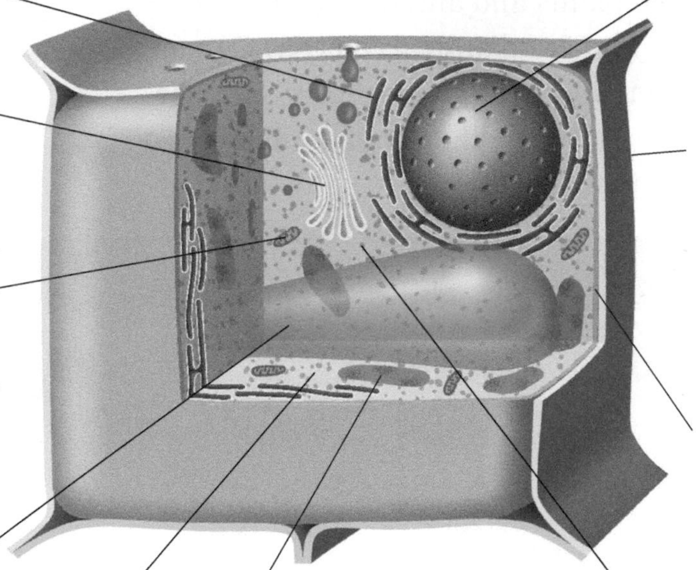

Figure 1.11 Photograph of a plant cell taken through a microscope. It shows chloroplasts (green), cytoplasm, vacuoles (large yellow areas), and the cell wall, among other structures.

endoplasmic reticulum A folded organelle that makes proteins.

Golgi apparatus A folded organelle that combines proteins made by the endoplasmic reticulum and delivers them to the rest of the cell and outside the cell.

mitochondria The powerhouses of the cell. These organelles break down food particles and release their stored energy. The cell uses this energy to fuel all of its activities. Mitochondria are surrounded by a membrane.

vacuole A large, sac-like organelle that stores excess food, waste, and other substances. Each vacuole is surrounded by a membrane.

cytoplasm Jelly-like material that fills the cell and surrounds the organelles. Food and oxygen move through the cytoplasm to the organelles.

chloroplasts Membrane-bound organelles that contain a green substance (pigment) called chlorophyll. In a process called **photosynthesis**, chlorophyll uses the Sun's energy to convert carbon dioxide and water into sugar (food) and oxygen. Chloroplasts are found in plant cells but not in animal cells.

nucleus A large organelle that is easy to see under magnification. It controls the activities of the cell, such as growth.

cell wall Found in plant cells but not in animal cells. The rigid structure that surrounds the cell membrane. It provides the cell with strength and support. Materials pass in or out of the cell through pores in the cell wall.

cell membrane The thin covering that holds the cytoplasm and the organelles inside the cell and controls the passage of materials in or out of the cell.

ribosomes Tiny organelles that help make proteins. There are many of these organelles in the cytoplasm.

Figure 1.12 This is a representation of the key parts of a plant cell. It does not represent all plant cells.

Animal Cells

Figures 1.13 and 1.14 show that animal cells have many of the same organelles that plant cells have. Compare the two diagrams and note any similarities or differences.

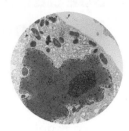

Figure 1.13 Photograph of an animal cell taken through a microscope. The nucleus (pink) takes up most of the cell. Outside the nucleus is the cell cytoplasm (green). The brown bodies at the top of the cell are mitochondria. The cell is surrounded by a cell membrane.

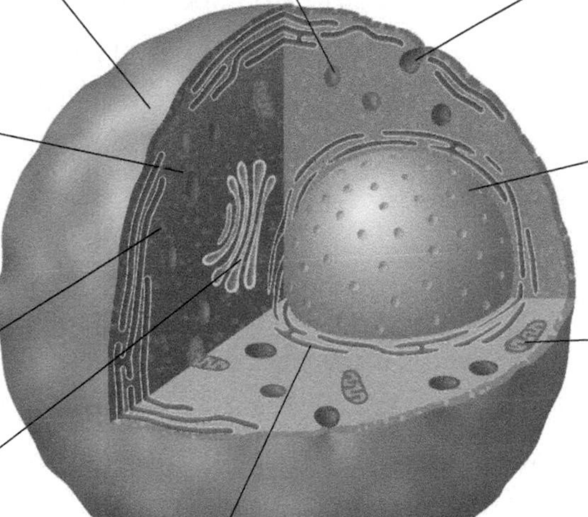

cell membrane The thin covering that surrounds the organelles inside the cell and controls the passage of materials in or out of the cell. The cell membrane is the outer boundary of an animal cell.

cytoplasm Jelly-like material that fills the cell and surrounds the organelles. Food and oxygen move through the cytoplasm to the organelles.

ribosomes Tiny organelles that help make proteins. There are many of these organelles in the cytoplasm.

Golgi apparatus A folded organelle that combines proteins made by the endoplasmic reticulum and delivers them to the rest of the cell and outside the cell.

lysosomes These organelles break down food and digest wastes.

endoplasmic reticulum A folded organelle that makes proteins.

vacuoles Sac-like organelles that store excess food, waste, and other substances. Animal cells have several small vacuoles.

nucleus A large organelle that is easy to see under magnification. It controls the activities of the cell, such as growth.

mitochondria The powerhouses of the cell. These organelles break down food particles and release their stored energy. The cell uses this energy to fuel all of its activities. The number of mitochondria varies according to the function of the cell.

Figure 1.14 This is a representation of the key parts of an animal cell. It does not represent all animal cells.

A9 *During Reading*

Thinking Literacy

Using Headings

Textbook headings are specifically organized to guide a reader's understanding of the information and indicate which topics are connected or related. As you read to the end of section 1.2, pay special attention to the headings and subheadings presented on these pages. In your notes, make a list of these headings as well as the different ways they are presented. Think about colour, type size, and other conventions used to highlight these headings. How does the visual presentation of the headings help you as a reader? Use the headings on these pages to explain the connections among these topics.

Special Technologies for Studying Plant and Animal Cells

When you first looked at cells under a microscope, you were likely looking at prepared slides, and the cells had been stained with a dye such as iodine. The cells and their organelles do not have much colouring, so light passes through them. Without colour or contrast, the organelles are difficult to see. Stains make some organelles visible (Figures 1.15 and 1.16). All of the cells shown in photographs in this text are micrographs of stained cells. **Micrographs** are photographs taken with a microscope.

The preparation of a specimen (sample) for viewing under the microscope involves a variety of steps that depend on the type of specimen. Typically, a very thin slice of the specimen is obtained without damaging the cells. Next, the specimen must be mounted on a slide.

Finally, the cells are stained. Researchers usually choose the type of stain best suited to the cell they are examining. For example, some stains are best for observing blood or bone marrow. Others are for distinguishing cells from surrounding tissues or to make carbohydrates visible.

Stains must be handled with care because some are toxic and others can damage the eyes. The most common stains for student purposes are:

- food colouring, which is non-toxic
- iodine, which is used to detect the presence of starch
- methylene blue, which is used on animal cells to make the nucleus visible

Take It _Further_

Biologists are not the only scientists who use microscopes. Earth scientists such as geologists also use them. Find out what a geologist uses a microscope for. Begin your research at ScienceSource.

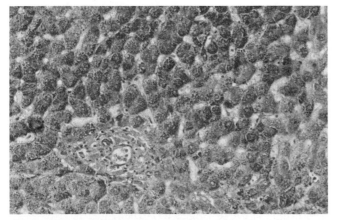

Figure 1.15 These liver cells were stained in order to reveal the organelles.

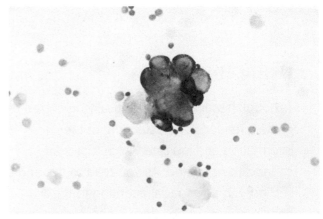

Figure 1.16 A stain was used in this sample to reveal the presence of cancer cells.

Building a Cell

Purpose

To design and construct a model of a plant or animal cell

> ### Materials & Equipment
> - building materials such as recycled objects OR
> - food items such as pasta or breakfast cereal that resemble the organelles they are representing.

Procedure

1. Choose the type of cell you will construct.

2. List the organelles to be represented and the function of each one in a chart.

3. Consider options for materials that will best represent the organelle.

4. Select the best building materials and construct your model.

Questions

5. Add the material you used to represent each organelle to the chart you created in step 2.

6. Justify your choice of materials.

7. What part of your model best represents an organelle? Explain your reasoning.

8. If you had more time or different materials, what would you change in your model? How?

Preparing Dry Mount Slides

Purpose

To learn how to correctly prepare dry mount slides of a variety of non-living things

> ### Materials & Equipment
> - compound light microscope
> - microscope slides and cover slips
> - tweezers
> - threads from different fabrics
> - other samples (e.g., hair, salt)

Procedure

1. Choose a few strands of thread from the fabric samples provided.

2. Place the threads at the centre of a clean, dry slide.

3. Hold a cover slip very carefully by its edges, and gently place it over the threads.

4. View the threads under the microscope using the medium-power lens.

5. With your teacher's permission, make dry mount slides of other samples, such as hair or salt.

Questions

6. Draw and label a sketch of the threads you saw.

7. Challenge your lab partner to figure out what fabric sample the thread on your dry mount came from.

8. Repeat steps 6 and 7 for the other specimens.

Preparing Wet Mount Slides

Prepared microscope slides are convenient to use, but in order to view your choice of specimens, you need to prepare your own slides. In order to view living or moving objects, you must prepare a wet mount.

Purpose

To learn how to correctly prepare wet mount slides of a variety of objects

Materials & Equipment

- compound light microscope
- microscope slides
- cover slips
- tweezers
- medicine dropper
- water
- a newspaper
- homogenized milk
- skim milk (optional)
- other samples (e.g., pond water)

Procedure

1. Obtain a clean, dry microscope slide and cover slip. Place the slide in front of you.

2. Carefully cut a lowercase "e" from the newspaper.

3. Use the medicine dropper to place 1 or 2 drops of water in the middle of the microscope slide.

4. Use tweezers to place the "e" right side up on the drop of water.

5. Hold the cover slip very carefully by its edges, at an angle of about 45° to the surface of the slide. Gently lower the cover slip over the sample. If any air bubbles get trapped, carefully move the cover slip with your finger to free them.

6. View the sample under the microscope. Start with low power and then move to medium power.

7. Make a wet mount of homogenized milk, and view it under medium power.

8. Get permission from your teacher to make wet and dry mount slides of other samples, such as pond water.

9. Draw a sketch of the specimens you viewed. Give your sketch a name and a date.

10. Challenge your lab partner to figure out what your sketch represents.

Questions

11. There are many white blobs visible on the wet mount of homogenized milk. What might these be? Test your theory by making a wet mount slide of skim milk. Draw and label a sketch comparing both milk samples.

12. Why do you think it was important to get rid of any air bubbles?

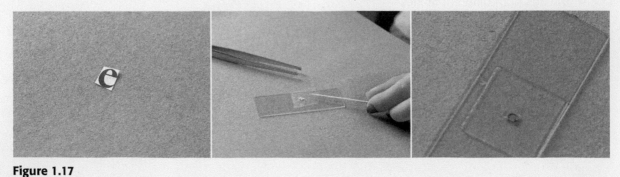

Figure 1.17

Key Concept Review

1. Prepare a chart listing the organelles of a plant cell and their functions. Label the columns in your chart and give your chart a name.

2. Prepare a chart listing the organelles of an animal cell and their functions. Label the columns in your chart and give your chart a name.

3. When would you use a dry mount to view a specimen under a microscope? When would you use a wet mount?

4. What is a micrograph?

Connect Your Understanding

5. Plant and animal cells have some of the same types of organelles. List these organelles, and explain why you think this is the case.

6. Plant cells have some organelles that are different from those found in animal cells. List these organelles, and explain why you think these organelles are needed.

Practise Your Skills

7. You have obtained specimens of a piece of meteorite and water from the pond it landed in. Describe the procedure for preparing to view each of them under a microscope that has been set up.

For more questions, go to ScienceSource.

A13 Thinking about Science, Technology, and Society

S T S E

"Perfecting" Plants

Farmers have saved seeds for crops almost since the beginning of agriculture. They have also experimented with breeding plants in the hope of developing better ones.

Scientists began to assist farmers, and in Canada, research studies led to the development of wheat that could grow in our climate. This success enabled Canadian farmers to become major producers of wheat, an important part of Canada's economy.

Scientists are now able to breed plants that resist insects or can grow better in more challenging conditions. Sometimes the seeds of those plants are engineered so that they cannot develop into new plants. This ensures that

farmers will always buy seeds from the company that paid for the research.

Consider This

With a classmate or as a whole class, discuss these questions.

1. Companies are usually allowed to own the technology they invent. Should companies be able to own technologies that relate to living things? Explain your reasoning.

2. If scientists can change plant cells to improve the world's supply of food, should they be allowed to do so? Who should decide?

The Flow of Materials into and out of Cells

Here is a summary of what you will learn in this section:

- The cell membrane can control the substances that move into or out of a cell because the membrane is selectively permeable.
- Diffusion is a process where substances in areas of high concentration move to areas of low concentration.
- Osmosis is a special type of diffusion involving water and a selectively permeable membrane.

Figure 1.18 On a windy, rainy day only the right type of jacket will keep the wearer warm and dry.

When it is wet and windy outside, you need to wear a jacket that keeps the rain and cold air away from your body. A clothing designer must choose from the few fabrics that have the right properties for a wet-weather jacket. If the jacket is made of cotton, you will be wet and cold. Cotton is **permeable**, which means water and air can pass through it easily.

If the jacket is made of a plastic material, you may still be wet and perhaps cold. Plastic is **impermeable.** Although rain cannot pass through it, you will get hot and sweaty because the air heated by your body cannot escape through the plastic. Then the moisture in the heated air will condense on the inside of the jacket and conduct heat away from your body. The best jacket material keeps the rain out but lets some water vapour pass through. Such material is selectively permeable (Figure 1.18). **Selective permeability** refers to the property of a barrier that allows only certain substances to pass through it.

A14 *Starting Point* Skills Ⓐ Ⓒ

Finding Buried Treasure

A sieve is an example of a selectively permeable membrane. It allows some items to pass through it while other items cannot.

If you lost your ring in a pail of sand, you could use a soil sieve or a kitchen sieve to retrieve it.

Consider This

1. If you were using a sieve to sift through sand to find your ring, what is the most important quality of the selectively permeable membrane you are using?

Cells and Permeability

The cell walls and membranes you see in Figures 1.19a and 1.19b below are selectively permeable. Each structure functions as a barrier that separates the inside of a cell from the outside environment and keeps the cell intact. In addition, these selectively permeable cell structures allow certain substances, such as water, oxygen, carbon dioxide, carbohydrates, and waste created within the cell, to pass through it. Large molecules that may harm the cell are blocked by the membrane or cell wall.

Without selective permeability, the cell would be sealed. It would be unable to access the supply of materials the organelles need to carry out cell activities, and the cell would be unable to get rid of the wastes generated by its activities. Instead, every cell in your body (and in every other organism) is bringing water, food, and gases in and removing wastes at every moment of the day.

This movement of substances into and out of a cell is called **cellular transport**. Cellular transport involves several different processes. Diffusion and osmosis are two types of cellular transport processes.

(a)
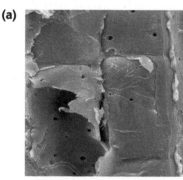

(b)

Figure 1.19 Both plant (a) and animal (b) cells have selectively permeable membranes and walls (in the case of plant cells). Substances such as air and water move into the cells and waste moves out of the cells.

A15 *Learning Checkpoint*

Build a Mind Map

A mind map is an excellent tool to help you remember what you are reading. In the information that follows, you will be introduced to two different forms of cellular transport — diffusion and osmosis. Create a mini-mind map to help you summarize their roles in ensuring the survival of a cell.

Begin by writing "cellular transport" in the centre of a piece of paper. Then build your understanding about the key ideas of diffusion and osmosis. Note definitions, functions, and examples of the two forms of transport as you read through the rest of this section.

Figure 1.20 The smoke from this fire moves through the air by diffusion, dispersing its particles evenly throughout the air.

Diffusion

Diffusion is the movement of particles from an area where there are many of them (a higher concentration) to an adjoining area where there are few of them (a lower concentration) (Figure 1.20). Diffusion continues until both areas have the same number (concentration) of particles (Figure 1.21).

Diffusion happens all around you. Diffusion occurs when you place a tea bag into boiling water to make tea. Diffusion is at work when you can smell the aroma of pizza coming from the kitchen. Everything you can smell is because of diffusion. Diffusion causes the fragrance of cologne or perfume to spread through a room. A classroom is usually not a good place to wear these products because of the effectiveness of diffusion in such a small space, and because some people are very sensitive to fragrances.

For a cell, diffusion is how resources such as oxygen are transported (moved) into it through its selectively permeable membrane. When the concentration of oxygen is lower inside a cell than it is outside the cell, oxygen diffuses into the cell, where it is used by the mitochondria. As the oxygen is used to produce energy, more will diffuse into the cell to keep the concentration almost the same inside and outside the cell.

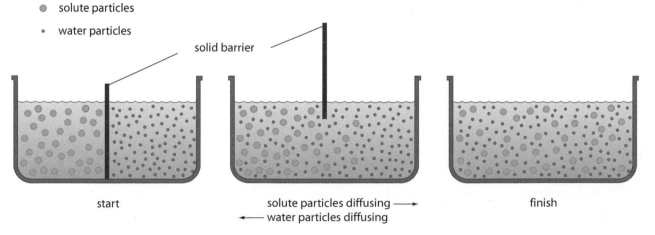

solute particles
water particles
solid barrier

start

solute particles diffusing ⟶
⟵ water particles diffusing

finish

Figure 1.21 The process of diffusion

Osmosis

Osmosis is a special kind of diffusion that involves only the movement of water through a selectively permeable membrane (Figure 1.22). The concentration of water inside a cell must stay fairly constant, and therefore water diffuses into and out of cells continuously. Osmosis (this movement of water into and out of cells) is vital to the cells' survival.

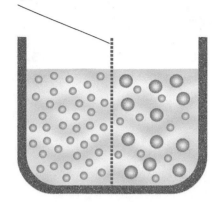

selectively permeable membrane

water particles

solute particles

Figure 1.22 During osmosis, water moves from an area of higher concentration of water to an area of lower concentration of water through a selectively permeable membrane. In the diagram, the water particles move from left to right.

The process of osmosis also depends on the difference in the concentration of particles. In the case of cells, if the concentration of water particles inside the cell is higher than it is outside the cell, water will move out of the cell by osmosis. If the concentration of water particles outside the cell is higher, the water particles will move into the cell.

If you let the soil around the plant dry out, the plant would begin to droop as the concentration of water particles inside the cell dropped. With no water in the soil, there is no water to move into the cells. If you examined the cells in the stem, they would look shrunken. The cell walls would not be rigid, giving the plant a wilted appearance. This process is easiest to detect in plants (Figure 1.23).

If you were to look at one of the cells in the stem of a firm plant under the microscope, you would see that it has a very full shape. The cell has so much water in it that if the thick cell wall were removed, the cell would burst.

Take It *Further*

Bottled water is not pure water. It has dissolved substances in it. Find out more about these substances and how they may help your cells to function properly. Report back to your class. Begin your research at ScienceSource.

Figure 1.23 Osmosis is involved in giving plants the rigidity they need to reach up for sunlight. Compare the drawing of a cell in a wilted plant (left) to the one in the healthy plant.

Diffusion Detective

During diffusion, molecules move randomly as they shift from a high concentration to a low concentration. This activity will allow you to observe diffusion.

Question

Do all liquids diffuse in the same way?

Materials & Equipment

- 3 clean 400-mL beakers or clear glass containers
- water
- electric kettle
- food colouring
- vegetable oil
- tea bag
- medicine dropper

Figure 1.24 Get as close to the surface as possible (within 5 mm) before adding the substance to the water.

Procedure

1. Add approximately 300 mL of water to two of the containers.

2. Add approximately 300 mL of boiling water to the third container. Be careful with the hot water. It can scald you.

3. Carefully hold the food colouring container 5 mm above the surface of the water in the first container, and gently add 3 to 5 drops to the surface of the water.

4. Use the medicine dropper to carefully add 3 to 5 drops of vegetable oil to the surface of the water in the second container.

5. Carefully lower the tea bag into the third container.

6. Do not bump or move the containers or agitate, swirl, or stir the liquid inside them.

7. Observe what happens over a 5-min period.

8. Draw and label a series of diagrams that records what happened in each container.

Analyzing and Interpreting

9. Compare your observations with those of a classmate. In one sentence, describe the pattern of movement you observed for each of the substances added to the water.

10. Did you observe any differences in the way the substances moved in the water? Suggest an explanation.

Skill Builder

11. Do you think the activity was a fair test to compare the diffusion of different substances? Explain why or why not.

12. If necessary, suggest how the activity could be changed to make it a fair test.

Forming Conclusions

13. What factors, if any, do you think might affect diffusion?

Food for Thought

Question

How will plain water and a saltwater solution affect plant cells?

Materials & Equipment

- two 400-mL beakers
- water
- 2 pieces of each food: carrot, celery stalk, raisin
- spoon
- salt
- plastic food wrap

Procedure

1. Fill each beaker with 300 mL of water.

2. Label one beaker A and the other beaker B.

3. Add salt to beaker B and stir. Continue to add salt until no more will dissolve (a small pile will remain on the bottom no matter how much you stir).

Figure 1.25

4. Create a chart to record your observations. In your chart, record the shape of each food item, what it feels like, and what it looks like. Add 1 carrot, 1 celery stick, and 1 raisin to each of your beakers.

5. Cover each beaker with a piece of plastic food wrap. Predict what will happen to each food item in each beaker. Create a chart to record your predictions.

6. Let the beakers sit for a day or less.

7. Record your observations in your chart.

Analyzing and Interpreting

8. How did the plain water and the saltwater solution affect the food items?

Skill Builder

9. Compare your predictions to your results. Discuss any differences.

10. Use words and pictures to show how osmosis occurred in this activity.

Forming Conclusions

11. Should you store plant-based foods in plain water or a saltwater solution? Explain your reasoning.

Key Concept Review

1. Define the term "permeable" in your own words.

2. Use the term "concentration" in a sentence about liquids that conveys its meaning.

3. List three examples of a selectively permeable material or item. Explain where it is found or used and why a selectively permeable material is needed.

Connect Your Understanding

4. If you wrap fresh celery in foil, it will stay crunchy when you store it in the refrigerator. Explain why you think this happens.

Practise Your Skills

5. You need to put a new roof on your house. Describe how you would test possible materials for permeability. What would be the criteria for success?

For more questions, go to ScienceSource.

A18   *Thinking about Science, Technology, and Society*

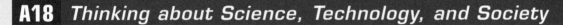

The Artificial Kidney

Your kidneys help filter waste materials out of your blood. If they become damaged, you may need to have your blood filtered artificially. This process is called dialysis.

Dialysis works by using the principles of diffusion and osmosis. Tubing hooks the patient up to a machine, known as a dialyzer, and blood is pumped from one of the patient's arteries into the dialyzer (Figure 1.26). This blood is rich in waste materials.

The compartment in the dialyzer is divided by a selectively permeable membrane. A special dialysis fluid, called dialysate, flows through the dialyzer on the other side of the membrane.

This system can filter the waste materials from the patient's blood. The clean blood is returned to the body by being pumped into a vein.

Consider This

With a classmate or as a whole class, discuss the following questions.

1. A dialysis treatment can take from three to five hours and must be done three or four times a week. Every year, another 2000 Ontarians require dialysis. Should those who can afford it be asked to contribute to the cost? Explain your reasoning.

2. A kidney transplant is an alternative to dialysis. Should people be encouraged to donate their organs for transplant? Explain your reasoning.

Figure 1.26 Patients with damaged kidneys need regular dialysis treatment.

Solving the Mystery of Viruses

Figure 1.28 A skin cell seen under a compound light microscope

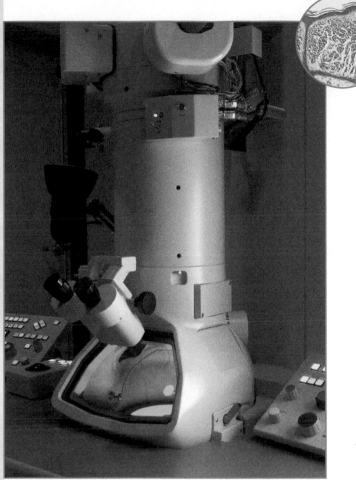

Figure 1.27 Transmission electron microscope

Figure 1.29 Skin cells seen under a scanning electron microscope

Viruses are extremely tiny agents that cause infection. They are smaller than bacteria, and they are unable to grow or reproduce on their own. Instead, they must invade a living cell. They use the resources of the cell to develop and multiply.

Researchers did not see viruses until after the electron microscope was developed in the late 1930s (Figure 1.27). Compound light microscopes are limited to magnifications of 500x or 1000x. This level of magnification did not allow researchers to see the details inside organelles such as the nucleus or mitochondria (Figure 1.28). Nor could they see tiny viruses. In order to see that level of detail, scientists needed microscopes that could magnify objects by 10 000x or more.

An electron microscope uses a focussed beam of electrons instead of light to create an image of a specimen. Magnetic lenses help contain and focus the beam. The interactions of the electrons and the specimen are transformed into an image (Figure 1.29).

Since the mid-1960s, when scanning electron microscopes became more widely available, there have been a number of breakthroughs in the study of viruses. In addition to solving the mystery of how West Nile virus is transmitted, researchers have studied everything from the common cold to the outbreak of SARS (severe acute respiratory syndrome).

Question

1. A compound light microscope costs hundreds of dollars, depending on the model. An electron microscope can cost hundreds of thousands of dollars, depending on the technology supplied with it. Should governments provide funds for researchers to acquire specialized electron microscopes? Explain your reasoning.

Key Concept Review

1. Where is the diaphragm located on a microscope? Explain what it is used for. *k*

2. (a) Identify the type of cell in the diagram shown here, and name all numbered parts. *k*

   (b) Describe the function of the parts numbered 1, 3, 5, and 6. *k*

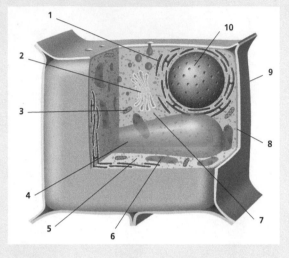

3. Compare and contrast the processes of osmosis and diffusion. Give an example of each. *k*

4. Your teacher has given you a sample of soil to examine. Would you use a dry mount or a wet mount to examine it? Explain your reasoning. *t*

5. If you were looking at a cell specimen through a microscope, how could you tell that the cells belonged to a plant? *t*

6. Use the term "selectively permeable" in a sentence that demonstrates its meaning. *k*

Connect Your Understanding

7. What would happen if cell membranes suddenly became permeable instead of selectively permeable? Could cells remain alive? Explain your thinking. *a*

After Reading Thinking Literacy

Reflect and Evaluate

Brain research indicates that the brain is a pattern seeker. As we read increasingly more complex text, the brain tries to draw on what it already knows about how the text works in order to understand new information.

With a partner, develop a chart to list the text features related to scientific vocabulary that you have encountered in chapter 1. What is the purpose of each of these text features? How does each feature help you as a reader? What other text features did you encounter in chapter 1? Include them in your chart.

ACHIEVEMENT CHART CATEGORIES
k Knowledge and understanding *t* Thinking and investigation *c* Communication *a* Application

8. What would be the impact on the environment if an artificial virus that attacked and destroyed chloroplasts in plant cells was accidently released by a research company? *a*

9. When you put the groceries away, you forgot to put the celery in the refrigerator. When you found it on the counter, it was soft and limp. How could osmosis help the celery? Explain what you would do and why it would work. *a*

Practise Your Skills

10. Describe the steps involved in preparing a wet mount of a specimen. *k*

11. You have mounted your specimen on the stage of the microscope. Describe the process of focussing the lens on the specimen. *k*

12. Describe the steps involved in making a drawing of what you see under a microscope. *k*

13. List three safety steps you must follow when carrying a microscope. *k*

Unit Task Link

Cells are the basic unit of life, and it is important to understand what they look like and how they function. Make a list of the key features of plant and animal cells and describe their function.

A19 Thinking about Science, Technology, and Society

Reverse Osmosis

During osmosis, water moves across a selectively permeable membrane from an area of high water concentration to an area of low water concentration. In other words, pure (100 percent) water will move across a selectively permeable membrane to water that has dissolved substances in it like salt.

During reverse osmosis, water particles are forced to move in the opposite direction — from a low concentration to a high one. High pressure is applied to the low water concentration (usually saltwater) side, and the water particles there are forced through the tiny holes of the selectively permeable membrane. They move to the high water concentration side, and the salt is left behind.

Consider This

With a classmate or as a whole class, discuss these questions.

1. How could this technology be used by shipwreck victims on an island in the ocean?

2. If viruses are smaller than salt molecules, is this filtering method 100 percent safe? Explain your reasoning.

The basic needs of large, small, and microscopic organisms are met at the cellular level.

In this chapter, you will:

- examine unicellular and multicellular organisms
- explain cell specialization
- describe plant and animal cell processes

Skills You Will Use

In this chapter, you will:

- demonstrate the proper use of a microscope
- observe and draw organisms observed under a microscope

Why This Is Important

Living things include unicellular and multicellular organisms. Understanding cellular processes helps us to understand how every organism on Earth — from an amoeba to us to a blue whale — meets its basic needs.

Before Reading

Thinking Literacy

Reading and Interpreting Graphical Text

Writers use graphical text forms such as pictures, diagrams, and charts to communicate information in a concise and visual way. Complex ideas and concepts can sometimes be communicated more easily in a picture or diagram. These visual elements provide important clues to the main ideas and concepts in the written text.

Take a "picture walk" through chapter 2. Use what you see to write a prediction about the main idea of this chapter. Consider how most of these pictures are similar to each other but different from pictures you saw in chapter 1.

Key Terms

- unicellular
- multicellular
- specialized cells
- cell division

2.0 Getting Started

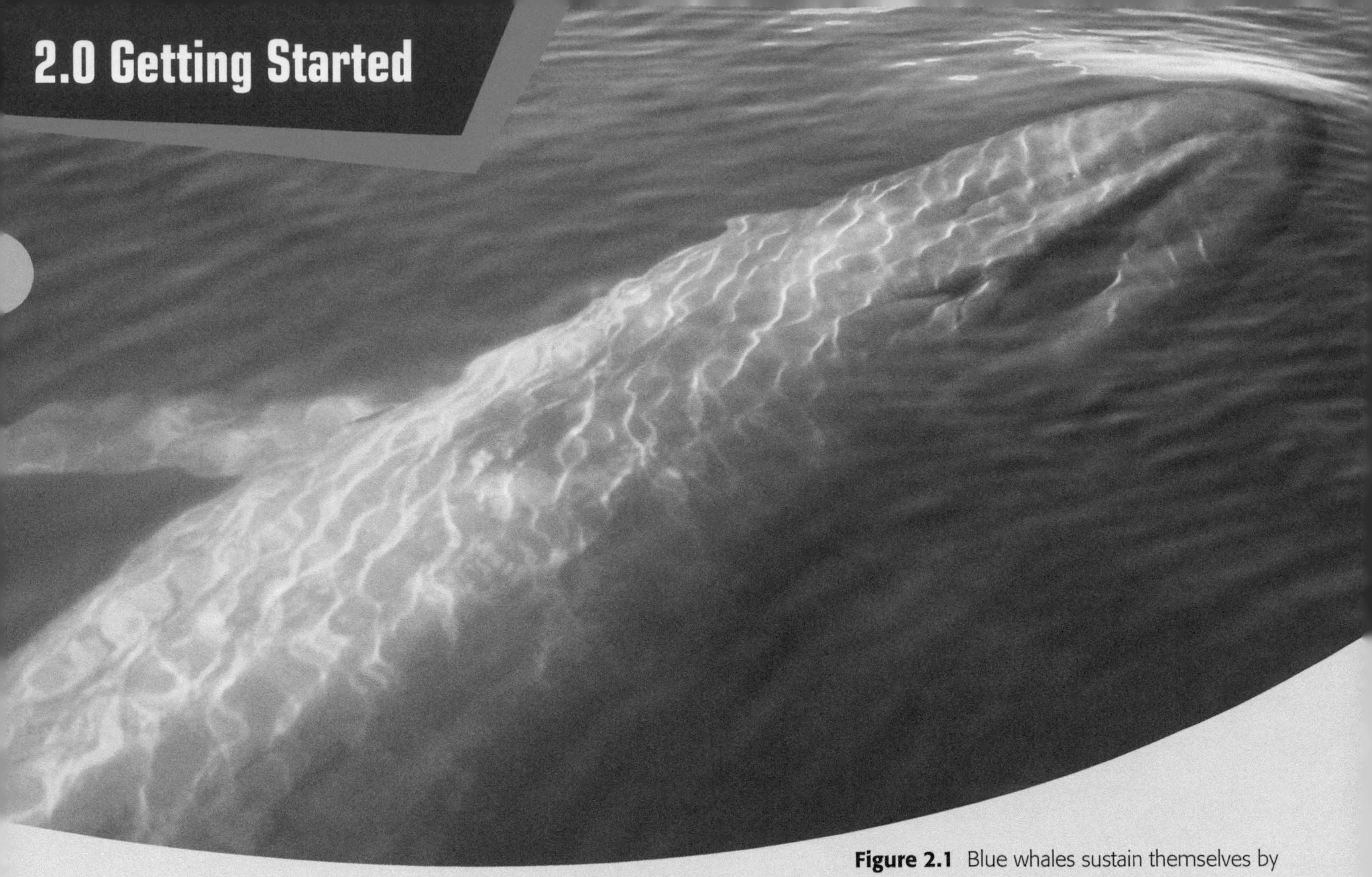

Figure 2.1 Blue whales sustain themselves by eating huge quantities of zooplankton.

The blue whale is the largest type of animal on Earth (Figure 2.1). It can grow to be about 25 m long. An adult often weighs more than 150 tonnes. The whale feeds on zooplankton, which is one of the smallest animals on Earth. The blue whale and zooplankton are just two of the estimated 1.75 million different kinds of living things found on Earth. All living things, whether they are plants, animals, fungi, protists, or types of bacteria, are made of cells. It is the activities of cells that allow each living thing to meet its basic needs.

The obvious structures of the living things you see around you — jaws, teeth, eyes, limbs, and wings or fins; leaves, stems, or roots — may appear to be the means of meeting basic needs. In fact, these structures are working together to supply the organism's cells with the water, oxygen, and nutrients that the cells need to carry out their activities.

The visible structures of organisms may look very different. They make it possible for the organism to get what it needs to live from its environment. They also ensure that the necessities of life are processed to get to the cells. The real work of survival happens within the cells.

The co-ordinated activity involved in getting the oxygen, water, and nutrients to the cells happens without any awareness on the part of the organism. This is true when these activities take place in your own body. While you may taste the food you eat, or notice that the water you drink is hot or cold, you rarely breathe consciously. Once the oxygen, water, and food are inside your body, the various parts of your body take care of the processing. You are unlikely to notice any of this activity unless something goes wrong. Yet without it, you would not be able to survive.

A20 *Quick Lab*

Meeting Basic Needs for Survival

Living things must perform certain functions in order to stay alive. These functions may include moving, responding to stimuli, gathering food, taking in oxygen, and building a home.

Purpose

To decide what structure each organism uses to perform the activities that keep it alive

Materials & Equipment

- pen and paper

Procedure

1. Prepare a chart with five columns.

2. Down the left-hand column, list the functions that living organisms perform in order to survive. Name the organisms shown on the right in the headings for the remaining columns. (Note: A **microorganism** is an organism that can only be seen with a microscope.)

3. Fill in your chart to indicate which structure you think each organism uses to perform each function. (Some functions may not be applicable.)

4. Compare your chart with one prepared by a classmate.

Questions

5. Did your classmate list functions that you did not? Which ones?

6. Which functions did most people name?

7. Did each organism shown have a structure for each of the functions you listed?

Figure 2.2 Microorganism

Figure 2.3 Plant

Figure 2.4 Mammal

Figure 2.5 Fish

Unicellular Organisms

Here is a summary of what you will learn in this section:

- Unicellular organisms are essential for the continuance of life on Earth.
- Unicellular and multicellular organisms carry out many of the same activities to meet their basic needs.
- Unicellular organisms are varied in structures and adaptations.

Figure 2.6 Phytoplankton are unicellular organisms that supply most of Earth's oxygen.

Unicellular organisms are living things made of a single cell. They are usually smaller than a speck of dust, and they live everywhere that can sustain life: in water, in soil, and in or on multicellular organisms. There are millions of species. Scientists believe these organisms could have been on Earth for as long as 3.8 billion years.

While some unicellular organisms, such as some forms of bacteria, are harmful, many more are essential for life on Earth to continue. Phytoplankton are unicellular organisms that live in the oceans (Figure 2.6). They contain chlorophyll to convert the Sun's energy into food. Phytoplankton provide most of the oxygen in Earth's atmosphere and are the foundation of the ocean food chain.

Unicellular decomposers, such as bacteria, are another group of single-celled organisms that are essential for life on Earth. They complete the cycling of matter by converting nitrogen in soil into a form of nitrogen that can support plant life and the terrestrial food chains.

A21 *Starting Point*   Skills Ⓐ Ⓒ

What is going on in the Composter?

Have you ever looked inside a composter after the decomposers have been at work for a while? What did it look like in there, and how did it smell? Did you turn away in disgust? Or were you fascinated?

Consider This

With a classmate or as a whole class, discuss the following questions.

What to Do

1. List the conditions decomposers need to do their work.

2. List the basic needs of decomposers. Are these needs the same or different from the basic needs of other living things?

3. What should be done with the contents of a composter? Explain your reasoning.

A Single Cell Is a Living Thing

Most unicellular organisms, such as the diatom, paramecium (pl. paramecia) and the amoeba, are microscopic, although some can be seen with the unaided eye. Diatoms (Figure 2.7) live inside glass-like shells, which they make themselves. Like plants, diatoms make their food through photosynthesis.

It is often assumed that unicellular organisms are simple because of their simple structure. And yet, they perform the same basic activities that complex plant and animal organisms perform. They move, eat, respond to stimuli, reproduce, and expel waste that results from cellular activity.

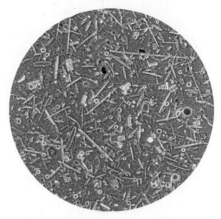

Figure 2.7 Diatoms are unicellular organisms. They live in lakes, oceans, and moist soil and are an important part of the food chain.

How Unicellular Organisms Move

Unicellular organisms move in a variety of ways. Paramecia have cilia, which are tiny hairs that act like oars and propel the organism along (Figure 2.8). *E. coli* bacteria move by rotating a flagellum that looks a bit like a tail (Figure 2.9). These organisms "swim" along. An amoeba moves by changing shape and forcing its cytoplasm into extensions called pseudopods.

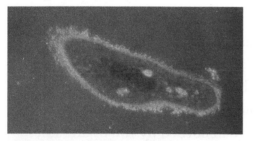

Figure 2.8 Paramecia are unicellular organisms that use cilia to propel themselves.

Figure 2.9 *E. coli* are unicellular organisms that move by rotating a flagellum.

A22 *During Reading*

Thinking Literacy

Visualizing with Combination Notes

Taking notes while reading is a good way to check understanding and clarify thinking. The "combination notes" strategy allows you to record information in a variety of ways, including visually. Draw a line two-thirds of the way down the middle of your page. On the left side of the top two-thirds of the page, record key information as you read "The Amoeba." Use the right side to visually display your understanding in pictures, diagrams, or a web. Use the bottom one-third of the page to record summaries of main concepts.

Figure 2.10 Coloured scanning micrograph of *Amoeba proteus*, one of the largest species of amoebas.

Take It *Further*

Diatoms, paramecia, and bacteria are examples of unicellular organisms. Choose two types of unicellular organisms, and find out how they obtain and digest their food. Prepare a chart comparing the two processes. Begin your research at ScienceSource.

The Amoeba

Do not mistake the microscopic amoeba for a mere blob. It is a fascinating organism. Amoebas thrive in water-based environments and are found in both fresh and salt water. They can also live in wet, decaying vegetation on the forest floor, in wet soil, or in other living organisms (including humans). There are many, many species of amoebas (Figure 2.10). Most are harmless to humans, but some cause disease.

Amoebas have many of the characteristics typical of animal cells. The body is surrounded by a selectively permeable cell membrane. Commonly visible organelles include one or more nuclei (depending on the species), cytoplasm, food vacuoles, and a special vacuole that pumps water out of the cell to prevent it from bursting. Water enters the amoeba by osmosis. Oxygen diffuses into the organism, and carbon dioxide waste diffuses out of the organism.

Amoebas can be carnivores, herbivores, or omnivores. Despite their usual microscopic size, amoebas are predators — they prey upon organisms such as algae and bacteria. The amoeba's hunting skills are based on its ability to change shape, a result of having a very soft cell membrane and cytoplasm. (The word "amoeba" comes from the Greek word for change.) The organism changes shape as it moves and captures prey (Figure 2.11).

As the amoeba completes the capture of its prey, the food it has engulfed becomes a vacuole. Chemicals called enzymes digest the food, the nutrients are absorbed by the organism, and the vacuole disappears. Waste products are eliminated through the cell membrane.

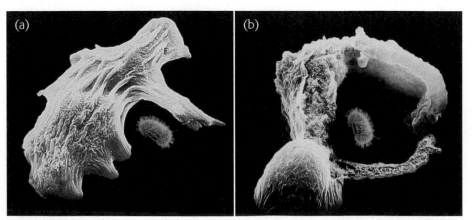

Figure 2.11 When food is detected nearby, an amoeba extends pseudopods to capture it. These images show an amoeba (a) surrounding and then (b) engulfing its prey.

Observing Unicellular Organisms

Question

What cell structures can be seen under a compound light microscope?

Materials & Equipment

- microscope
- microscope slides
- cover slips
- medicine dropper
- pond water sample (supplied by your teacher)
- small jar
- methyl cellulose (optional)
- prepared slides of amoebas (optional)

CAUTION: Handle microorganisms with care. Wear safety gloves, wash your hands thoroughly after the activity, and dispose of the specimens as instructed by your teacher.

Procedure

1. Turn to Toolkit 9 to review how to set up and use a microscope.

2. Prepare a wet mount slide of the pond water.

3. Set your slide up on the microscope stage, and use the low-power objective lens to observe your sample.

4. View the slide systematically for evidence of unicellular organisms.

5. Switch to the medium-power lens. Concentrate on what you are observing, and keep your sample in focus. Try the high-power lens.

NOTE: If the organisms in your sample are moving too quickly for you to observe them, use the medicine dropper to add a tiny amount (less than a drop) of methyl cellulose. This will thicken the water. Do not touch the sample or the methyl cellulose during this procedure.

6. If you are not successful in locating amoebas, paramecia, or diatoms, use the prepared slides to view these microorganisms.

7. Prepare a drawing of one of the organisms you observe. Indicate the shape, relative size, colour, and any cell structures that you can see. Label your drawing. Note the magnification you are using.

Analyzing and Interpreting

8. If you are observing pond water, describe how your organism moves.

9. If you used the methyl cellulose, what impact did it have on the specimens in your sample?

Skill Builder

10. You have made drawings of your observations. Do you think words would be a better way to communicate your observations? Explain your reasoning.

Forming Conclusions

11. What cell structures did you see?

12. Did all of the organisms you saw move in the same way? Describe any differences.

Figure 2.12 Always wear safety gloves when working with microorganisms.

Key Concept Review

1. Explain why something with only one cell can be considered to be an organism.

2. Name three unicellular organisms.

3. Name three ways in which unicellular organisms can move. Describe one of them.

4. Where did the amoeba's name come from? Explain why it was given that name.

Connect Your Understanding

5. Describe two things that would happen in an ecosystem if there were no unicellular organisms.

Practise Your Skills

6. Describe three things you should do when handling microorganisms.

7. Explain how you would prepare a drop of water containing an amoeba for viewing under a microscope.

For more questions, go to ScienceSource.

A24 *Thinking about Science, Technology, and Society*

Cooking and Freezing

Unicellular organisms such as bacteria thrive in warm temperatures and moist conditions. These conditions are ideal for composting; however, they must be avoided when preserving, storing, or preparing food. Past and present technologies for the preservation and storage of food focus on creating conditions that are cold and/or dry. Cooking raises the internal temperature of foods high enough to kill microorganisms.

What to Do

1. Research one of the following technologies to find out how it preserves food.

   (a) air drying of foods such as fish

   (b) canning of foods such as vegetables

   (c) freezing of foods such as meat

2. Review Health Canada's guidelines for the safe handling of food.

Consider This

With a classmate or as a whole class, discuss the following.

3. Explain how each of the preserving techniques ensures that the food will not contain harmful microorganisms.

4. How do the guidelines for handling food help to ensure that food is free of microorganisms that could contaminate it?

5. What do you think would happen if we did not have these guidelines?

Figure 2.13 Drying racks are a traditional way of preserving fish.

Multicellular Organisms and Cell Specialization

Here is a summary of what you will learn in this section:

- Diffusion and osmosis limit the size of cells.
- Multicellular organisms use specialized cells to carry out activities to meet basic needs.
- Specialized cells in multicellular organisms interact with and depend on other specialized cells.

You have seen how an amoeba captures a meal. Think of how the frog in Figure 2.14 does it. Unicellular organisms rely on one cell to perform all the functions that meet their basic needs. **Multicellular** organisms rely on a variety of types of cells to perform cellular functions. These types of cells are called **specialized cells**. They perform specific functions, such as digestion or movement. They must interact with other types of cells in the organism in order to carry out their tasks successfully.

Specialized cells in various parts of the frog — including eyes, muscles, and tongue — must work in perfect co-ordination in order to capture an insect for dinner. The average frog performs this task many times each day. Once the frog catches the insect, the cells in the frog's digestive system take over, extracting the nutrients and expelling cellular wastes.

Figure 2.14 The specialized cells in a frog work together to help the organism catch a meal.

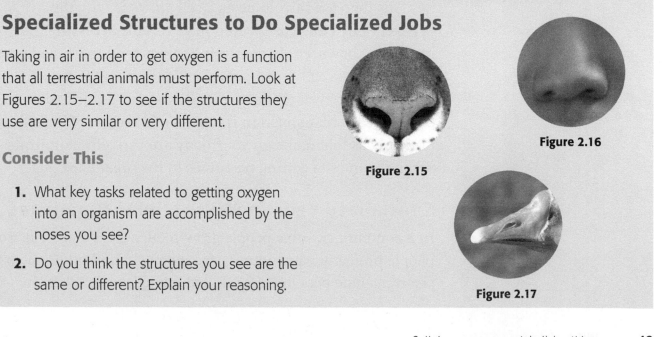

A25 *Starting Point*

Skills Ⓐ Ⓒ

Specialized Structures to Do Specialized Jobs

Taking in air in order to get oxygen is a function that all terrestrial animals must perform. Look at Figures 2.15–2.17 to see if the structures they use are very similar or very different.

Figure 2.15

Figure 2.16

Figure 2.17

Consider This

1. What key tasks related to getting oxygen into an organism are accomplished by the noses you see?

2. Do you think the structures you see are the same or different? Explain your reasoning.

Figure 2.18 *Acetabularia* is one of the world's largest unicellular organisms.

Figure 2.19 Multicellular organisms have a variety of specialized cells.

More Cells for Bigger Organisms

There are a few unicellular organisms that are so big you can see them with your unaided eye. One of the members of the algae family, *Acetabularia*, can grow to be 5 to 7 cm in diameter (Figure 2.18). Some amoebas may reach 1 cm, but unicellular organisms are usually microorganisms.

Unicellular organisms are usually micro-sized because cellular activities are performed most efficiently at that size. The limitation is related to the processes of diffusion and osmosis. The processes that deliver gases and water to cells and remove wastes are effective across very short distances. For example, an oxygen particle can diffuse over a distance of 0.01 mm in a fraction of a second. To diffuse over a distance of 1 mm would take 100 times as long.

This large increase in distance is because in a bigger cell, even though the surface area of the selectively permeable cell membrane would increase as the cell's size increased, the cell's volume would increase even more. You can imagine the same principle on a bigger scale if you picture the difference between a golf ball and a beach ball. The distance to the middle of the golf ball is many times shorter than the distance to the middle of the beach ball. For a cell to be bigger in the same proportion, gases and water would have to travel much farther to reach all of the organelles in the cytoplasm. If a unicellular organism were many times bigger than 1 mm, diffusion and osmosis could take several minutes instead of fractions of a second.

This increase in volume as a cell grows is why the organelles in a huge cell would have trouble accessing the resources they need. Larger living things tend to be made up of more than one cell. In an organism made up of dozens, thousands, or even millions or trillions of cells, diffusion and osmosis can still happen in fractions of a second. The trillions of tiny cells that make up your body are very efficient units when it comes to getting resources to the organelles.

Specialized Cells in Multicellular Organisms

In a community, some people grow food; others deliver it. Some people protect the community from danger, and others help to clean up. One person is not skilled enough to do all of the different jobs expertly. Nor could one person meet all of the demands of a community.

The same is true for multicellular organisms. One type of cell cannot do all of the different jobs in a complex organism. In the same way that a community needs specialists, multicellular organisms are made up of specialized cells rather than cells that are exactly the same. While the specialized cells have the same kinds of organelles as other plant or animal cells, the organelles may be better adapted to performing the cell's tasks.

Specialized Animal Cells

The number of types of cells in a multicellular organism depends on the complexity of the organism. The hydra is a simple multicellular organism (Figure 2.20). It has "skin" cells on the outside and digestive cells on the inside. The skin cells protect the insides from the outside environment and act as "gatekeepers" to control the substances that can get into and out of the organism in the same way that the cell membrane protects a cell.

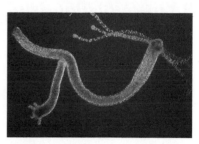

Figure 2.20 The hydra is a simple multicellular organism. Hydras are best viewed under a microscope.

A complex organism such as a human has hundreds of different types of cells. We have types of cells that function as protection and gatekeepers (Figure 2.21, skin cells), and cells responsible for digestion. We have cells that make up bones and cells that specialize in converting lots of energy (muscle cells) (Figures 2.22 and 2.23). Humans also have cells that are primarily for transmitting electrical impulses (nerve and brain cells) (Figures 2.24 and 2.25). Eyes have special cells that detect light. Blood cells transport oxygen and carry away wastes of cellular processes. Storage cells keep unused energy on hand in the form of fat, to be released and burned when the need arises (Figure 2.26).

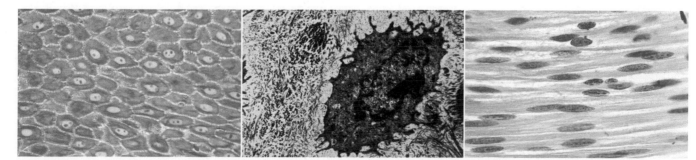

Figure 2.21 Human skins cells make up the largest organ in the human body.

Figure 2.22 Human bone cells make up the structure that supports the body.

Figure 2.23 Human muscle cells have more mitochondria than other cells, so they can transform more energy.

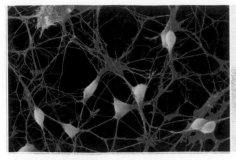

Figure 2.24 Human nerve cells transmit electrical impulses along pathways to the brain.

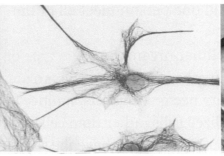

Figure 2.25 Human brain cells receive and transmit electrical impulses.

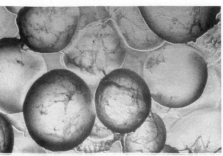

Figure 2.26 Human fat cells store energy in the form of fat, which can be accessed and burned when resources for fuel are low.

A26 *Learning Checkpoint*

Explaining the Size

1. In your own words, explain why diffusion and osmosis limit the size of cells.

2. In your own words, explain why multicellular organisms have specialized cells.

Take It Further

Plants and animals have cells with the special job of defending the organism against invaders. In humans, these cells work in the immune system. Four of these types of cells are called killer T cells, helper T cells, memory T cells, and antibodies. Find out what job two of these types of cells do and how they do it. Report back to the class. Begin your research at ScienceSource.

Specialized Plant Cells

Multicellular plants also have specialized cells. Some transform the Sun's energy into sugars. These cells are found primarily in the leaves (Figure 2.27). The job of cells in the stem is primarily to transport food and water to the rest of the plant, store some food, and support the plant (Figure 2.28). The cells in the roots store food, absorb water from the soil, and transport water and nutrients to the stem (Figure 2.29).

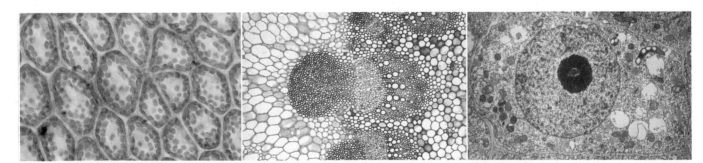

Figure 2.27 These leaf cells contain chloroplasts, which convert the Sun's energy into food.

Figure 2.28 The cells in a plant stem transport water and materials throughout the plant.

Figure 2.29 The cells in a plant root absorb water and nutrients from the soil and transport these resources to the stem.

Observing Multicellular Organisms

Question

What multicellular organisms can be seen under a compound light microscope?

Materials & Equipment

- microscope
- microscope slides
- cover slips
- medicine dropper
- pond water sample (supplied by your teacher)
- small jar
- methyl cellulose (optional)
- prepared slides of hydras (optional)

CAUTION: Handle microorganisms with care. Wear safety gloves, wash your hands thoroughly after the activity, and dispose of the specimens as instructed by your teacher.

Procedure

1. Turn to Toolkit 9 to review how to set up and use a microscope.

2. Prepare a wet mount slide of the pond water.

3. Set your slide up on the microscope stage, and use the low-power objective lens to observe your sample.

4. View the slide systematically for evidence of multicellular organisms.

5. Switch to the medium-power lens. Concentrate on what you are observing, and keep your sample in focus. Try the high-power lens.

NOTE: If the organisms in your sample are moving too quickly for you to observe them, use the medicine dropper to add a tiny amount (less than a drop) of methyl cellulose. This will thicken the water. Do not touch the sample or the methyl cellulose during this procedure.

6. If you are not successful in locating a hydra, use the prepared slides to view these microorganisms.

7. Prepare a drawing of the multicellular organisms you observe. Indicate the shape, relative size, colour, and any cell structures that you observe. Label your drawing. Note the magnification you are using.

Analyzing and Interpreting

8. If you are observing pond water, describe how the organisms move.

9. How many different organisms did you see in your sample?

Skill Builder

10. Describe the steps you must follow to observe a pond water sample with a compound light microscope.

Forming Conclusions

11. Were the organisms you observed plants or animals? Justify your reasoning.

Figure 2.30 Pond water can supply a number of multicellular organisms.

A28 *Design a Lab*

Toolkits 2,9

SKILLS YOU WILL USE
- Designing an experimental procedure
- Designing a fair test

Cells and Solutions

Question

How will the cells in an onion membrane respond to pure water, salt water, and vinegar?

Design and Conduct Your Investigation

1. Make a hypothesis. Refer to Toolkit 2 for help with this procedure.

2. Decide what materials and equipment you will need to test your hypothesis. For example:

   (a) List the lab equipment you will require to make your observations.

   (b) List the materials such as samples or solutions you will require.

3. Plan the steps in your procedure. Include any safety precautions.

4. Write up your procedure. Include steps to ensure that it will be a fair test of your hypothesis. Explain how you will document your results.

5. Ask a classmate to read the procedure and ask about any steps that are not clear. Show your revised procedure to your teacher.

6. Carry out your investigation. Refer to Toolkit 9 to review how to set up and use a microscope. Refer to "Preparing an Onion Membrane" in the next column for tips on handling your sample.

7. Compare your results with your hypothesis. Did your results support your hypothesis? If not, what possible reasons might there be?

8. Was your investigation a fair test? Justify your answer.

9. Was your procedure complete? How would you change it if you were going to do the investigation again?

10. Share and compare your design and results with your classmates. How were they similar? How were they different?

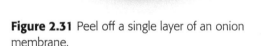

Figure 2.31 Peel off a single layer of an onion membrane.

Preparing an Onion Membrane

1. Select a clean glass slide and cover slip.

2. Carefully remove a piece of thin, semi-transparent membrane from between two inner layers of the onion.

3. Pick up the membrane with the tweezers. Take the microscrope slide, and hold it at a 45° angle. Carefully drape the membrane onto the middle of the slide. Avoid trapping air bubbles between the membrane and the slide.

4. After you have applied the solution, pick up the cover slip and slowly lower it over the membrane specimen. Avoid trapping air bubbles between the cover slip and the specimen.

Key Concept Review

1. Name five different types of cells that can be found in the human body.

2. Name three different types of plant cells, and describe their key functions.

3. Explain why a tiny cell is a more efficient basic unit of life than a large cell.

Connect Your Understanding

4. What are the advantages of having specialized cells? Are there any disadvantages? Explain your answer.

Practise Your Skills

5. Describe the steps to be followed to make a drawing of organisms observed under a microscope.

For more questions, go to ScienceSource.

A29 *Thinking about Science, Technology, and Society*

Water for Cells

Two-thirds of the average human body is water. Close to 70 percent of that water is inside the body's cells, 20 percent is in the space surrounding the cells, and the remainder is in the bloodstream. The water moves into and out of cells as necessary through osmosis.

When your body is properly hydrated, it has enough water to maintain cellular activities. When the body does not have enough water, it is dehydrated. Making sure that your body has enough water is one way to keep your body cells healthy.

What to Do

1. Calculate the amount of fluids that you consume in one day.

2. List the fluids you consume regularly. Check the ingredient lists of your favourite commercial drinks, and compile a list of the first three ingredients.

3. Research the most common effects of dehydration. Start your research at ScienceSource.

Consider This

With a classmate or as a whole class, discuss the following questions.

4. Compare the amount of fluids you each consume daily. Calculate the average.

5. Compile a list of the first three ingredients in fluids commonly consumed to find out what is being consumed along with water.

6. Suggest ways in which people are most likely to become dehydrated and what steps can be taken to avoid dehydration.

7. Some people think that bottled water is bad for the environment. They are concerned about the waste of water in unfinished bottles and the plastic bottles that end up in landfill sites. Suggest ways to meet the body's water needs without creating environmental problems.

Plant and Animal Cellular Processes

Here is a summary of what you will learn in this section:

- Cellular processes are continuous.
- The conversion and transport of energy are key cellular processes.
- Cells are replaced through the process of cell division.

Figure 2.32 When yeast interacts with sugar, it produces carbon dioxide as a waste product.

Whether you are awake or asleep, sitting watching a show or playing soccer, your cells are busy places. Just like a busy factory, materials are arriving in your cells, being used in production, and the waste and final products are being transported out.

The materials entering a cell through diffusion and osmosis and other transport mechanisms are raw materials to be used by the various organelles. Those organelles are breaking materials down to convert energy, transporting energy, building proteins, and sending chemical messages.

Cells also expel waste products. While a tiny cell regularly emits a tiny amount of waste, an organism with a trillion cells finds itself with a lot of waste in its system.

A30 Starting Point

Skills **A** **C**

Yeast in Action

Yeast is a unicellular fungus used in the preparation of baked goods. Its dried form is mixed with warm water and sugar and added to flour to make light-textured breads and cakes.

How does this work? Yeast cells consume sugar and use the starches in flour to make more sugar. They generate carbon dioxide as a waste product during the process (Figure 2.32). The gas is trapped in the dough, creating small bubbles. The carbon dioxide is eliminated during baking, and the final product is filled with small pockets of air.

You can test for yeast in action.

What to Do

1. Inflate a balloon several times to stretch it out. Set it aside.

2. Pour 250 mL of warm water into a 500-mL recyclable water bottle. Add one package of baker's yeast and about 30 mL of granulated sugar. Swirl the mixture.

3. Stretch the balloon over the mouth of the bottle.

Question

4. What change did you see in the balloon? What is causing this change?

Visualizing the Cell as a Factory or a City

Visualizing as you read helps you use experiences, senses, and prior knowledge to better understand what you are reading. As you read pages 51 and 52, note the different organelles and their specialized jobs in cells.

What to Do

Using the metaphor "the cell is a factory" or "the cell is a city," visualize how each part of a cell could be represented by a part in a factory or a city. Draw your cell as a factory or city. Use a legend to identify organelles and their visual counterparts, and explain the workings of your cell factory or cell city to a partner. What other metaphors could you create for a cell?

Transforming Energy

All cellular activities such as growth, repair, and reproduction need energy. Mitochondria provide energy for the cell by transforming oxygen and sugar (food) into carbon dioxide and water. This process is called **cellular respiration**, which occurs in both plant and animal cells.

In plant cells, chloroplasts produce the sugar needed by the mitochondria in a process called **photosynthesis**. In photosynthesis, the chlorophyll in chloroplasts captures the Sun's energy so the chloroplast can convert carbon dioxide and water into sugar and oxygen. In this way, energy is transformed from sunlight into sugar in plants (photosynthesis) and then sugar is consumed to release useable energy in both plant and animal cells (cellular respiration).

Processing and Transporting Materials

What happens when water, gases, and nutrients enter cells through the cell membrane? Materials move through the cytoplasm to the various organelles. The endoplasmic reticulum makes proteins from raw materials that come into the cell and passes them to the Golgi apparatus. The Golgi apparatus processes protein molecules and secretes them outside the cell to be used elsewhere in the organism. Lysosomes break down food and digest wastes. All of this cellular activity is controlled by the nucleus.

Figure 2.33 This paramecium has ingested (eaten) two smaller organisms, called euglena. The green euglena are visible inside the paramecium near the bottom of the micrograph. Through the process of digestion, the paramecium extracts sugars produced in the chloroplasts of the euglena and provides them to its own mitochondria for energy production.

Reproducing

Cells have a lifespan — amoebas live for approximately two days. Human brain cells live between 30 and 50 years. Human red blood cells live for 120 days. Skin cells live for 20 days. What does this mean? In the case of your skin, it means that your skin cells are replaced approximately every 20 days.

In fact, in the average human body, with its several hundred trillion cells, approximately three billion cells die every day. Cells die because they have been damaged, because they have not received enough water or food, or because they have reached the end of their lifespan. Given these losses, you might expect that multicellular organisms are constantly shrinking. This does not happen, however, because before the cells die, they create a replacement for themselves through cell division.

During cell division, cells split in half to form two smaller cells. The nucleus splits into two first. The rest of the cell then divides.

Cell division is easiest to see in a unicellular organism. Figure 2.34, below, shows the process. First, the cell's nucleus splits in two. Then the membrane begins to pinch near the middle to divide the cytoplasm, including its organelles, and ensure that each new cell has a nucleus. The two new cells are identical. The same process occurs in the cells of your body.

Take It Further

Using your muscles frequently and with increased intensity will increase the number of mitochondria in your muscle cells. Find out more about how using your muscles will increase your ability to transform energy. Begin your research at ScienceSource.

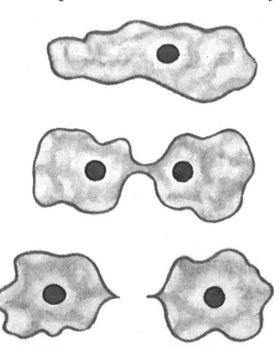

Figure 2.34 First, the nucleus divides into two. Then the cell membrane pinches to divide the cytoplasm. Two new, identical cells result from cell division.

In the case of a plant cell, instead of pinching in half after the nucleus divides, a new cell plate develops across the cell to create a new cell wall between the two nuclei (Figure 2.35).

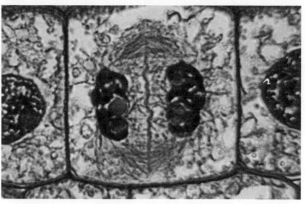

Figure 2.35 Plant cells divide by developing a new cell wall.

Modelling Diffusion

Purpose

To model the diffusion of molecules through a selectively permeable membrane

Materials & Equipment

- 600-mL beaker
- 250-mL beaker
- water
- cornstarch
- measuring spoons
- non-resealable plastic sandwich bag
- twist tie
- iodine

CAUTION: Iodine will stain skin and clothing.

Procedure

1. Put approximately 200 mL of water in the large beaker. Add about 10 drops of iodine, and set the beaker aside. Note the colour of the solution.

2. Put approximately 100 mL of water in the smaller beaker. Measure 2 tablespoons of cornstarch into the water and mix it thoroughly. Pour the solution into the bag. Seal it with a twist tie. Note the colour of the solution.

3. Submerge the bag with the cornstarch solution in the iodine water bath. Keep the twist tie above the level of the liquid. Leave the bag in the bath for approximately 10 min.

4. Remove the bag from the iodine bath, taking care not to drip the iodine solution onto clothes or other surfaces.

5. Observe the cornstarch solution in the bag.

6. Follow your teacher's instructions in cleaning up everything you used.

Questions

7. What colour was the cornstarch solution at the beginning of the activity? What colour was the cornstarch solution at the end of the activity?

8. What colour was the iodine bath at the beginning of the activity? What colour was the iodine bath after the bag with the cornstarch solution was submerged in it?

9. Did the cornstarch diffuse out of the bag into the iodine solution? How do you know?

10. Did the iodine diffuse through the bag into the cornstarch solution? How do you know?

11. Explain your results.

Key Concept Review

1. Name three cellular processes.

2. What time of the day or night is best for cellular activities?

3. Describe the process of cell division in your own words.

4. Name three reasons why cells die.

Connect Your Understanding

5. Explain how cell division is linked to cell theory.

6. This is a picture of a plant cell. Describe what is happening in this picture.

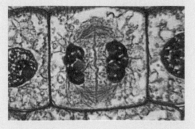

Practise Your Skills

7. Explain how building a model can help you understand scientific processes.

For more questions, go to ScienceSource.

A33 *Thinking about Science, Technology, and Society*

Helping Cells, Harming Cells

Healthy human cells divide to produce new cells on a regular basis. When cancer develops, cells are dividing uncontrollably, and the body is harmed. Some cancers are hard to detect and result in premature death.

Finding technology to stop the cancer process is a goal of cancer research. Current treatment is based on two key therapies: chemotherapy and radiation therapy (Figure 2.37). Both therapies are expensive.

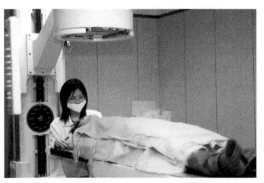

Figure 2.37 Radiation therapy can harm both cancer cells and healthy cells.

What to Do

Go to ScienceSource to research the topics in steps 1 and 2.

1. Find out how the two therapies work, and write an explanation of each in terms of what you know about cells.

2. Find out and describe the effect of each of the two therapies on cancer cells and on healthy cells.

Consider This

With a classmate or as a whole class, discuss the following points.

3. Use what you know about cells and cellular processes to explain how cancer patients can recover from these therapies.

4. As the number of cases of cancer increases, how can society make sure that all patients can get the treatment they need?

Microbiologists at Work

Figure 2.36 Microbiologists study cells and cellular processes, as well as other microorganisms.

Many early researchers studying "things too small to be seen with the unaided eye" were inspired by a desire to understand what caused disease. The earliest suggestion that microorganisms were a factor was published in 1835 after a study of fungi affecting silkworms. The theory that germs were responsible for many illnesses was being discussed by 1847. Louis Pasteur published the theory in 1857.

As the germ theory gained acceptance, the medical profession began to change their practices to include more attention to cleanliness and sterilization. Many more of their patients survived as a result.

The Role of Improved Technology

German electrical engineer Ernst Ruska constructed the first electron microscope in 1931. Since Ruska's innovation, microscopes and techniques for studying cells have become more advanced. At the same time, the discoveries by microbiologists have become increasingly influential in the way diseases are diagnosed and treated.

Careers in Microbiology

The study of microbiology has expanded steadily since the 1930s and has become increasingly specialized. There are now a variety of careers in a variety of fields.

- **Bacteriologists** study bacteria.
- **Environmental microbiologists** study microorganisms in the environment.
- **Food microbiologists** study microorganisms that spoil food and cause illness.
- **Industrial microbiologists** study microorganisms in order to make useful products (biotechnology).
- **Medical microbiologists** are doctors studying diseases caused by microbes.
- **Microbial epidemiologists** study the role of microorganisms in illnesses and health.
- **Mycologists** study fungi.
- **Protozoologists** study protists.
- **Virologists** study viruses.

Questions

1. Research a career in microbiology. Start your reseach at ScienceSource.

2. Prepare a report that includes the following information:

    (a) the education required

    (b) a place of work

    (c) a description of possible main duties

    (d) a recent important discovery in the field

Reflect and Evaluate

The study of science is often a study of similarities and differences or comparisons and contrasts. A study of ecosystems, for example, is about biotic and abiotic factors. A study of fluids can be about fast or slow, thick or thin. This study of cells is about same or different, unicellular or multicellular, plants or animals.

Research tells us that our brains work in the same way. They store information based on similarities and retrieve information based on differences.

With a partner summarize what you have learned from this chapter in the form of a 5-4-3-2-1 organizer.

List:

- 5 new learnings
- 4 similarities and differences between plant and animal cells
- 3 key differences between unicellular and multicellular organisms
- 2 ways visualization helps you as a reader
- 1 question you still have

Key Concept Review

1. Define the term "cell specialization" in your own words. (k)
2. How do diffusion and osmosis help amoebas survive? (k)
3. How do diffusion and osmosis limit the size of a cell? (k)
4. Explain why visible structures, such as fins, beaks, and tails, look so different on different organisms. (k)
5. Unicellular organisms move in many different ways. Use words and pictures to explain how each of the following organisms moves: (k)
   (a) paramecium
   (b) *E. coli* bacteria
   (c) amoeba

Connect Your Understanding

6. Phytoplankton are unicellular organisms that live in the ocean. How is their existence important to your survival? (t)
7. A unicellular organism is a living thing that meets all of its basic needs with just one cell. A multicellular organism can require up to several trillion cells to do the same thing. Which one do you consider to be more advanced? Explain your reasoning. (t)
8. You need to collect a live sample of an amoeba for study in class. Where would be the best natural environment to collect this sample? Why? (a)

Practise Your Skills

9. What is the correct procedure for handling a sample of pond water? (k)
10. Some algae reproduce every 24 hours if conditions are ideal. If it takes 15 days for the algae to half-fill a pond, how long will it take to fill the whole pond? What assumption did you make in order for this to happen? How likely is this to occur? Explain your reasoning. (a)

ACHIEVEMENT CHART CATEGORIES
(k) Knowledge and understanding (t) Thinking and investigation (c) Communication (a) Application

11. You are examining a sample of pond water, and you notice organisms passing through your field of view. You are out of methyl cellulose, so your teacher suggests making a new wet mount and adding a few threads of cotton from a cotton ball to the slide before adding the cover slip. What effect will this have? ⓣ

12. Sean and Krista were working on the Modelling Diffusion activity (A32) in class. They observed no change in the cornstarch solution. Suggest and explain two possible reasons why this might have happened. ⓣ

Unit Task Link

Review the list of key features and functions that you made at the end of Chapter 1. Use the list to make notes on the cellular processes you learned about in this chapter. Remember to include diffusion and osmosis.

A34 Thinking about Science, Technology, and Society

Protecting Cells in the Environment

Synthetic chemicals are chemicals that are produced in a laboratory. Synthetic chemicals are used for cleaning, preserving, and decorating as well as for fuelling our machines. Think of the bleaches, soaps of all kinds, hair gels, make-up, polishes, perfumes, varnishes, paints, gasoline, and oil you use or come into contact with during your regular activities. Synthetic medicines help treat illnesses. All of these synthetic materials are helpful to society.

Many of the chemicals that make up these materials have entered the soil and water systems and are now found in the cells of plants and animals. Some synthetic chemicals are suspected of disrupting cell processes in one of two ways: either by causing uncontrollable cell reproduction (cancer) or by interfering with the reproductive processes of organisms and causing sterility or physical deformities.

What to Do

1. Create a two-column chart. In the first column, list the synthetic chemicals and medicines you have used or have been in contact with in the past week.

2. In the second column, note how the materials are disposed of. For example, are they thrown in the garbage or put into the water system?

Consider This

With a classmate or as a whole class, discuss these questions.

3. Do you think new chemicals should be made available for use before their effects on cells are known? Explain your reasoning.

4. Many people think that the disposal of chemicals should be regulated carefully. Suggest ways in which this could be done.

Magnetic resonance images (MRIs) like this one can be used by doctors to determine if a person's lungs are healthy or damaged.

What You Will Learn

In this chapter, you will:

- explain the roles of cells in plant and animal tissues and organs
- explain the roles of tissues and organs in plants and animals
- evaluate the role of technology in studies of cell biology and the social impact of these studies

Skills You Will Use

In this chapter, you will:

- use analytic skills to evaluate issues
- use appropriate science and technology vocabulary
- use a variety of forms to communicate

Why This Is Important

Understanding the interactions of cells, tissues, and organs helps researchers develop new technologies to fight disease and repair cellular damage that may threaten our health.

Before Writing

Thinking Literacy

Preparing to Write a Newspaper Article

Newspapers include articles on current issues, including science. Journalists reporting the stories often present both facts and opinions to readers.

Find examples of science news in your local newspapers. Highlight the facts and opinions being presented by using a different colour for each. Create a definition explaining the difference between facts and opinion..

Key Terms

- tissue
- organ
- organ system
- paralysis
- tumour

3.0 Getting Started

Figure 3.1 In order to be successful, a team requires healthy players who can fulfil their designated roles.

When Toronto FC (Football Club) plays a soccer game, you see 11 players on the field: a goalkeeper, four defenders, four mid-fielders, and two strikers. Each player has a job to do, but the team requires a lot more than these 11 individuals. There are coaches, managers, team doctors, physiotherapists, trainers, accountants, marketing experts, sponsors, media consultants, and more. All the elements in the team's organization work together. Without the individual parts, there would be no team. Without a team, the parts would have no purpose. And without co-ordination among the parts, the team would be in chaos.

The body of a multicellular organism, like the human body, is much more complex than a soccer team. Your body is made up of trillions of cells that are organized into tissues that make up organs (such as lungs) and organ systems (such as the respiratory system).

Most of your body's functions happen without your being aware of them. This co-ordinated activity among cells, tissues, and organs keeps you (the organism) functioning.

Figure 3.2 Arriving at school on time and ready to work involves a lot of co-ordinated activity.

You co-ordinate events in your life every day, beginning with the not-so-simple task of getting ready for school in the morning, balancing activities with family and friends, and scheduling homework and recreation. Keeping track of everything can be difficult. Like you, your body keeps track of all of its activities, but at the cellular level. Scientists are still learning how all of the cells and parts of the human body work together to keep you healthy.

A35 *Quick Lab*

Amoeba Race

The amoeba is the unicellular organism that moves from place to place by sending out pseudopods (false feet). Simulating how an amoeba co-ordinates its life activities can help you understand how any cell co-ordinates its functions to survive.

Purpose

To simulate the movement and the eating habits of an amoeba

Materials & Equipment

- open area
- 5 soccer balls
- outdoor play area (optional)

Procedure

1. Form three groups:
   - Group 1, about 1/2 of the class, will be the cytoplasm.
   - Group 2, about 1/2 of the class, will be the cell membrane.
   - Group 3 will consist of two people who will act as the nucleus.

2. The nucleus pair must link elbows in order to stay together.

3. The cytoplasm group crowds around the nucleus.

4. The cell membrane group links hands and surrounds the nucleus and the cytoplasm.

5. Try these amoeba challenges.
   (a) Move like an amoeba across the room.
   (b) Move from the classroom into the hall.
   (c) Divide to form two identical cells. The nucleus will have to separate.
   (d) Move around the schoolyard to collect soccer balls on the ground. The schoolyard represents a pond, and the soccer balls represent food. A cell can touch the food only with its feet. See which cell can collect the most food.

Questions

6. Describe any difficulties you experienced while being part of a cell.

7. How do you think it is possible for a simple unicellular organism to co-ordinate its movements?

From Cells to Tissues to Organs

Here is a summary of what you will learn in this section:

- Most multicellular animals and plants are made up of cells that are organized into tissues and organs.
- There are four main types of animal tissues — connective, muscle, nervous, and epithelial.
- There are three main types of plant tissues: protective, transport, and photosynthetic.

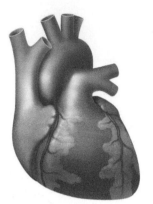

Figure 3.3 The heart is the organ that pumps blood through the veins and arteries. Heart muscle tissue is made up of specialized muscle cells.

The many specialized cells in a multicellular organism are not scattered randomly throughout the organism. Specialized cells that are similar in structure and function are grouped together in **tissues**. **Organs**, such as the heart, are made of tissues that work together to perform a specific task (Figure 3.3).

There are four main types of animal tissue and three main types of plant tissue. The cells in each type of tissue share the same basic design and perform the same function. Each tissue cell works with and depends on the others as it performs its own tasks. The way in which the various types of tissue cells perform their basic processes may vary, and those cells may have a special role, but all cells transform and transmit energy, expel wastes, and reproduce during their existence.

A36 *Starting Point*   Skills Ⓐ Ⓒ

Your Body Can Heal Itself

What happens when you get a cut on your skin?

What to Do

1. With a partner, write down all the things that you remember happening when you last got a cut. List sensations, such as pain, as well as activities, such as bleeding. What happened after that?

Consider This

2. How long did it take your cut to heal?

3. How much of the activity related to the healing of your cut did you control consciously?

4. How do you think your skin cells "know" what to do?

Animal Tissues in Organs

The four main types of animal tissue are connective, muscle, nervous, and epithelial (tissue that forms the outer layer of a structure). The cells in these tissues work together to support their own lives as well as the life of the whole organism.

The four types of tissues are found in different combinations in most of the organs in your body (Figure 3.4). The organs made of these tissues work together in a number of organ systems.

Take It *Further*

Many animals, including humans, have hair on their bodies. Choose one hair-covered animal. Find out how the hair is structured and describe its function. Report your findings to your class. Begin your research at ScienceSource.

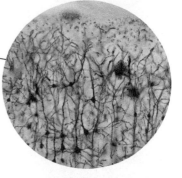

Nervous tissue transmits and receives nerve impulses. The brain, spinal cord, and nerves are all made of nervous tissue.

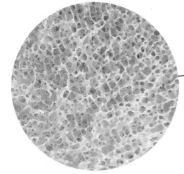

Connective tissue supports and connects different parts of the body. Blood is a connective tissue. Fat, cartilage, tendons, and bone (shown above) are also connective tissues.

Epithelial tissue covers the surface of your body. It also lines the inside of organs such as the small intestine.

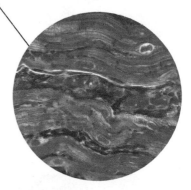

Muscle tissue contracts to cause motion. One type of muscle allows your body to move. Cardiac muscles (shown above) contract rhythmically to pump blood. The contraction of smooth muscles helps move food along your intestines.

Figure 3.4 There are four main types of tissue in the human body.

Figure 3.5 Plant organs contain three different types of tissues: protective, transport, and photosynthetic.

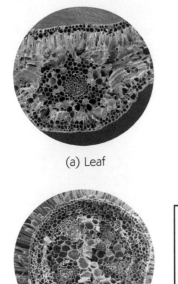

(a) Leaf

(b) Stem

(c) Root

Plant Tissues in Organs

The three types of plant tissue are protective, transport, and photosynthetic (Figure 3.5). All of these types of tissue are found in the three organs of a plant: leaves, roots, and stems (Figure 3.6). As in animals, the organs of the plant interact and depend on each other. One organ cannot live without the substances and activities provided by the other two organs. Plant organs make up two organ systems: the root system (which is below ground) and the shoot system (which is made up of anything that is above ground).

Protective tissues form a covering on most plants that helps prevent water loss and protects the plant.

Photosynthetic tissues transform the Sun's energy into sugar.

Transport tissues contain hollow, tube-like cells that move food and water through the plant.

Figure 3.6 The tissues of a leaf

A37 *Learning Checkpoint*

Note Taking

Summarizing information in your notes is an important step in comprehending and recalling text. Create a chart with two rows to summarize the information about animal and plant tissues. Use three columns to list the type of tissue, its function, and where it can be found. Do you think this three-column chart would work better here than a Venn diagram? Explain your reasoning.

Special-Effects Technician

Recognize a Need

A new science fiction movie is being filmed in your area, and the director has put a job posting in the local newspaper for special-effects technicians. Technicians will need to create realistic representations of creatures from a variety of planets in our solar system.

Problem

Design, draw, and label a realistic creature from another planet in our solar system.

Materials & Equipment

- print and media resources, including the Internet (ScienceSource)
- blank drawing paper
- coloured pens and pencils

Criteria for Success

- Your creature must be adapted to the physical conditions on its home planet.
- You must refer to your knowledge about cells, tissues, and organs when you describe how your creature is adapted to its environment.

Brainstorm Ideas

1. Decide which planet in our solar system will be the creature's home planet.
2. What features and processes of cells should be considered when you create your creature?
3. Which tissues and organs will your creature have?

Figure 3.7
The creator of this creature took the physical conditions on the proposed home planet into account when deciding what its cells and tissues would be like.

Make a Drawing

4. Draw and label a diagram of your creature that shows how its cells, tissues, and organs are adapted to the conditions on its home planet.

Test and Evaluate

5. Review the criteria for success and the planet's physical conditions to determine if you have met the criteria.

Communicate

6. Prepare an oral report to present your creature to the film's director. This presentation will be part of the "job interview." Good luck!

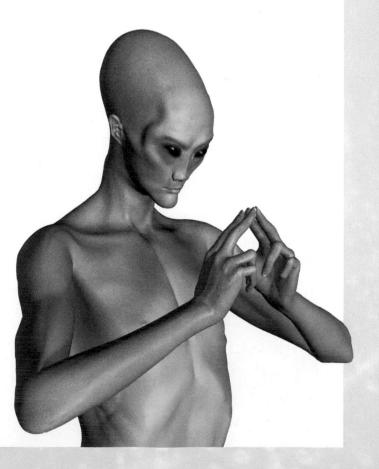

Key Concept Review

1. Create a two-column chart. In the left-hand column, name four types of animal tissue. In the right-hand column, describe their functions.

2. Create a two-column chart. In the left-hand column, name three types of plant tissue. In the right-hand column, describe their functions.

3. Name a plant organ, and identify the tissues that make up this organ.

4. Give two examples of:

   (a) connective tissue in animals

   (b) muscle tissue in animals

   (c) nervous tissue in animals

Connect Your Understanding

5. How does the distribution of animal tissues in an organism differ from the distribution of tissues in a plant?

6. Describe the relationship between organs, cells, and tissues.

7. Do you think multicellular organisms could function without specialized cells? Explain your reasoning.

Practise Your Skills

8. Draw a diagram of the tissues in a leaf.

For more questions, go to ScienceSource.

A39 *Thinking about Science, Technology, and Society*

X-Rays and Magnetic Resonance Imaging

X-ray technology uses electrons to produce an image of dense tissue. Magnetic resonance imaging (MRI) uses protons to produce images of the body. MRI technology excels at imaging soft tissue and organs such as the heart, the brain, the muscles, and the tendons and cartilage of joints like the knee. Each of the knees shown below has a form of arthritis.

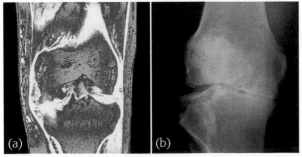

Figure 3.8 (a) MRI (b) X-ray

Consider This

With a classmate or as a whole class, discuss the following questions.

1. X-ray technology is older than MRI technology. Are new technologies always better than old ones? Explain your reasoning.

2. Many professional athletes have to wait a few days or less to have an MRI done on their injuries. Wait times for most other people are far longer. Do you think this should be the case? Explain.

3. Should the Ontario government allow private MRI clinics to open in the province? What are the benefits and drawbacks?

Interdependent Organ Systems

Here is a summary of what you will learn in this section:

- Individual organs perform specific functions.
- Organ systems are made of two or more different organs working together to do a task.
- Organ systems work together to keep an organism functioning properly.

Your organs do not work in isolation. It is true that your lungs deliver oxygen to your blood, but without blood vessels and a heart it would be difficult to keep muscle cells in your foot alive. They would not get enough oxygen to survive. Organs must be linked to other organs in order to carry out all of the functions required within an organism. The linking of organs to form organ systems is the next level of biological organization (Figure 3.9). As with tissues, humans have many different organ systems: the respiratory system, the circulatory system, and the skeletal system, to name a few.

The healthy functioning of organ systems, organs, and tissues depends on the health of the cells in the tissues. Cells that receive the materials they need through the organ systems sustain the organism.

In the next activity, you will discover how your muscles and blood circulation are connected.

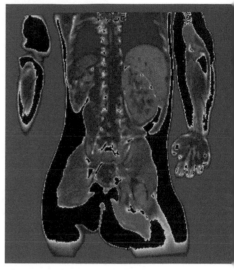

Figure 3.9 In a multicellular organism, there is a highly structured organization of the different body parts. All parts work together to make sure the organism functions properly.

A40 Starting Point

Skills **A C**

An Open and Shut Case

When muscles work very hard, they need a constant supply of blood to deliver oxygen and remove wastes such as carbon dioxide.

Try this with a partner.

1. One partner uses a watch and acts as the timer.

2. The other partner squeezes a clothespin between index finger and thumb (the other three fingers must be extended straight out) as fast as possible for 30 s, counting the number of squeezes. Rest for 10 s. Repeat two more times.

3. Switch roles and repeat steps 1 and 2.

What do you notice about your performance over the three trials?

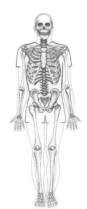

Figure 3.10 Skeletal system

Figure 3.11 Muscular system

Figure 3.12 Circulatory system

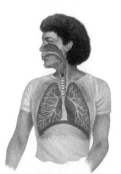

Figure 3.13 Respiratory system

Human Organ Systems

Organ systems are made up of more than one organ and perform one or more specific functions in the body. The organs in an organ system work together. Over the course of your life, these systems work very closely with each other.

The **skeletal system** is made up of bones and cartilage (Figure 3.10). This system provides support for movement, attachment points for other tissues, and protection of other organs (for example, the spine protects the spinal cord).

The **muscular system** is made up of skeletal muscles, including tendons and ligaments (Figure 3.11). This system enables you to move from place to place. It also moves substances through your body. For example, swallowing food involves a series of muscle contractions to force food down the esophagus and into the stomach.

The **circulatory system** is made up of the heart (an organ), plus blood vessels and blood (Figure 3.12). Its main purpose is to deliver nutrients, move gases, and remove waste products.

The **respiratory system** is made up of the nose, trachea, and lungs (Figure 3.13). This system allows oxygen from the air to enter the body and waste carbon dioxide to exit the body. This process is called **respiration**.

The **nervous system** is made up of the brain, spinal cord, and nerves that exist in every part of the body (Figure 3.14). This system sends and receives nerve messages throughout the body. It also controls behaviour, movement, and processes such as digestion and circulation.

The **digestive system** is made up of the mouth, salivary glands, esophagus, stomach, liver, gall bladder, pancreas, and small and large intestines (Figure 3.15). This system breaks food down so that nutrients can be absorbed by the blood and transported to all cells. The colon also expels all solid waste from the body.

The **excretory system** is made up of the kidneys, ureters, bladder, and urethra (Figure 3.16). This system filters the blood and removes liquid waste and extra water from the body.

The **integumentary system** is made up of skin, hair, nails, and sweat glands (Figure 3.17). The skin, hair, and nails cover and protect the body. Sweat glands are involved in maintaining normal body temperature.

Figure 3.14 Nervous system

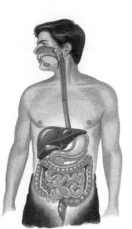

Figure 3.15 Digestive system

Figure 3.16 Excretory system

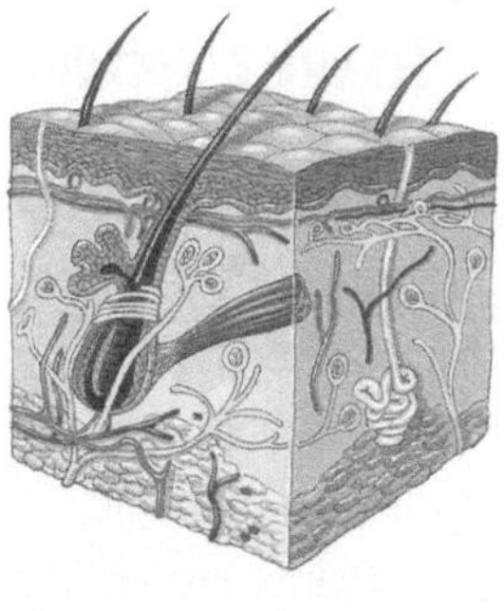

Figure 3.17 Skin segment of the integumentary system

The **endocrine system** is made up of several glands that produce hormones. Hormones are chemicals that regulate every bodily function. Glands such as the pituitary, thyroid, and pancreas all produce hormones that carry messages to other parts of the body. In the brain, the hypothalamus acts as the control centre for the endocrine and nervous systems.

The **lymphatic system** is made up of lymph, lymph nodes, lymph vessels, and lymphoid tissue. This system protects the body. It is responsible for destroying and removing any invading organisms and abnormal cells.

The **reproductive system** is made up of organs for producing offspring.

*Take It **Further***

Organ transplant techniques are continually improving. An increasing number of human parts and organs can be transplanted successfully. Make a list of all of the parts and organs that are currently available for transplant. Which ones are most commonly transplanted? Report your findings to your class. Begin your research at ScienceSource.

A41 *During Writing*

Thinking Literacy

The Structure of a Newspaper Article

Cell biology is a rapidly growing field of study that looks at challenges, developments, and technologies that affect the health of both plants and animals. Newspapers often report on the latest research and developments.

Revisit the newspaper science articles you collected and look at the structure of this form of writing. What information is presented in the first paragraph? How are the next paragraphs different? How are facts and opinions reported? What does the writer do in the last paragraph of the news article? Share your observations with the class to develop a framework for your writing.

As you read section 3.3, think about which area of research is of most interest to you as you prepare to write a newspaper article.

Flower Power

No one organ system in an animal's body, such as yours, is more important than another. If your circulatory system is working fine, but your immune system does not work properly, you could become ill.

Plants are multicellular organisms. Their organs also work together in organ systems. In this activity, you will determine if the root system that draws water up into a plant is more important than the shoot system, which is responsible for photosynthesis.

Question

Is one organ system more important for plant survival than the other?

Materials & Equipment

- ■ 3 white carnation plants in pots
  (each plant must have at least 5 blooms)
- ■ 2 balloons
- ■ 2 elastic bands
- ■ blue food colouring
- ■ four 400-mL beakers
- ■ water

Procedure

1. Place one plant in regular light and give it enough water.

2. Place a second plant in total darkness and give it enough water.

Figure 3.18

3. Take cuttings from the third plant following these instructions:
   - Place 1 flower and stem in plain water.
   - Place 1 flower and stem in water with 10 drops of blue food colouring.
   - Place 1 flower and stem, with a balloon placed over the end of the stem, in plain water. (Use the elastic band to make sure the balloon does not fall below the level of the liquid in the beaker.)
   - Place 1 flower and stem, with the other ballon over the end of the stem, in water with 10 drops of blue food colouring. (Use the elastic band to make sure the balloon does not fall below the level of the liquid in the beaker.)

4. Leave the plants for about one week.

5. Write a paragraph describing the health of the plants in regular light and total darkness after one week.

6. Write a paragraph describing the health of the cuttings after one week.

Analyzing and Interpreting

7. What was the purpose of putting one plant in regular light and one plant in total darkness?

8. What was the purpose of the set-up for the four different cuttings?

Skill Builder

9. Describe another way to record and report the results of this activity.

Forming Conclusions

10. Which organ system, the root system or the shoot system, is more important for the health of a plant? How do you know?

Key Concept Review

1. Create a chart to summarize the human organ systems and their key functions.

2. Name the plant organ systems and explain their function.

3. What are hormones? What is their function?

Connect Your Understanding

4. You arrived at science class today! Write a paragraph that explains how 10 of your organ systems contributed to your arrival.

5. "The brain is the most important organ in your body." Do you agree or disagree with this statement? Explain your reasoning.

6. Explain how the health of cells in your lungs could affect the health of the rest of your body.

7. List at least three different organ systems that you used to read the words on this page. Justify your choices.

Practise Your Skills

8. The ability to conduct a fair test is an important scientific skill. List five things that were done in the Flower Power Inquiry Activity (A42) that helped to make it a fair test.

For more questions, go to ScienceSource.

A43 Thinking about Science, Technology, and Society

How Loud Is "Too Loud"?

Hearing damage can be caused by many factors, but one of the main contributors to the problem is the use of earbud-style headphones. Excessively loud music played for a long time can damage the delicate nerve cells in the inner ear. These cells transmit sound impulses to the brain. If they are damaged, irreversible hearing loss will occur.

Using volume-limiting technology, reducing the amount of time spent listening to a music system, or using over-the-ear headphones are all ways to help reduce the chances of doing permanent damage to hearing.

Consider This

With a classmate or as a whole class, discuss the following questions.

1. What volume setting do you usually use on your listening device?

2. How long do you usually listen to your music?

3. Do you use volume-limiting technology to protect your hearing from permanent damage?

4. Would you use the 60-60 rule, which means no more than 60 minutes at 60 decibels (6 on the dial or 60 percent of the scale)? Why or why not?

The Impact of Research in Cell Biology

Here is a summary of what you will learn in this section:

- Improved understanding of cellular processes requires improved technology for studying cells.
- Advances in knowledge of cell biology will have an impact on human health, agriculture, and the environment.
- As our ability to manipulate cells increases, society will need to decide what will be allowed.

Figure 3.19 *Staphylococcus aureus* is a common bacterium that lives in many places, including on human skin and in nostrils. This bacterium can cause serious infection if it enters the body. (Look closely at the photo. The bacteria that look pinched in the middle are in the process of reproducing.)

As microscope technologies become more effective, researchers are able to see and understand more about cellular processes. They can also gain more insight into the roles that different types of cells play in some of the world's biggest health and environmental challenges. Research projects in cell biology include working to:

- stop the development of cancers
- regenerate nerve cells to repair spinal cord injuries
- develop vaccines to prevent disease
- discover biological tools to clean up pollution
- prepare to stop the spread of infectious diseases not yet known
- increase world food production

A44 *Starting Point*   Skills Ⓐ Ⓒ

Simple Solutions

Technology has helped medicine solve many serious health issues. Sometimes, however, the solution to a health problem is simple.

In the past 50 years, bacteria, such as the staphylococcus shown in Figure 3.19, that live on skin or in nostrils have become common in and outside of hospitals. While on the skin, the bacterium does no harm. However, if it gets inside the body through a cut, it can cause very serious infection called a "staph" infection.

How can you protect yourself? Wash your hands. Clean and protect cuts and scrapes.

Consider This

With a classmate or as a whole class, discuss the following questions.

1. When should you wash your hands? How many times a day do you wash your hands?

2. What is the proper way to wash your hands? Why would it be effective?

3. What procedures can you use to protect cuts and scrapes against infection?

Ongoing Research in Cell Biology

Cell biology is a growing and highly varied field of study. New technologies have opened new areas of study. As well, new health challenges have required the development of new technologies.

Working to Stop Cancers

Cancer is a disease related to the uncontrolled and rapid reproduction of cells through cell division (Figure 3.20). Normal, healthy cells proceed with their activities. They divide and reproduce at certain times according to signals issued by their organelles.

Cancerous cells continue to reproduce rather than carrying out their required cellular activities. The result is a **tumour**, a mass of cells that are continually reproducing but are otherwise non-functional. Tumours can appear in any organ in the body and can spread from one organ to another.

The work of cell biologists and other specialists has focussed on a number of areas, including how to turn off the cells' non-stop reproduction, how to destroy tumours, and finding out why the process begins. Research on prevention has looked into factors related to characteristics that can be inherited, lifestyle choices such as smoking, and environmental issues such as chemical pollution in air and water.

Successful studies have led to the development of effective treatments for some cancers, improved technology for the detection of many cancers, and insights into lifestyle choices that can help us protect ourselves from some cancers.

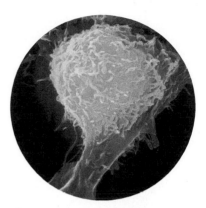

Figure 3.20 A cancer cell. Cancer is the result of the uncontrolled reproduction of cells.

Repairing Damaged Spinal Cords

The body's spinal cord includes cells that transmit nerve impulses from the senses to the brain and carry impulses from the brain to various muscles to instruct them to move. The spinal cord is located in the body's spine, connecting to nerves branching out into various parts of the body.

Damage to the nerves branching out into the body can create problems with numbness and problems sending sensory information to the brain. Damage to the spinal cord that severs it results in a loss of both information from the senses and the means of instructing the muscles to move. **Paralysis** is the inability to move muscles. If the spinal cord is severed below

Figure 3.21 Improved technologies related to mobility have helped people with spinal cord injuries.

the shoulders, the lower body and legs are paralyzed. If the spinal cord is severed in the neck area, all four limbs can be paralyzed.

Successful technologies have been developed to compensate for the lack of mobility. Wheelchairs have improved (Figure 3.21). Access to buildings and transportation has been redesigned to assist those who have been paralyzed. Cell biologists, however, continue to work to solve key problems relating to regenerating the cells in spinal tissue that transmit the impulses. While skin, bone, and muscle cells can repair themselves, finding a way to trigger similar repair in cells in spinal tissue is a challenge.

Preparing for New Infectious Diseases

Improvements in technologies for studying cells and cellular processes have led to successful treatments for many infectious diseases. Smallpox, polio, malaria, and tuberculosis have been brought under control in much of the world. The challenge for researchers in cell biology and related fields is to know how bacteria and viruses are adapting to create new infectious diseases.

Researchers have recently solved some of the mysteries related to diseases such as West Nile virus and Lyme disease, which are transmitted to humans through insect bites. A bigger challenge was the emergence of severe acute respiratory syndrome (SARS), which was first reported in November 2002 and lasted until July 2003. Documented cases of infection totalled 8096, and 774 deaths were attributed to the disease.

Researchers around the world struggled to discover how the disease was transmitted from one human to another. Until they understood that, it was difficult to control (Figure 3.22). Researchers eventually concluded that SARS was a virus transmitted through contact either with airborne water droplets or with contaminated surfaces. They did not find a successful treatment.

Health officials around the world remain on alert for the next outbreak of an unknown infectious disease.

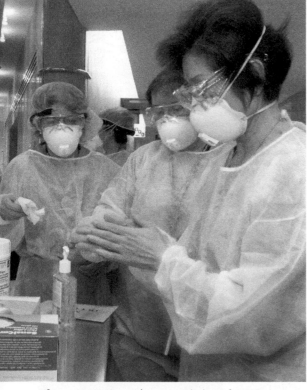

Figure 3.22 Once the transmission of SARS was understood, staff treating SARS patients were given a variety of protective gear and practices in order to prevent the spread of the disease.

Improving World Food Production

Plants are at the beginning of every food chain, and the successful cultivation of healthy plants is the key to feeding the world's population. In the past, farmers experimented with techniques such as crossbreeding to increase the amount of food their crops produce. Cell biologists changed plants so they can grow in different conditions, such as regions that are colder or drier than the original plant could tolerate or regions with a shorter growing season.

More recently, researchers have found ways to modify plant cells to improve an organism's resistance to insects and the chemicals that are used to kill weeds, rodents, and bugs. For example, a form of corn, known as Bt corn, can kill an insect known as the European corn borer (Figure 3.23). The insect has destroyed millions of dollars worth of crops each year.

Cell biologists have also changed plants to increase their nutritional value. In 2000, Swiss researchers announced the development of a modified type of rice, which they named golden rice. This rice has higher vitamin A and iron content than other rices. It was created by introducing genes and enzymes from beans, wild rice, daffodils, and a fungus called aspergillus. It is now grown and eaten in a number of countries (Figure 3.24).

Supporters believe that this kind of research will solve many of the world's problems with the supply of nutritious food. Critics are concerned that this kind of food contains modified cells that animals and humans have never digested before. They fear that the food may affect human cells in ways that no one has anticipated.

Figure 3.23 Infestations of the European corn borer have ruined acres of crops in the Atlantic provinces, Quebec, and as far west as the Rockies.

Figure 3.24 Dr. Swapan Datta, a plant biotechnologist, inspects golden rice plants in the Philippines.

Take It *Further*

Many farmers and consumers are concerned about the use of chemicals on food crops. Organic food is grown without using chemicals. Find out what techniques are used instead. Report your findings to your class. Begin your research at ScienceSource.

Thinking Literacy

A45 | *During Writing*

What's your opinion?

Choose one of the topics discussed in this section and create a plus, minus, interesting (PMI) chart. Share your chart with a classmate who chose the same topic and add one point that your partner had. Write a summary sentence that expresses your opinion on this topic now. Use the information in your PMI chart, as well as what you have learned about the topic and the structure of a newspaper science article, to write your own newspaper article. Remember to include your classmate's opinion in your writing.

A46 *Decision-Making Analysis*

Toolkit 4

SKILLS YOU WILL USE
- Identifying ethical issues
- Communicating

DI Anchor Activity

Stopping the Spread of Infectious Disease

Issue

While researchers work to find causes of and cures for new infectious diseases, some procedures for stopping the spread of disease are well known. However, many, including personal and public hygiene practices or isolation, can be very disruptive to personal lives as well as to economic activity. Should a community or society be able to force individuals to comply with orders relating to the spread of infectious disease?

Background Information

- Before health officials understood the cellular processes of disease, they knew that disease could be transmitted through physical contact. As early as the 1500s, public officials tried to stop the spread of infectious disease through the use of quarantines, publicly enforced periods of isolation of individuals who had or might have had certain illnesses.
- Quarantines have been used throughout Canada's history. In the 1890s, Canada strengthened its quarantine procedures for new immigrants in an effort to avoid a repeat of four previous outbreaks of deadly cholera.
- Quarantine of individuals and families continued well into the 1940s for a variety of illnesses. The practice was increasingly felt to be an infringement on personal freedom, and eventually, it was thought that isolation should be voluntary.
- During the SARS outbreak in 2002, individuals suspected of coming into contact with the infection were asked to stay home. Many health-care workers did isolate themselves from the public and their families.

Other members of the public refused and insisted on continuing to go about their business.

- Many people have suggested that if everyone suspected of coming into contact with infected people was quarantined, there would be a huge disruption of economic activities such as the distribution of food and water, as well as great financial losses.
- In today's world, travel by air and other means moves goods, animals, and people from almost anywhere in the world to another location in a matter of hours or days.
- Quarantines are currently enforced for live animals being brought into Canada, as well as for animals that have shown signs of diseases.

Analyze and Evaluate

1. If there is an outbreak of another new infectious disease like SARS somewhere in the world, what do you think Canadian officials should do? What should world health officials do? What might be the social impact of their actions?

2. Should people in the area where the new disease has been found be allowed to leave? Where could they go?

3. Do you think governments should be able to restrict travel and personal activities during outbreaks of a new infectious disease? How could the restrictions be enforced?

4. Prepare a report or presentation that outlines your ideas on the types of actions communities should take during an outbreak of a new infectious disease.

A47 *Decision-Making Analysis*   Toolkit 4

Growing Bt Corn and Other Modified Plants

Issue

Scientifically modified plants are developed for specific purposes. For example, *Bacillus thuringiensis*, or Bt, corn was developed to save corn crops that were being destroyed by an insect called the European corn borer. Scientists altered the cells of the plant to add a toxin that kills the insect.

A number of people have concerns about these kinds of modifications, fearing that the new product may cause unintended harm or become an invasive species. How can we decide if modifying plants scientifically is a safe practice?

Background Information

■ The larvae of the European corn borer eat the leaves and ears of corn. Bt corn contains a toxin that allows lethal bacteria such as *E. coli* to enter the larvae's digestive tracts and kill them.

■ Some people do not support the development of new varieties of plants such as Bt corn. They believe that natural cross-pollination of the modified plants and native plants may affect the seeds of native plants.

■ Some countries have banned the import of grains and other foods that have been modified scientifically. Officials in others have suggested that such grains and foods must be labelled so that consumers can decide whether to buy them or not.

■ Some researchers are concerned that there may be unintended consequences of the scientific modification of plants, such as the development of new allergies, or there could be an unknown, longer-term harmful animal or human health impact resulting from consuming these plants.

Analyze and Evaluate

1. Consider one of the following three viewpoints about the use of scientifically modified organisms.

    (a) The practice should be banned because of known or potential environmental and social risks.

    (b) Scientifically modified plants should be used wherever possible.

    (c) The use of scientifically modified plants can be approved for social benefit, but it should be closely regulated.

2. Develop some specific questions that relate to the issue and your chosen point of view.

3. Go to ScienceSource to conduct your electronic search for information.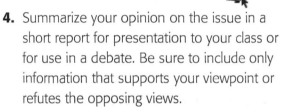

4. Summarize your opinion on the issue in a short report for presentation to your class or for use in a debate. Be sure to include only information that supports your viewpoint or refutes the opposing views.

Figure 3.25 A field of Bt corn looks much the same as a field of non-Bt corn. Do you think it should be labelled?

Key Concept Review

1. What are five examples of research projects in cell biology?

2. What is the relationship between cancerous cells and a tumour?

3. What causes paralysis?

4. List three ways in which scientific research has improved the production of food crops.

5. What is the main challenge faced by biologists researching infectious diseases?

6. Describe how officials tried to prevent the transmission of infectious diseases before they understood how disease was transmitted. Explain why you think it would or would not work.

Connect Your Understanding

7. "The study of cell biology is directly linked to technology." Do you agree or disagree with this statement? Explain your answer.

8. What is the role of scientific research in solving human health problems? Explain your answer.

9. List three societal issues that are related to microbiology. Write a brief paragraph to explain why one of them is the most important one and should receive public funding for research.

Practise Your Skills

10. Describe the steps you would take in order to analyze and evaluate an issue.

For more questions, go to ScienceSource.

A48 *Thinking about Science, Technology, and Society* S T S E

What Kind of Testing Should Be Done?

Scientists in labs can use cells in test tubes to test their ideas about a new treatment for a disease or a condition such as paralysis. They can consult their colleagues from around the world to get their opinion on whether it will work or not. They can also create computer models that might suggest whether the treatment will be successful.

At some point, however, they have to test it on living organisms. For many years, such tests were done using animals. Some people feel that this practice is inhumane and should be stopped. How can researchers find out if their ideas for treatments will work on people?

Consider This

With a classmate or as a whole class, discuss the following questions.

1. Should researchers be allowed to test new treatments or procedures on animals?

2. If your group decides the answer is "no," how will researchers find out if their treatments will work on people?

3. If your group decides the answer is "yes," should there be any rules or restrictions? Who should enforce the rules?

Making Connections

Jay Ingram

Jay Ingram is an experienced science journalist and is the host of *Daily Planet* on Discovery Channel Canada.

Wow! Bacteria

It will probably surprise you to know that human cells are not the most plentiful cells in your body – bacterial cells are. There are an estimated 500 different species of bacteria in each one of us, and their total population is something like 100 000 000 000 000. Or maybe it's 1 000 000 000 000 000. There might be as many as 100 bacterial cells in your body for every 1 of your human cells.

Most people react to this news by thinking, "Ewwwwwww!" But they're wrong. The vast majority of those bacteria do not cause disease. Instead they help us by doing things like making food easier to digest or producing valuable vitamins in our intestines.

We're not the only ones that provide a home for bacteria: every single creature does, and some of them make use of bacteria in the strangest ways. My favourite is an animal called the bobtail squid. It's a small squid – you could hold one easily in the palm of your hand – and it has a typically squiddy appearance, with tentacles extending from a short little body. But if you saw one of these squid at night, you'd be impressed.

The bobtail squid glows. It emits a blue-green light from a pit in its belly as it swims near the surface of the ocean collecting food. Scientists think the light confuses predators lurking below, who think they are seeing starlight or moonlight. That is clever enough, but the nature of that light is simply astonishing. It is not produced by the squid the way that fireflies produce their own cold light. Instead, a living colony of bacteria, nestled in the squid's light organ, generates the light.

Immediately after hatching, the squid trap these bacteria in a special bacteria-collecting organ. Funnily enough, even though there are millions of different bacteria in the ocean, only this one, light-generating species can colonize the organ. Once the bacteria have been taken in, the collecting organ is changed – *by the bacteria* – into a *light* organ! In a way, the squid is not a squid until it has collected its bacteria.

Back to us. Remember, we each have trillions of bacteria in us. Are we, in some as-yet-undiscovered way, the product of the bacteria in our gut or on our skin? If so, "Ewwwwwww!" should really be "Wow!"

Figure 3.26 Bobtail squid

Key Concept Review

1. What types of systems do living things have, and how are they organized? ⓚ

2. Why is the co-ordination of activities among organs important to multicellular organisms? ⓚ

3. Could you survive without any of your organ systems? Why or why not? ⓣ

4. How would the health of an organ be affected if many of its cells were damaged? Give reasons to support your opinion. ⓣ

5. (a) Name a plant organ. ⓚ

   (b) Identify the tissues that make up this organ.

   (c) Describe the cells that make up each of the tissues in this organ.

6. Create a concept map to show how three organ systems noted in this chapter are related. ⓚ

7. What key areas are cell biologists focussing on for cancer research? ⓚ

Connect Your Understanding

8. Flu shots are available each year. Explain why you think researchers have not developed a one-time vaccination for this illness. ⓣ

9. Diffusion happens throughout your body. Use the concept of diffusion to explain how oxygen gets from the air around you to a cell in your foot. List the organs and organ systems that help deliver the oxygen. ⓐ

10. Explain how an understanding of cells and cellular processes can help in diagnosing and treating disease. ⓐ

11. Human understanding of cellular processes has potential for both benefit and harm to human health and the environment.

After Writing · *Thinking Literacy*

Reflect and Evaluate

Review the newspaper article you wrote, then take five minutes to share your article with a classmate who wrote on a different topic. Listen to a reading of your classmate's article. What was the most important information you heard?

Write a paragraph explaining your concerns about possible health challenges in the modern world and how scientific knowledge and discovery can play a role in facing these challenges.

Share your opinions and observations with the class.

ACHIEVEMENT CHART CATEGORIES
ⓚ Knowledge and understanding   ⓣ Thinking and investigation   ⓒ Communication   ⓐ Application

Give one example of a potential benefit and one of a potential harm. Do you think the potential for benefit outweighs the potential risk of harm? Justify your opinion. ⓐ

12. The photo opposite was taken during the SARS crisis in Toronto in 2003. Identify precautions taken to prevent the transmission of the disease. Explain why you think they would or would not be effective. ⓐ

Practise Your Skills

13. You have been asked to take part in a debate about the use of animal testing in science. Describe the steps you will take to analyze and evaluate the information and prepare your presentation. ⓐ

14. Select a discovery related to microbiology that you feel is important. Make a T-chart, and list at least three potential benefits and three potential risks to society. ⓒ

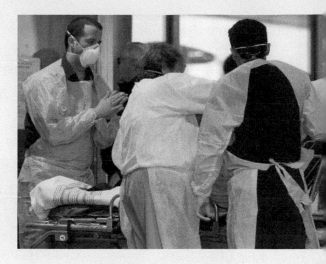

Unit Task Link

Make a list of human organ systems and explain the role cells play in those systems.

A49 *Thinking about Science, Technology, and Society* STSE

Public Choices Affect the Health of Cells

The lungs are lined with cells that have tiny hairs like the ones seen on the paramecium, and they are also called cilia. In this case, the cilia work like tiny brooms and sweep out the lungs to keep them free of materials that do not belong.

The nicotine in tobacco smoke paralyzes the cilia, and they stop sweeping. Burning tobacco also releases a multitude of other chemicals. The chemicals build up in the lungs and become available to cells throughout the body as the respiratory system passes materials on to the circulatory system. This is why smoking has been linked to a variety of illnesses, including lung cancer, bronchitis, and heart disease.

What to Do

Use the information you have learned about diffusion, osmosis, cells, and organ systems as you consider whether smoking in public should be allowed or should be banned.

Consider This

With a classmate or as a whole class, discuss the following social issue.

Smoking is a personal choice. Smoking is also the cause of many diseases, and second-hand smoke is a problem for many people. Should smoking be allowed in public places? What should be considered a public place?

1.0 Cells are the basic units of all living things.

KEY CONCEPTS

- Cell theory
- Differences between plant and animal cells
- Diffusion and osmosis

CHAPTER SUMMARY

- Cells in all organisms come from existing cells.
- Many organelles in plant and animal cells perform similar functions.
- Plant cells have chloroplasts that contain chlorophyll, a substance involved in photosynthesis.
- Materials flow into and out of cells through the processes of diffusion and osmosis.
- The study of cells was not possible until the microscope was developed and improved.

2.0 Cellular processes sustain living things.

KEY CONCEPTS

- Unicellular and multicellular organisms
- Specialized cells in multicellular organisms
- The basic cellular processes that sustain plant and animal cells

CHAPTER SUMMARY

- Unicellular organisms are essential for the continuance of life on Earth.
- Osmosis and diffusion limit the size of cells.
- Cell specialization helps multicellular organisms meet their basic needs.
- Cellular processes include transforming energy, processing and transporting materials, and reproduction.

3.0 Healthy organisms depend on the interaction of healthy cells, tissues, and organs.

KEY CONCEPTS

- Specialized cells in tissues and organs
- Interdependent organ systems
- The influence of studies in cell biology on human life and health

CHAPTER SUMMARY

- Cells make up four main types of animal tissue and three main types of plant tissue.
- Specialized tissues make up organs.
- Organ systems are made up of two or more organs working together to do a task.
- Organ systems work together to keep an organism functioning and healthy.
- Studies in cell biology lead to breakthroughs in human health-care, agriculture, and the environment.

Come and Visit "The Cell"!

Getting Started

You are the marketing director at a theme park. You have been given the task of promoting it to teachers, parents, and students. This is no ordinary theme park, however. You work for the park known as "The Cell." Every organelle, process, and function related to cells is represented at a regular, life-sized theme park.

Visitors will witness the aspects of cell structure and activity that have been presented in this unit. Thrill-seeking visitors will be looking for the excitement that they have come to expect at theme parks. Your challenge is to convince potential visitors that The Cell is a great place.

Your Goal

You will create a marketing brochure for "The Cell" theme park. Using graphics, text, and creative layout strategies, the finished product will clearly relate all aspects of the structure, function, and processes of a cell to matching components of an actual theme park.

What You Need to Know

You have explored the basics of cell structure and function. You are aware of major events and technological innovations that have aided the study of the cell in even greater detail, such as the improvement in microscope capability.

Review your notes to recall the processes that occur within the cell and across the cell membranes. Consider that some cells are specialized in order to carry out specific tasks within tissues.

Steps to Success

1. Gather a variety of marketing brochures in order to familiarize yourselves with this sales tool. Discuss the common features. Focus on those that are particularly effective. (Or not!)

2. Using the Internet or print resources, make yourself familiar with the aspects of a modern amusement park that you could relate to cell structures, functions, and processes. Start your Internet research at ScienceSource.

3. Brainstorm the matching of structures, functions, and processes between the actual cell and the theme park. Remember to stress the visual aspects for the brochure.

4. Collect (or create) pictures, art, or graphics that could be used in your layout. Use magnified images of the actual structures wherever possible.

5. Create text boxes that provide information as well as excite and intrigue the viewer.

6. Don't forget to include a site plan as a final visual reference.

How Did It Go?

7. Do your amusement park features relate to structures and functions that exist in a real cell?

8. Are processes such as osmosis, diffusion, and reproduction reflected in aspects of your theme park?

Key Terms Review

1. Create a mind map that shows your understanding of the terms listed below. You may need to add some words of your own to show how the terms are connected. *k*
   - animal cell
   - cell division
   - cell theory
   - diffusion
   - microscope
   - multicellular
   - organ
   - organ system
   - organelle
   - osmosis
   - plant cell
   - selective permeability
   - specialized cells
   - tissue
   - unicellular
   - virus

2. Use the words below in a paragraph that explains how materials pass through a cell membrane. *k*
   - carbon dioxide
   - cell membrane
   - diffusion
   - organelle
   - osmosis
   - oxygen

Key Concept Review

1.0

3. Describe one difference between: *k*
   (a) plant cells and animal cells
   (b) an amoeba and a hydra

4. "Cells are the basis of life." Do you agree or disagree with this statement? Explain your reasoning. *a*

5. In your own words, state the three key ideas that make up the cell theory. *k*

6. In your notebook: *k*
   (a) name all the parts numbered in the cell diagram
   (b) explain the functions of three of those parts

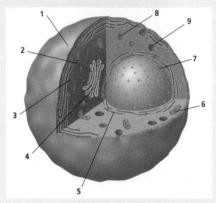

7. Draw a plant cell, label all of the parts, and explain the function of each one. *k*

8. If a cell membrane suddenly became permeable to all substances, could the cell remain alive? Explain your answer. *t*

2.0

9. Name four characteristics of living things. *k*

10. Examine the two micrographs (a) and (b) below. Identify each one as either a plant or an animal cell. Explain your choice. *k*

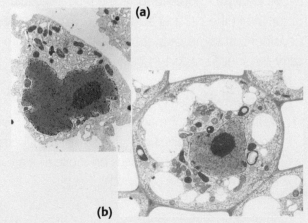

(a)

(b)

ACHIEVEMENT CHART CATEGORIES
k Knowledge and understanding   *t* Thinking and investigation   *c* Communication   *a* Application

11. Name and describe the function of the parts of the microscope numbered in the photograph below. Ⓚ

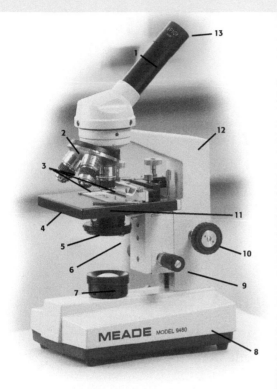

12. Examine the photograph below. What is the student doing? Ⓐ

13. Examine the diagram on the right. In which direction will the water (smaller particles) move? Explain why. Ⓚ

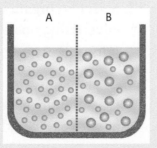

14. What critical needs of an organism are jaws, limbs, teeth, and eyes necessary for? Ⓚ

15. What role does the environment play in defining the appearance of an organism? Ⓚ

16. What important role do unicellular organisms play in sustaining life on Earth? Ⓚ

17. Volcanic eruptions like the one on the island of Krakatoa in Indonesia in 1883 can send huge quantities of ash into the atmosphere. This ash can partially block out the Sun's rays for days or weeks. What effect would this have on unicellular and multicellular plants? Ⓣ

18. Describe the link between multicellular organisms and the concept of specialized cells. Ⓐ

19. Explain why cells are typically very small. Ⓣ

20. Plants have specialized cells. What is the role of each type of specialized plant cell? Ⓚ

21. Your body sends you signals to tell you when you are hungry. Why do organisms require food? Ⓚ

22. (a) Why is it important for a multicellular organism to have a very efficient waste removal system? Ⓣ

(b) Name one cellular waste product, and describe how it is removed. Ⓚ

23. Use words and pictures to describe basic cell division. (k)

3.0

24. Multicellular organisms are very complex and need to co-ordinate trillions of cells and cellular processses. At the start of Chapter 3, this concept was introduced by comparing it to a soccer team. Make this comparison with a different organization, for example, a school board or a city. (a)

25. Organize the terms shown below from basic to more complex. For each word, name one example. (k)

individual, organelle, tissue, cell, organ system, organ

26. Tissues are collections of similar cells that perform the same function. Can tissue survive on its own? Explain your answer. (t)

27. Your organ systems do not function independently. Consider the following scenarios, and explain how two different organ systems are working together. (a)

(a) You step on hot pavement in the summer and quickly pull your foot back.

(b) After running up the stairs, you breathe a little harder.

(c) A friend has a cold, and three days later you have a cold too.

28. Look at the photographs below. Name each type of tissue, and state whether it comes from a plant or an animal. (k)

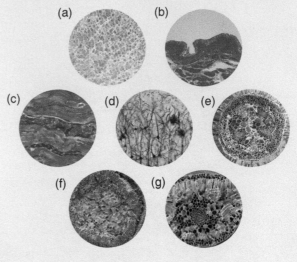

(a)   (b)
(c)   (d)   (e)
(f)   (g)

Connect Your Understanding

29. What makes your hands wrinkle after a long bath or shower? (a)

30. The muscle cells responsible for bumblebee flight have a large amount of mitochondria. Explain why. (t)

31. Cell biologists have modified plants so that they can grow in different conditions or have different nutritional value. Do you think cell biologists should alter human cells to make us stronger or faster? Explain your reasoning. (t)

32. Select an organelle. Design and create an advertising poster to promote it as the most important organelle in the cell. (c)

33. Explain why an understanding of cells is essential for making informed decisions about your health. (t)

ACHIEVEMENT CHART CATEGORIES
(k) Knowledge and understanding   (t) Thinking and investigation   (c) Communication   (a) Application

Practise Your Skills

34. Design an experiment using a potato to illustrate the process of osmosis. Include a purpose, hypothesis, materials list, procedure, and data collection chart. *a*

35. With your teacher's permission, carry out the experiment you designed in question 34. *a*

36. List 10 different technologies mentioned or illustrated in this unit that improve our understanding of cells and how they function. *a*

37. You see a skunk on the far side of your schoolyard. Several minutes later, you smell its distinctive aroma. Use words and pictures to describe why this is an example of diffusion. *t*

Revisit the Big Ideas

38. Identify which of the following statements are false. Reword the false statements to make them true. *k*

(a) Organelles are the smallest unit of life.

(b) Healthy cells contribute to healthy organisms.

(c) Cells, tissue, organs, and organ systems work independently of each other.

39. In your own words, explain the meaning of this statement: "Each cell is a system within a system." *t*

40. In what ways has learning about cells changed your thinking with respect to making healthy choices? *a*

A50 **Thinking about Science, Technology, Society, and the Environment**
S
T
S
E

What's the limit?

This unit began with a discussion of how the discovery of cells and the ability to study them led to an understanding of how living things, including humans, are structured and how they function. This knowledge led to the discovery of cures for some diseases and to the development of special crops to help feed the world. Cell research has allowed us to change or modify the basic unit of life — changing when and how plants grow, healing wounds, and sometimes ending the development of cancers.

Consider This

With a classmate or as a whole class, discuss the following.

1. Should there be a limit to how far we can go in changing the basic unit of life? If so, what should that limit be? Explain your reasoning.

2. Do you think there should be restrictions on who is allowed to do work that changes the cells of living things? Explain your reasoning.

Systems in
Action

Unit Overview

Fundamental Concepts

In Science and Technology for grades 7 and 8, six fundamental concepts occur throughout. This unit addresses the following two:

- Systems and Interactions
- Continuity and Change

Big Ideas

As you work through this unit, you will develop a deeper understanding of the following big ideas:

- Systems are designed to accomplish tasks.
- All systems include an input and an output.
- Systems are designed to optimize human and natural resources.

Overall Expectations

By the end of this unit, you will be expected to:

1. assess the personal, social, and/or environmental impacts of a system, and evaluate improvements to a system and/or alternative ways of meeting the same needs

2. investigate a working system and the ways in which components of the system contribute to its desired function

3. demonstrate an understanding of different types of systems and the factors that contribute to their safe and efficient operation

This rock climber, with his system of ropes and pulleys, enjoys the natural freshwater system of Ontario.

Exploring

The da Vinci Surgical System® is a mechanical system used for robotic surgery.

Chances are that a system woke you up today and several systems helped you make your breakfast. You may also have used a transit system and a school system. A **system** is a group of individual parts or procedures that work together to accomplish a desired task. All the different parts of a system are called **components**. Society runs smoothly and efficiently because of its many systems.

Systems can be classified into two categories. A mechanical system is composed of physical parts working together, for example, a bus. The physical parts of the bus act together to provide transportation. A non-mechanical system is a set of procedures, methods, or rules that accomplish a task. Bus schedules and routes are examples of non-mechanical systems. Many systems in society include both mechanical and non-mechanical systems.

Some systems, such as the solar system, occur naturally. Other systems are developed to meet the needs of society. Many of those systems evolve as our society changes. One system that is continually changing is a health-care system.

Robotic Surgery

One recent addition to our health-care system is robotic surgery, the use of robots to perform surgery. Laparoscopic devices, such as fibre optic cables, miniature cameras, and surgical instruments, are inserted into the body through small incisions. These are controlled by the surgeon at a special console. This type of robotic surgery is called minimally invasive surgery (MIS). MIS surgery means less trauma and pain for the patient, who recovers more quickly.

Robotic surgery has now progressed to the point where a machine, instead of a surgeon, operates on a patient. The surgeon sits at a console and manipulates the robot's four arms. One robotic arm controls the camera while three arms manipulate the instruments. With this machine, surgeons have better precision and dexterity as well as full stereoscopic vision.

Dr. Anvari keeps an eye on the monitor while operating robotically.

Remote Surgery

With these new systems, surgery can now be done remotely, with the surgeon and the patient in different locations. In February 2003, Dr. Mehran Anvari of Hamilton, Ontario, operated on a patient in North Bay, over 400 km away. This was the first remote surgery (telesurgery) in Canada. The Canadian military may use remote surgery for injured soldiers in distant combat zones.

In the future, automatic surgery may be possible. The techniques of expert surgeons, stored in computers, will allow robot systems to perform surgery without direct human input.

Society has to decide if this is an ethical and acceptable addition to our medical system. Part of our responsibility as citizens is to assess each system's impact on society and on our environment.

The robotic instruments are closing the wound.

...MORE TO EXPLORE

Clothes Peg Surgery

In this lab, you will design something that works in the same way that robotic surgery does.

Purpose

To design and construct a mechanical system to retrieve a coin from the bottom of a jar

Materials & Equipment

- glass jar
- $1 coin
- plasticine
- clothes peg

Procedure

1. Place a $1 coin (loonie) on edge in a small piece of plasticine. Place the plasticine and coin at the bottom of a tall jar.

2. Design a device to retrieve the coin from the jar using a clothes peg and other materials. Your device must allow you to pick up the coin without your fingers entering the jar.

3. Make a sketch of your design. Get your teacher's approval before you proceed.

4. Construct your device and attempt to pick up the coin from the bottom of the jar.

Questions

5. Was your design successful? (a) If yes, describe two modifications that could improve your design. (b) If no, suggest modifications to your design that might make it work properly.

6. Make a list of the components of your mechanical system and state their purposes in the overall task.

Components of a System

Systems are made up of individual components that work together to perform a task or function.

What to Do

1. Choose one of the systems listed below.
   - health care system
   - legal system
   - school system
   - respiratory system
   - Aboriginal clan system
   - waste management system

2. List the components of this system.

Consider This

3. What task does this system perform?

4. Choose one component of the system from your list. Suppose that component was removed from the system. Describe how this would affect the system.

5. Describe the long-term effects of removing the component from the system. Include any societal, technological, and environmental impacts.

UNIT B

Contents

Unit Task

In your Unit Task, you will design, construct, and test a mechanical system that uses only the energy stored in a spring-bar mousetrap to perform a function other than catching mice. You will use skills that you learn in this unit to efficiently transfer the energy stored in the mousetrap. Your investigations on forces, work, mechanical advantage, and efficiency will help you develop your mechanical system.

Essential Question

How does a mousetrap work, and how does each component contribute to the system's desired function?

Getting Ready to Read

Thinking Literacy

Creating a Word Wall

Scan the unit and identify 10 key words whose meaning is unknown to you. Make a class list of unknown words. Arrange these words alphabetically and make them into a word wall. With your group, discuss possible meanings of each word. Think of related words to help you, then use the Glossary that starts on page 405 to verify your meanings. In your own words, record the meanings of your 10 unknown words in your notes.

In the circus, an acrobat jumps on one end of the teeter-totter to launch another acrobat into the air.

What You Will Learn

In this chapter, you will:

- describe the characteristics of a system and define a mechanical system
- identify the purpose, inputs, and outputs of a mechanical system
- explain how heat is produced
- understand the relationship between work, force, and distance moved

Skills You Will Use

In this chapter, you will:

- measure force using a spring scale
- calculate the work done to move objects
- calculate the mechanical advantage of a mechanical system

Why This Is Important

Riding a bike, climbing stairs, and throwing a ball are examples of using forces to transfer energy. Mechanical systems are often involved in these energy transformations.

Before Reading

Thinking Literacy

Activating Prior Knowledge

Chapter 4 focuses on four main topics: mechanical systems, force, work and energy, and mechanical advantage. Draw a mind map to record what you already know about each topic from earlier science classes, as well as from your daily life. Revisit your mind map as you read the chapter, and add and modify meanings and connections.

Key Terms

- work
- force
- friction
- mass
- weight
- mechanical system
- energy
- gravity
- mechanical advantage
- ideal mechanical advantage

4.0 Getting Started

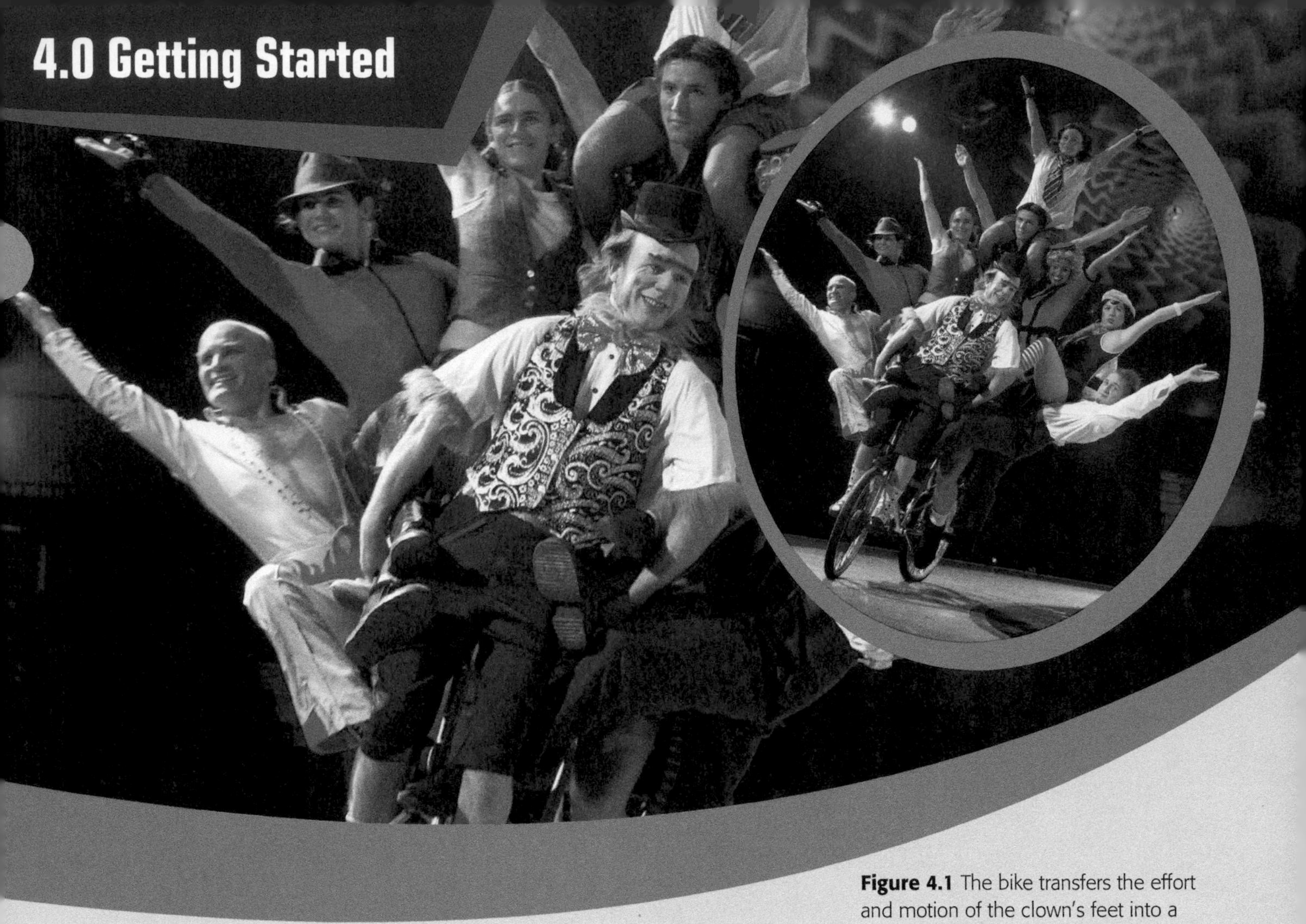

Figure 4.1 The bike transfers the effort and motion of the clown's feet into a different motion for all the riders.

When we watch acrobats and clowns perform at a circus, we do not tend to think of science. But circus performers need to understand the science of mechanical systems in order to perform acts of strength and balance. A **mechanical system** is a group of physical parts that interact with each other. The parts function as a whole in order to complete a task.

The bicycle in Figure 4.1 is a mechanical system. Many individual parts of the bicycle work together to allow the clown to carry the passengers relatively easily. Although the clown's feet move in small circles, the bicycle is travelling in a straight line. As well, the clown can push hard enough on the pedals to move all the passengers.

Figure 4.2 If the riders sit at different distances from the centre, they can balance the teeter-totter.

Mechanical systems are more than just bicycles. Consider the teeter-totter in your local playground. The downward motion of one person is transferred into the upward motion of the other. By adjusting how far the two people sit from the centre of the board (the fulcrum), you can compensate for the people having different masses (Figure 4.2). Circus performers use a more complex version of the teeter-totter (Figure 4.3).

Figure 4.3 The smaller acrobat is able to move the larger acrobat by changing location.

B3 *Quick Lab*

Lift This

The human body is also a mechanical system. Muscles, bones, and joints work together to perform various tasks. Imagine that you have a ball in your hand. By controlling all the parts that make up your human mechanical system, you can move the ball in a circle or throw it in a straight line. Depending on how much effort you exert and the technique you use to throw the ball, you can control how fast the ball travels.

Purpose

To examine how the amount of effort required to lift a mass can vary depending on where the mass is located

Materials & Equipment

- piece of string, 50 cm long
- 1- to 2-kg mass

Figure 4.4

Procedure

1. Make a loop from the piece of string. Hang the mass from the string.

2. Stand up. Hold your forearm horizontally, with your elbow tight against the side of your body. Loop the string over your hand (Figure 4.4).

3. Keeping your elbow stationary, lift your arm slowly. Make mental notes of how much effort you need to lift the object and of the distance you were able to raise the object.

4. Move the loop of string to your wrist and repeat step 3.

5. Move the loop of string to your forearm and repeat step 3.

Questions

6. At which string location did you need the least effort to lift the object?

7. Explain the relationship between the distance of the string from your elbow and the amount of effort you required to lift the object.

8. Which string location allowed you to lift the object the farthest? Compare the effort needed at this location to those needed at the other locations.

Here is a summary of what you will learn in this section:

- A force is a push or a pull that acts on an object.
- Forces can be classified as either contact forces or action-at-a-distance forces.
- Mass is the amount of matter in an object.
- Weight is the force of gravity acting on an object.
- For an object on Earth, the force of gravity, in newtons, is the product of the object's mass, in kilograms, and the gravitational field 9.8 N/kg.

"May the Force be with you" is a popular line from the *Star Wars* movies. The use of the word "force" in the movie is different from force in a science classroom. In science, **force** is a push or a pull that acts on an object.

B4 *Starting Point*   Skills Ⓐ Ⓒ

Identifying Forces

Any object that is being pushed or pulled is experiencing a force. Looking at Figure 4.5, we could say, "The leash applies a force on the dog." With a partner, make a list of the forces that you can find in Figure 4.5.

Figure 4.5

In order to slide your textbook across your desk or kick a football, you must apply a force to the object (Figure 4.6). A magnet can move a steel paper clip without even touching it. Forces can also stop objects from moving, such as when you catch a ball. Even objects that are at rest have forces acting on them. For example, as you sit at your desk, you are being pulled to the ground by Earth's force of gravity. As well, your chair seat is pushing upward on you so that you do not fall. Every object in the universe experiences forces. So in terms of the *Star Wars* definition, the force is with you.

Figure 4.6 The football begins its motion as a result of the force of the player's foot.

Classifying Forces

All the different forces shown in Figure 4.5 can be classified as contact forces or action-at-a-distance forces.

Contact forces must touch the object that they push or pull, for example, hitting a tennis ball (Figure 4.7). Another common contact force is friction. **Friction** is a force that opposes the relative motion of an object. If you slide a hockey puck across a wooden floor, it slows down and stops because friction resists its motion. If you slide the same hockey puck across ice instead of the floor, the puck slides farther before stopping because ice applies less friction on the puck than the wooden floor does.

Action-at-a-distance forces can push or pull an object without touching it. Gravity, static electricity, and magnetism produce action-at-a-distance forces, as shown in Figure 4.8. These are also called non-contact forces.

The most common action-at-a-distance force, the force of **gravity**, is the attraction between two objects due to their mass. The amount of attraction depends upon the amount of each object's mass and the distance between the two objects. For example, when we let go of a ball, the ball is pulled to the ground by the force of gravity, even though nothing is touching it. This is because the ball and Earth both have mass and therefore attract each other.

Figure 4.7 The racket applies a contact force when hitting the ball.

Figure 4.8 (a) The static charge on the balloon attracts the water. (b) Magnets apply an action-at-a-distance force.

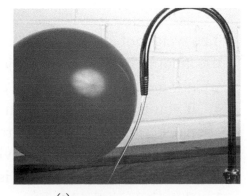

(a)

(b)

Making Connections

Making connections is an important strategy for readers. This ongoing process of interacting with the text helps readers connect with their prior experience and knowledge. This helps them visualize, infer, and remember what they have read better.

As you read the next section, record the following in a three-column chart:

1. key words that spark a meaningful connection

2. your connection as a reader

3. how this connection helps you better understand the text

Figure 4.9 If you were an astronaut, your mass would be the same on both Earth and the Moon. Your weight would be less on the Moon, however, because the Moon has less gravity.

Table 4.1 Masses and Weights of a 50-kg Person on the Surface of Various Objects in the Solar System.

Location	Mass (kg)	Weight (N)
Earth	50	490
Moon	50	80
Mars	50	160
Jupiter	50	1140

Mass

Once we have identified the type of force, we often need to measure the amount of force. Before we do this, we must understand the difference between mass and weight. **Mass** is the amount of matter in an object. The mass of a bowling ball is greater than the mass of a tennis ball because it contains more matter. The metric unit for measuring mass is the kilogram (kg). For example, the mass of 1 L of water is 1 kg. Smaller masses are often measured in grams (g). There are 1000 g in 1 kg, so we could say that the mass of 1 L of water is 1000 g.

Since mass is the amount of matter in an object, the object's mass does not change as a result of gravity. If you have a mass of 50 kg on Earth, your mass on the Moon, where gravity is one-sixth Earth's gravity, is still 50 kg (Figure 4.9). This is because the amount of matter in your body has not changed on your trip to the Moon.

Weight

The weight of an object is not the same as its mass. **Weight** is the amount of force on an object due to gravity. Therefore, weight means the same thing as the force of gravity.

If you travelled from Earth to the Moon, your weight would change because the force of gravity on Earth is about six times stronger than the force of gravity on the Moon (Table 4.1). This means that your weight is about six times greater on Earth as it is on the Moon.

The Unit of Force

The metric unit for force is the newton (N), named after Sir Isaac Newton (1643–1727). Since weight is the force of gravity, it is measured in newtons (N). On Earth, a 1.0-kg mass has a weight of 9.8 N.

Outside of the science classroom, you may have used a scale to "weigh" fruit or vegetables. Most of these scales are marked in kilograms. When you do this, you are not finding the weight, in newtons, but instead finding the mass, in kilograms.

Measuring Force

Most meters that measure force contain a spring or elastic component that stretches or compresses when a force is applied. The most common force meter is called a Newton gauge or **spring scale**, as shown in Figure 4.10. A spring scale consists of a spring with a hook on the end. As more force is applied to the hook, the spring stretches farther. The spring scales used in your classroom have been calibrated to display the relationship between the amount of force and the distance of stretch. This allows you to read the amount of force directly from the spring scale.

Spring scales can measure forces other than weight. If you needed to know how much force you need to slide an object across your desk, you simply attach the spring scale to the object and pull at a constant speed, as in Figure 4.11. By pulling parallel to the desk at a constant speed, you are measuring the force of friction between the object and your desk.

Figure 4.10 The spring scale shows the weight of an object in newtons.

Suggested Activity • • • • • • • • •
B7 Quick Lab on page 103

Calculating the Force of Gravity (Weight)

It is useful to determine the weight of an object without having to use a spring scale. Scientists discovered that the mass of an object and its weight are directly proportional. That means that an object with twice the mass has twice the weight. On Earth, a 1.0-kg mass suspended from a spring scale has a weight of 9.8 N. A 2.0-kg mass has a weight of 19.6 N. Thus, if you multiply any mass by 9.8 N/kg, you get its weight on Earth. This value, 9.8 N/kg, is called Earth's gravitational field strength and is symbolized by g.

Figure 4.11 Spring scales can be used to determine the force required to move an object.

Take It **Further**

The bathroom scale you might use at home to weigh yourself does not look like the spring scale shown in Figure 4.10. Compare and contrast these two scales used for weighing. Begin your search at ScienceSource.

The force of gravity (F_g) on any mass (m) near the surface of Earth can be calculated by:

Force of gravity = (mass of object) × (the strength of Earth's gravitational field)

Using symbols, this word equation can be expressed as:

$$F_g = mg$$

where mass is in kilograms (kg) and g is 9.8 N/kg.

For example, to find the weight of a 50-kg student on Earth:

$$F_g = mg$$
$$= (50 \text{ kg})(9.8 \text{ N/kg})$$
$$= 490 \text{ N}$$

Suggested Activity •·········
B8 Inquiry Activity on page 104

A 50-kg student weighs 490 N on Earth.

B6 *Learning Checkpoint*

Weight and Mass

1. Use the words "mass" or "weight" to correctly complete the following sentences.

   (a) Even if gravity changes, the _____ of an object does not change.

   (b) The _____ of an object would change if the gravity changed.

   (c) Kilogram (kg) is the metric unit for _____.

   (d) The newton (N) is the metric unit for _____.

2. The following masses are located on Earth. Calculate the weight of each object.

   (a) 25 kg

   (b) 40 kg

   (c) 150 kg

3. An object has a mass of 5.0 kg on the surface of the Moon. What would be the object's:

   (a) mass on Earth?

   (b) force of gravity on Earth?

Measuring Force with a Spring Scale

An object at rest requires a force to start it moving. To lift an object, a force must be applied that overcomes the force of gravity on that object. To slide an object across a surface, the applied force must overcome the force of friction. This force can be measured by using an appropriate spring scale.

Purpose

To measure the force required to move some common objects

Materials & Equipment

- different spring scales (0–5 N, 0–20 N)
- string
- scissors
- 4 small objects (less than 1 kg each)

CAUTION: Handle sharp objects like scissors very carefully.

Procedure

1. Copy Table 4.2 into your notebook.

Table 4.2 Measuring Force with a Spring Scale

Object	Force Required to Lift the Object (N)	Force Required to Slide the Object (N)

2. Choose four different objects from your backpack, pencil case, or classroom. Record the name of each object in your data table.

3. If any of the objects does not have a place to attach the hook of the spring scale, tie a loop of string to the object.

4. Place your first object on your desk and connect it to the hook of your smallest spring scale. Holding your spring scale vertically, slowly begin to lift the object with the spring scale. If the reading on the spring scale is approaching the maximum and the object is still on your desk, change to a larger spring scale. Measure the force required to lift the object and record this value in your data table.

5. Now reconnect your first object to the hook of your smallest spring scale. Holding your spring scale horizontally, slowly try to slide the object across your desk by pulling the spring scale. If the reading on the spring scale is approaching maximum and the object is still not moving, switch to a larger spring scale. Measure the force required to slide the object across your desk and record this value in your data table.

6. Repeat steps 4 and 5 for your remaining three objects.

Questions

7. If you needed approximately 3.0 N to lift an object, would it be better to use a 0–5 N scale or a 0–20 N scale? Explain your answer.

8. When measuring the force needed to slide your object, explain why it was important to hold the scale horizontally (parallel to the table) and not at an angle.

9. In general, does it take more force to lift an object off the desk or to slide the object across the desk?

DI Anchor Activity

B8 *Inquiry Activity*

SKILLS YOU WILL USE
■ Performing and reporting
■ Analyzing and interpreting

Toolkits 2,8

The Force of Gravity

A graph is sometimes a good way to find the relationship between two variables. If the data produce a straight-line graph that passes through the origin, then we say that the two variables are directly proportional.

Question

What is the relationship between mass and the force of gravity (weight)?

Materials & Equipment

- spring scale
- set of hooked masses
- graph paper

Procedure

1. Copy Table 4.3 into your notebook, with space for five trials.

Table 4.3 The Force of Gravity

	Mass (g)	Mass (kg)	Weight (N)
1			
2			

2. Choose one of your hooked masses and record its mass, in grams, in the data table. Convert this value to kilograms and record this as its mass in kilograms.

Figure 4.12

3. While holding your spring scale stationary vertically, hang the mass and measure its weight (Figure 4.12). Record this value in your data table.

4. Repeat steps 2 and 3 for four more masses. You may have to combine masses to get enough readings. For example, hook a 50-g and a 100-g mass together to get a 150-g mass.

5. Use your data to plot a weight-versus-mass graph. Plot the weight on the vertical axis and the mass, in kilograms, on the horizontal axis.

6. Draw a best-fit line through the data points plotted on your graph.

Analyzing and Interpreting

7. As you increased the mass, what happened to the weight?

8. Choose three points on the best-fit line of your graph. For each point, calculate the weight divided by the mass. Are the results of these three calculations similar to each other?

9. On Earth, the ratio of weight to mass is approximately 9.8 N/kg. How do your results compare to this ratio?

10. Did your best-fit line pass through all your data points? If no, what are some of the sources of error in your experiment?

Skill Builder

11. Explain how you could use your best-fit line to find the weight of a mass without hanging it from a spring scale.

Forming Conclusions

12. Your data are best represented by a straight line on a weight-versus-mass graph. What is the relationship between weight and mass?

Key Concept Review

1. Define "force." State the correct units for measuring force.

2. What are the two categories of force? Give an example of a force for each category.

3. What force causes a sliding object to slow down?

4. What is another word for "force of gravity"?

5. Explain how weight is different from mass.

6. What device is commonly used to measure force?

7. You weigh yourself on your bathroom scale at home. Would the same scale give the same measurement if you weighed yourself on a different planet? Explain.

Connect Your Understanding

8. Calculate the weight, in newtons, of each of the following masses.

   (a) 25 kg (b) 6.0 kg (c) 250 g

Practise Your Skills

9. An astronaut measures the force of gravity on various masses on the surface of two different planets. The data for Planet A and Planet B are shown below. Which planet has the larger gravitational field? Explain your answer.

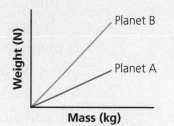

For more questions, go to ScienceSource.

B9 *Thinking about Technology, Society, and the Environment*

The Right Shoe

A lot of research goes into the design of shoes for specific sports, such as soccer shoes, bowling shoes, and basketball shoes. Often, the shoe is designed either to increase the force (e.g., a better grip in soccer shoes) or to decrease the force (e.g., shock absorption in basketball shoes and sliding ability in curling shoes).

Consider This

1. Choose a modern sports shoe. What need was the shoe designed to meet?

2. How has modern shoe technology affected the sport?

3. Did the development of this shoe have any economic impacts? environmental impacts? societal impacts?

Work and Energy

Here is a summary of what you will learn in this section:

- Work is done when a force causes something to move and energy is transferred.
- When a force causes an object to move a distance in the same direction as the force, then work = force × distance.
- Energy is the ability to do work.
- Kinetic energy is the energy due to an object's motion.
- Potential energy is stored energy.

Suppose you stopped 10 people on the street and asked them the question, "What is work?" For most people, work is what you do to earn money. You or your friends might work as baby sitters, newspaper deliverers, or hamburger flippers. What if your job was to hold a poster against a wall without moving? In this case, have you done work?

In science, the term "work" is used differently from how it is in everyday language. In science, **work** is the amount of effort spent when a force causes an object to move a distance. This means that when you kick a soccer ball, work is done on the ball since the force of your foot moved the ball a distance. When you write notes, you apply a force to the pen to move it across the page; you are doing work. What about holding that poster against the wall without moving? You are definitely applying a force, but since the poster is not moving a distance, no work is done on the poster.

B10 *Starting Point*

Skills Ⓐ Ⓒ

What Is Work?

For each of the photographs in Figure 4.13, use the scientific definition of "work" to decide if work is being done on the object. Justify your answer to a partner. Would people who do not know the scientific definition consider any of these photographs as being "work"?

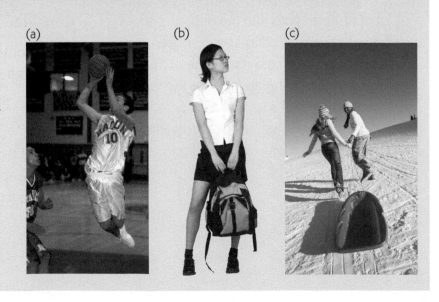

(a) (b) (c)

Figure 4.13 (a) Shooting a basketball, (b) holding a backpack, (c) pulling a sled

Making Connections

Good readers stay engaged with the text they are reading by making meaningful connections to themselves, to the world, and to other texts. These connections are often coded as text to self (T–S), text to world (T–W) and text to text (T–T). As you read this section, record and code the connections you make. Which connection helps you understand what you are reading best?

Work and Energy

At the end of a long run in your PE class, you might feel as if you have little energy left. At home we turn off the lights or turn down the heat to save energy. Most people are familiar with the word "energy," but what does this word mean? In science, **energy** is defined as the ability to do work. The metric unit for energy is the joule (J), named after James Joule (1818–1889). Work is done when a force causes an object to move. Therefore, energy is the ability to apply a force and move an object. The bowling ball in Figure 4.14 applies a force to the pins and moves them a distance while knocking them down. Since the bowling ball did work on the pins, the rolling bowling ball had energy.

To knock all the pins down, the bowling ball does not have to hit every pin. When the bowling ball does work on the first pin that it strikes, it transfers some of its energy to that pin. The first pin now has energy to knock down another pin. When work is done, energy is transferred from one object to another or from one form of energy to another form of energy.

During any transfer of energy, the total amount of energy remains constant. This means that you cannot create energy, nor can you destroy energy. You can only transfer the energy from one object to another or transform the energy from one form to another. This is called the law of conservation of energy.

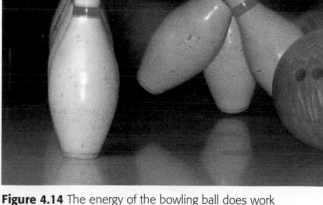

Figure 4.14 The energy of the bowling ball does work on the pins that the ball hits.

Forms of Energy

The various forms of energy can be classified into two categories: kinetic energy and potential energy. The bowling ball was able to do work because it was moving. A stationary bowling ball cannot knock down the pins. When an object is moving, the energy it has is called **kinetic energy**. Sometimes the motion is hard to detect. For example, electricity, thermal energy, and sound are forms of kinetic energy since the particles involved in each of these energies are in motion.

In earlier grades, you learned that all matter is made of tiny particles. All these particles are in motion all the time, so they have kinetic energy. Thermal energy is the total amount of all the kinetic energy of all the particles in an object or substance. When this energy transfers to another object or substance, it is called heat.

Energy does not always involve motion. An object can store its energy to do work later. Any energy that is stored is called **potential energy**.

You are able to do work because of the chemical potential energy in the food you eat. As plants and animals grow, they store chemical energy, and they convert it into other forms of energy when they need to. Gasoline and batteries also store chemical potential energy. A bow stores elastic energy until it is released (Figure 4.15).

Figure 4.16 shows a heavy rock directly above a tent peg stuck in the ground. When the rock is dropped, it will apply a force to the peg and move it a distance into the ground. Since the rock can do work on the tent peg if it is dropped, the stationary rock held above the tent peg has potential energy. The potential energy of an object that is able to fall is called **gravitational potential energy**.

Figure 4.15 In this position, the bow has potential energy.

Figure 4.16 An object that can fall has gravitational potential energy.

Work Produces a Change in Energy

According to our definition of potential energy, a backpack at rest on the floor has no gravitational potential energy since it cannot fall. When you lift the backpack, you are doing work since you are applying a force over a distance, as shown in Figure 4.17. As you do this work on the backpack, the backpack now has the ability to fall. Therefore, the work done on the backpack caused a change in the backpack's gravitational potential energy. Similarly, when you pluck a guitar string, some of the work done on the string is changed into sound energy. In all situations, whenever work is done on an object, there is a change in the object's energy.

Work Done by Friction

As mentioned earlier, energy is neither destroyed nor created. Energy can only be transferred from one object to another or transformed from one form of energy to another. When friction does work on an object, some of the object's energy is transformed into thermal energy. An increase in thermal energy makes an object warmer. Thermal energy is the total energy of the moving particles in a substance.

A person running the bases in a baseball game has kinetic energy. While sliding into a base, the player loses that kinetic energy when stopping (Figure 4.18). Since in any situation, energy cannot be lost, where does the player's kinetic energy go? The work done by the friction force transforms most of the kinetic energy into thermal energy. The part of the person's body sliding across the ground gets warmer. This is the same as warming your hands by rubbing them together: the kinetic energy is transformed into thermal energy.

In this unit, you are investigating how mechanical systems use forces to transfer energy. It is important to realize that all mechanical systems include frictional forces. As energy is transferred by a mechanical system, some amount of thermal energy is always produced.

Figure 4.17 When you do work by lifting the backpack, the backpack gains gravitational potential energy.

Figure 4.18 Work done by friction to stop the runner produces thermal energy.

Calculating Work

Since doing work changes an object's energy, then work must be measured in the same units as energy, which is the joule (J). Our definition of work can be used to derive an equation needed to calculate the work done on an object. The amount of work done depends on the amount of force exerted and the distance over which the force is applied. When the force causes the object to move in the same direction as the force, the amount of work done can be calculated as follows:

(Work in joules) = (Force in newtons) × (distance in metres)

This same equation can be written using symbols.

$W = Fd$

For example, suppose Jennifer pushes a box with a force of 150 N and the box moves 3.0 m. How much work does Jennifer do on the box?

$W = Fd$
$\quad = (150 \text{ N})(3.0 \text{ m})$
$\quad = 450 \text{ J}$

Jennifer does 450 J of work on the box.

If this box has a mass of 25 kg, how much work will it take her to lift it from the floor to 2.0 m in the air? We still use the equation $W = Fd$, but first we need to find the force needed to lift the box. In Section 4.1, we learned that the force of gravity is given by $F_g = mg$. To lift the box at a constant speed, you have to exert a force equal to its weight.

The force exerted on the box can be calculated as:

$F_g = mg$
$\quad = (25 \text{ kg})(9.8 \text{ N/kg})$
$\quad = 245 \text{ N}$

Therefore, the amount of work done by this force is:

$W = Fd$
$\quad = (245 \text{ N})(2.0 \text{ m})$
$\quad = 490 \text{ J}$

Suggested Activity •········
B13 Quick Lab on page 111

Take It **Further**

All devices transfer or transform energy. For example, a flashlight is a device that transforms the chemical energy stored in the battery into light energy and thermal energy. Choose a simple device and describe the energy transformations that take place when that device is used. Begin your search at ScienceSource.

Calculating Work

Use $W = Fd$ to solve the following questions.

1. Simon lifts a rock 1.5 m by applying a force of 20 N. How much work does Simon do on the rock?

2. Gravity pulls an apple 4.0 m to the ground with a force of 2.0 N. How much work does gravity do on the apple?

3. Jasjot does 450 J of work on an object by pushing the object 15 m at a constant speed. How much force does Jasjot exert on the object?

How Much Work Does It Take?

In order to calculate the work done on an object, we first need to know the amount of force needed to move the object a measured distance.

Purpose

To determine the amount of work, in joules, needed to move various objects in your classroom

---

Materials & Equipment

- spring scales
- various objects
- metre stick

Procedure

1. Copy Table 4.4 into your notebook.

Table 4.4

Object	Type of Motion (e.g., lifting, sliding)	Distance (m)	Force (N)	Work (J)

2. Choose four objects that you can move in a straight line by lifting, sliding, or opening. Record these objects in your data table.

3. Indicate the desired motion of each of these objects in your data table. Include the distance you plan to move the object.

4. Keeping the spring scale parallel to the motion of the object, measure the force exerted while moving each object the specified distance. Be sure to pull the object with a slow, constant speed. Record these force values in your data table.

5. Use the formula $W = Fd$ to calculate the work required to move each of your objects.

Questions

6. Which of your four object motions required the most work? The least work? Why?

7. Explain why it was important to pull with a constant speed. How would the force on the spring scale change if you did not pull at a constant speed?

8. Choose one of your objects. Describe the form(s) of energy that were changed as a result of the work being done on that object.

Key Concept Review

1. What is the scientific definition of "work"?

2. What is the definition of "energy"?

3. Classify each of the following as examples of kinetic or potential energy.

   (a) A car is driving along a level road.

   (b) An elastic band is stretched to twice its normal length.

   (c) A book is at rest on the top shelf of a bookcase.

   (d) A lightning bolt produces thunder that travels at 1250 km/h.

4. When you do work to lift an object, what form of energy does the object gain?

5. When frictional forces do work on an object or mechanical system, what form of energy is always produced?

6. Michelle pushes on a wall with a force of 45 N. Explain why Michelle is doing no work on the wall.

Connect Your Understanding

7. Calculate the work done in each of the following situations.

   (a) A horse pulls a wagon with a force of 1200 N and moves it 15 m.

   (b) A cable lifts an elevator 16 m by using a cable with a tension force of 2500 N.

8. (a) How much work is required to lift a 35-kg object from the ground 3.0 m into the air?

   (b) How much gravitational potential energy did this object gain?

Practise Your Skills

9. Three different books are lifted from the ground and placed on separate shelves of a bookcase. The force required to lift each book and the height of its shelf are recorded in the data table shown here. Which book required the most work to move?

Book	Force (N)	Height of Shelf (m)
1	22.0	0.50
2	9.0	1.4
3	3.0	2.1

For more questions, go to ScienceSource.

B14   *Thinking about Science, Technology, and Society*

Giving Society a Lift

The main idea for this chapter is "mechanical systems use forces to transfer energy." This means that mechanical systems do work to transfer energy. For example, an elevator is a mechanical system that does work to give objects gravitational potential energy. The passenger safety elevator was invented about 150 years ago.

Discuss with a group how the elevator has affected how people live. Create a word web displaying your ideas.

Here is a summary of what you will learn in this section:

- A machine is a mechanical system that reduces the force required to accomplish work.
- Machines make work easier by increasing the force, increasing the distance, or changing the direction of the force.
- The force applied to the machine is called the input force, and the force applied by the machine is called the output force.
- The amount by which a machine can multiply an input force is called mechanical advantage.
- Mechanical advantage can be calculated by using the equation $MA = F_{out}/F_{in}$.

When you think of a machine, chances are that you imagine something complex like a car or a bicycle. However, machines can be as simple as a wrench or a screwdriver. A **machine** is any mechanical system that reduces the force required to accomplish work. Removing a tight nut from a bolt using only your fingers is almost impossible since you cannot apply enough force. A wrench multiplies the amount of force that you can apply with your fingers in order to remove the nut (Figure 4.19).

Similarly, a ramp makes it easier to raise a mass a vertical distance. In this section, you will learn how machines make work easier.

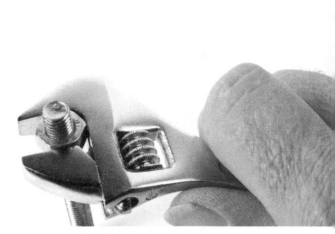

Figure 4.19 A wrench makes it easier to remove a nut from a bolt.

B15   *Starting Point*   Skills Ⓟ Ⓒ

Everyday Machines

A machine is any mechanical system that reduces the force needed to do work. For example, a car jack allows you to lift a car that you would not be able to lift without the jack. Work with a partner and make a list of as many machines as you can think of. Compare your list with those of two other groups and add any machines that are different from the ones on your original list. Keep this list for the next activity.

Functions of Machines

To move from the ground floor of a building to the second floor requires work. Usually this work is done by climbing stairs between the levels. Suppose that all the stairs were removed and replaced by a vertical rope (Figure 4.20). Most people would not be able to provide enough force to climb the rope to the next level. Stairs, therefore, are a machine that allows people to do the work more easily.

Machines make work easier in three ways:

- by increasing the force that can be applied to an object
- by increasing the distance over which the force is applied
- by changing the direction of a force

Figure 4.20 Stairs are an example of a machine that makes work easier.

Increasing the Force

It is almost impossible to crack a hard nut with your bare hands. A nutcracker is a machine that increases the applied force (Figure 4.21). When you apply a force to the handles, the jaws of the nutcracker apply a greater force on the nut.

However, the distance that you move each handle is greater than the distance that each jaw moves. Remember from the last section that work is the product of force and distance. When you work on the handles, you apply a small force over a large distance. The jaws of the nutcracker apply a large force over a small distance. However, the *work* done by the jaws of the nutcracker is no greater than the work done by you when you squeeze the handles. This is true for all mechanical systems.

Figure 4.21 The force that the jaws apply to the nut is greater than the force that the person applies to the handles.

Increasing Distance

The ramp in Figure 4.22 allows the cart to be loaded into the truck with less force than if it were lifted straight up. Regardless of how the cart is loaded, the cart in the truck has gained gravitational potential energy since it is now above the road. This means that work was done to move the cart into the truck.

Figure 4.22 The length of the ramp is greater than the height of the truck. By using a ramp to do the work over a longer distance, the person uses less force.

Lifting the cart straight up, without a ramp, requires a large force over a small distance (the height). When you use a ramp, the distance that the cart is moved increases and thus the force applied decreases.

Changing Direction

Some machines change the direction of the force you apply. The pulley used at the top of a flagpole is one example, as shown in Figure 4.23. When the soldier applies a downward force on the rope, an upward force is exerted on the flag.

Input and Output Forces

Whenever a machine is used to do work, two forces are always involved. When you exert a force on the machine, the machine exerts a force on the object. For example, suppose you need to lift a car using a jack, as shown in Figure 4.24. When you apply a force to the handle of the jack, the jack applies a force to the car. The force that is applied to the machine is called the **input force**, symbolized by F_{in}. The force that the machine applies to the object is called the **output force**, symbolized by F_{out}. In the case of our car jack, the input force is the person pushing on the handle, and the output force is the jack pushing up the car.

The input force (F_{in}) is defined as the force exerted on the machine. The output force (F_{out}) is defined as either the force that the machine applies to the object or the force required to move the object without using a machine.

The input force is sometimes called the effort force, and the output force is sometimes called the load force.

Figure 4.23 A flag can be lifted upwards by applying a downward force on the rope.

Figure 4.24 The input force, F_{in}, and output force, F_{out}, using a car jack

Describing Machine Forces

Copy Table 4.5 into your notebook. Using the list of machines from Activity B15, choose any 10 machines and record them in your data table. Write a title for your table.

For each machine, place an X in the column that you think best describes the function of that machine. For each machine, describe the input and output forces of that machine. An example has been done for you.

Table 4.5

Machine	Function			Input Force	Output Force
	Increase the Force	Increase the Distance	Change Force Direction		
Car jack	X		X	Person pushing on handle	Jack pushing up the car

Mechanical Advantage

Machines such as the nutcracker, ramp, and car jack make work easier because the output force is greater than the input force. The amount by which a machine can multiply an input force is called its **mechanical advantage**. Therefore, the ratio of the output force (F_{out}) to the input force (F_{in}) determines the machine's mechanical advantage.

Since mechanical advantage is the ratio of two forces, measured in newtons, mechanical advantage has no scientific units. You can calculate the mechanical advantage (MA) by using the following equation:

$$\text{Mechanical advantage} = \frac{\text{output force in newtons}}{\text{input force in newtons}}$$

$$\text{MA} = \frac{F_{out}}{F_{in}}$$

When jacking up a car, Wei pushes with a force of 250 N on the handle of a jack and the jack applies a force of 3000 N to the car. What is the mechanical advantage of this car jack?

*Take It **Further***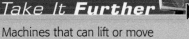

Machines that can lift or move heavy objects usually have a very large mechanical advantage. Tractors and bulldozers are examples of these types of machine. Choose a machine and investigate the maximum mechanical advantage of that machine. Begin your search at ScienceSource.

$$\text{MA} = \frac{F_{out}}{F_{in}}$$

$$= \frac{(3000 \text{ N})}{(250 \text{ N})}$$

$$= 12$$

The jack has a mechanical advantage of 12. This means that the jack will output 12 times the amount of force that Wei inputs.

Suppose that Jason and his wheelchair have a total weight of 910 N (Figure 4.25). A force of 130 N is required to push Jason up the ramp. In this example, we think of the output force as the force required to move the object without the ramp. Lifting Jason and the wheelchair up without the ramp would require a force of 910 N. Now we use our equation to calculate mechanical advantage.

Figure 4.25 The ramp has a mechanical advantage greater than 1 since the force needed to push the wheelchair up the ramp is less than the force needed to lift the wheelchair straight up.

$$\text{MA} = \frac{F_{out}}{F_{in}}$$

$$= \frac{(910 \text{ N})}{(130 \text{ N})}$$

$$= 7$$

The ramp has a mechanical advantage of 7.

Mechanical Advantage of 1

Not only can a machine multiply the input force and increase the distance over which the force is applied, but a machine can also change the direction of the force. Figure 4.26 shows an object attached to a rope that passes over a fixed pulley. If you pull down on the rope with a force, the same amount of force is applied to the object.

A fixed pulley is a machine that does only one thing: it changes the direction of the force. The mechanical advantage of this machine is 1 since the input and output force are the same size. Machines that have a mechanical advantage of 1 only change the direction between the input and the output forces. These machines do not make the work easier but are instead used for tasks in which the direction of the force must change.

Suggested Activity •·········
B19 Quick Lab on page 120

Figure 4.26 Machines that have a mechanical advantage of 1 only change the direction between the input and the output forces.

Mechanical systems use forces to transfer energy. **117**

Ideal Mechanical Advantage

In a real machine, some of the work done by the input force is converted to thermal energy by the friction in the machine. Because of this, the work done by the output force is less than the work done by the input force. An ideal machine has no friction, and therefore no energy is converted to thermal energy. The mechanical advantage of a machine that has no friction is called the **ideal mechanical advantage** (IMA). The ideal mechanical advantage can be calculated by finding the ratio between the distance over which the input force is exerted on the machine (d_{in}) and the distance over which the output force is exerted on the object (d_{out}).

Suggested Activity •·········
B20 Design a Lab on page 121

Ideal mechanical advantage can be calculated as follows:

$$\text{Ideal mechanical advantage} = \frac{\text{input distance}}{\text{output distance}}$$

$$\text{IMA} = \frac{d_{in}}{d_{out}}$$

Suppose Padma uses a hammer to pull a nail, as shown in Figure 4.27. If she moves the handle of the hammer 30 cm and the nail moves 5.0 cm, what is the ideal mechanical advantage of the hammer?

$$\text{IMA} = \frac{d_{in}}{d_{out}}$$

$$= \frac{(30 \text{ cm})}{(5.0 \text{ cm})}$$

$$= 6.0$$

Figure 4.27 The ideal mechanical advantage of the hammer can be determined by comparing the distance the handle moves to the distance the nail moves.

The ideal mechanical advantage of the hammer is 6.0.

Even though no real machines have zero friction, certain machines have such a small amount of friction that the ideal mechanical advantage is very similar to the real mechanical advantage. Machines like a hammer or a screwdriver have no sliding parts and therefore have almost no friction. The IMA can be close to the MA for machines such as these.

Ideal Mechanical Advantage of Less Than 1

Sometimes, the IMA is less than 1 and the output distance is greater than the input distance. This usually means that the speed at the output is higher than the speed at the input. Examples of machines with an IMA less than 1 are hockey sticks, baseball bats, and garden rakes. In each of these machines, the distance moved by the input force is less than the distance moved by the output force (Figure 4.28). When an increase in speed of motion is required, an IMA of less than 1 is sometimes necessary.

Figure 4.28 When you shoot with a hockey stick, the distance moved by the hands is less than the distance moved by the stick's blade. Thus, the speed of the blade (output) is greater than the speed of the input (hands).

B17 *Learning Checkpoint*

Mechanical Advantage

1. Laura pushes on the pedals of her bike with a force of 320 N. If the bike has an output force of 640 N, what is the mechanical advantage of this bike?

2. Laura squeezes the hand brakes of her bicycle with a force of 60 N. If the brake pads push on the wheel with a force of 300 N, what is the mechanical advantage of this bike's brake system?

3. The handle of a car jack is moved 75 cm and the car is lifted 2.5 cm. What is the ideal mechanical advantage of this car jack?

B18 *Learning Checkpoint*

Human Mechanical Advantage

If you did Activity B3, you lifted masses at various locations on your arm. When you used your elbow joint as a hinge, your muscles were the input force and the weight of the object was your output force (Figure 4.29). Since the mass was the same regardless of its location on your arm, the output force provided by your arm was always the same.

1. Explain what happened to the mechanical advantage of your arm as the weight was moved along your arm.

2. Do you think the mechanical advantage of your arm was ever greater than 1? Explain.

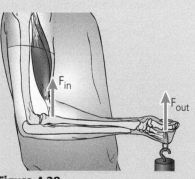

Figure 4.29

Calculating Mechanical Advantage

The mechanical advantage of a machine can be determined by calculating the ratio of the output force to the input force ($MA = F_{out} / F_{in}$). If the output force (F_{out}) is required to slowly lift an object, then the output force is equal to the weight of the object ($F_g = mg$).

Purpose

To determine the mechanical advantage of a metre stick, hinged at different locations and used to lift a mass

Materials & Equipment

- spring scale
- hooked masses
- ring stand or support
- metre stick
- string

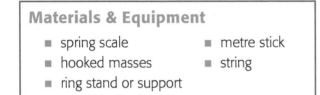

output force

input force

Figure 4.30

Procedure

1. Copy Table 4.6 into your notebook.

Table 4.6 Mechanical Advantage of a Simple Machine

Hinge Location (cm)	Output Force (N)	Input Force (N)	Mechanical Advantage
20			
30			
40			
50			
60			
70			

2. Suspend the metre stick from the support stand using a piece of string attached to the 20-cm location of your metre stick. This location is called the hinge location.

3. Attach your hooked mass to the 5.0-cm location of your metre stick using a second piece of string (Figure 4.30).

4. Using a spring scale attached to the 95-cm location of your metre stick, pull the metre stick until it is parallel to the ground. Record this force as the input force.

5. Record the output force provided by the metre stick. The output force is the force required to lift the hooked mass ($F_g = mg$).

6. Repeat steps 3–5 for the hinge locations in your data table.

7. Calculate the mechanical advantage of the metre stick at each of the hinge locations. Record these values in your data table.

Questions

8. As the distance from the output force to the hinge increased, what happened to the value of the mechanical advantage?

9. When the hinge was at the 70-cm location, the mechanical advantage has a value of less than 1. In a short paragraph, explain what a mechanical advantage less than 1 means in terms of input and output forces.

10. When the mechanical advantage is greater than 1, the distance moved by the output force is less than the distance moved by the input force. How do these distances compare when the mechanical advantage is less than 1?

My Bicycle's Mechanical Advantage

A bicycle is a mechanical system that transfers the force that you push on the pedals to a force on the ground provided by the wheel rims.

Multigear bikes can change the mechanical advantage depending on the gear. Gears are devices that change the speed, direction, or force of a transmitted motion. The mechanical advantage of a bicycle can be calculated by measuring the force on the pedals and the force on the wheel (Figure 4.31). Ideal mechanical advantage can be calculated by measuring the distance the pedal travels and the distance the bicycle travels.

Question

What are the mechanical advantage and ideal mechanical advantage of a bicycle?

Design and Conduct Your Investigation

1. Decide what materials you will need in order to record the measurements you need to be able to calculate both mechanical advantage and ideal mechanical advantage.

2. Plan your procedure. Think about these questions.

   (a) How will you measure the force on both the pedals and the wheel rim at the same time?

   (b) Since the pedals do not move in a straight line, what method will you use to measure the distance the pedals travel?

   (c) What steps will you follow to collect the data you need?

   (d) How will you record your results?

3. Write up your procedure. Be sure to show it to your teacher before going any further.

4. Carry out your experiment.

5. Share and compare your experimental plan and values with your classmates' plans and values. Did any other group plan their experiment exactly like yours? Similarly to yours? Completely different from yours? How did your bike's mechanical advantage compare to its ideal mechanical advantage? If the values were different, give an explanation.

6. Present your findings to the class or in a form suggested by your teacher.

Figure 4.31

Key Concept Review

1. Explain what is meant by the statement "a machine makes work easier."

2. What concept is represented by the ratio of the output force to the input force?

3. Jill applies a force of 15 N to a wrench. If the wrench applies a force of 150 N to a bolt, which of these values is the input force and which is the output force?

4. A pulley has a mechanical advantage of 1. What does this tell you about the size and direction of the input and output forces?

5. Use the concept of energy to explain why ideal mechanical advantage is not the same as mechanical advantage for real machines.

Connect Your Understanding

6. What is the mechanical advantage of a machine that exerts a force of 160 N on an object when a person exerts a force of 20 N on the machine?

7. A bicycle moves forward 4.0 m when the pedals are rotated through a distance of 1.0 m. What is the IMA of this bicycle?

Practise Your Skills

8. Ravi applies the same force to three different machines. The output force of each of these machines is shown here. List the three machines in order of highest to lowest mechanical advantage.

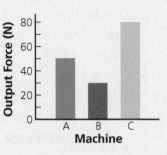

For more questions, go to ScienceSource.

B21 Thinking about Science, Technology, and Society

Can Opener

Can you imagine opening a can of soup without a can opener? A can opener is a mechanism designed to make the task of opening a can easier.

What to Do

1. Make a sketch of a manual can opener.

2. Identify the components of the can opener and label these parts on your sketch.

3. State the form and function of each labelled part.

Consider This

4. Most mechanisms are designed to meet a need. How well does your can opener address people's needs?

5. If every family had to destroy its can openers, describe the short- and long-term effects.

6. Describe possible environmental effects on the manufacturing, use, and disposal of your can opener.

Artificial Limbs

Artificial limbs or prostheses (singular: prosthesis) have been in use for more than 2300 years. An artificial leg was found that was made from copper and wood and dated from 300 B.C.E. A prosthesis is designed to replace a limb that is missing due to injury or disease, or from birth.

The last 50 years have seen the greatest advances in artificial limbs. Lightweight plastics and carbon fibres make the limb easier to move. The most exciting development is myoelectricity, which means that electric signals from the person's muscles can move the artificial limb. Sensors attached to the muscles transfer the muscle motion into electrical impulses. These electrical signals are sent to the areas of the prosthesis where motion is required.

Regardless of the technology used, an artificial limb is a machine that transfers forces. Interior cables pull hinged levers or use hydraulics. Designers of these high-tech devices are highly trained biomedical engineers. They must understand force, work, energy, and machines.

Prosthesis technology is now so advanced that some artificial limbs can perform better than a natural limb. Oscar Pistorius is a double-amputee sprinter who uses special composite prosthetic blades. He has run in many international competitions.

Questions

1. What technologies have created the greatest changes in prosthesis development?

2. What are two methods used to transfer forces in a prosthesis?

3. Do you think that athletes such as Oscar Pistorius should be allowed to compete against other athletes at the Olympics? In a short paragraph, give reasons for your answer.

Figure 4.32 In the 16th century, artificial limbs had moving parts that were controlled by straps attached to the body.

Figure 4.33 Each motion of the artificial limb is the result of the transfer of forces.

Figure 4.34 Oscar Pistorius, the "Blade Runner," with his carbon-fibre feet

Key Concept Review

1. A curling rock slides to a stop due to the force of friction. Is the force of friction a contact force or a force at a distance? ⓚ

2. Dan has a mass of 55 kg on Earth. What is his mass on a planet that has twice Earth's gravity? ⓚ

3. Explain how it is possible to do no work on an object even though you have applied a force to that object. ⓚ

4. For each of the following situations, state if the object has potential energy or kinetic energy. ⓚ

   (a) a bowling ball rolling down the alley

   (b) a book sitting on the top shelf of a bookcase

5. State the three functions of machines and give an example of a machine for each function. ⓚ

6. For a given machine, explain why the MA is usually less than the IMA. ⓚ

7. If you exert an input force over a greater distance than the distance exerted by the output force, for an ideal machine compare the sizes of the input and output forces. ⓚ

8. What concept is represented by the ratio of the input distance to the output distance? ⓚ

Connect Your Understanding

9. Suzy pushes against a brick wall with a force of 900 N for 1 minute. Her friend comments that she did no work during that minute. Is her friend correct? Explain. ⓐ

10. Ahmed inputs 250 J of work on a machine. Explain why that machine has an output of only 200 J of work. ⓐ

11. Make a sketch of each machine in the two photographs and label the input force and the output force in each. ⓣ

12. In a short paragraph, describe how you would determine the amount of work needed to pull a toboggan the length of a football field. Be sure to include the equipment list and describe the measurements that you will take. ⓐ

Reflect and Evaluate

After Reading Thinking Literacy

Reflect and Evaluate

Based on your learning, add and modify the mind map you began on page 95. How and where would you fit in the following words: machine, mass, weight, friction, and ideal mechanical advantage? Draw lines and arrows between the words on your mind map in a way that makes sense to you. Explain your mind map to a partner. How has the strategy of making connections helped you to understand this chapter better?

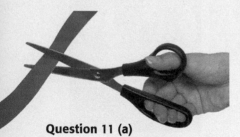

Question 11 (a)

Question 11 (b)

ACHIEVEMENT CHART CATEGORIES
ⓚ Knowledge and understanding ⓣ Thinking and investigation ⓒ Communication ⓐ Application

Practise Your Skills

13. What is the weight of a 3.0-kg mass placed on a spring scale in your classroom? ⓣ

14. Calculate the amount of work done in each of the following situations. ⓣ

    (a) A person lifts a 250-N child straight up 1.2 m.

    (b) A horse pulls a sled 12 m using a force of 2000 N.

15. A machine is able to lift a 50-kg mass when a 49-N force is applied to the machine. What is the mechanical advantage of this machine? ⓣ

16. The handle of a car jack is moved 150 cm in order to lift the car 5.0 cm. What is the ideal mechanical advantage of this car jack? ⓣ

17. A machine is often designed when the work required to move an object needs a force larger than a person can exert. Your task is to lift a 400-kg boulder from the ground and place it on a platform 3.0 m high. ⓣ

    (a) Make a sketch of a machine (or a combination of machines) that use the force provided by one person to accomplish this task.

    (b) Label the input and output force(s) on your sketch.

Unit Task Link

You will design, construct, and test a mechanical system that uses only the energy stored in a spring-bar mousetrap. This system must have a function other than catching mice. Will your design require a mechanical advantage greater than 1 or less than 1? How will your design produce the required mechanical advantage?

B22 Thinking about Science, Technology, and Society

Garden Rake versus Leaf Blower

For many people in Ontario, the beauty of autumn becomes the chore of gathering and disposing of the fallen leaves. Not that long ago, the garden rake was the only machine used to gather leaves. Some people now use electric- or gas-powered leaf blowers.

What to Do

1. Draw the following data table so that it fills a full page in your notebook.

	Environmental		Societal	
	Cost	Benefit	Cost	Benefit
Garden rake				
Leaf blower				

Consider This

With some classmates,

2. Brainstorm possible environmental and societal costs and benefits for the garden rake and the leaf blower. Record your results in the table.

3. Discuss why people saw a need for leaf blowers.

5.0

Mechanical systems involve machines that are designed to do work efficiently.

Sailors use pulleys and winches to help them raise the sails up the mast.

In this chapter, you will:

- analyze the uses of a variety of machines
- determine the mechanical advantage of a variety of machines
- determine the efficiency of a machine and suggest ways to increase its efficiency

Skills You Will Use

In this chapter, you will:

- manipulate simple machines in order to change their mechanical advantage
- design and construct a mechanism to perform a specified task

Why This Is Important

Every day you use a variety of mechanisms to perform tasks that require work to be done. Understanding the simple machines that make up these mechanisms allows you to complete the tasks efficiently.

Before Reading

Thinking Literacy

Predict-Read-Verify

Topics introduced in this chapter include:

- Simple Machines
- Ideal Mechanical Advantage
- Efficiency
- Increasing a Machine's Efficiency

Write down each of these topic titles and discuss what you think the topic means. Make a prediction about what you will learn.

Key Terms

- mechanism
- simple machine
- lever
- fulcrum
- pulley
- inclined plane
- screw
- wedge
- efficiency
- wheel and axle

Figure 5.1 A mountain bike has several different moving parts.

Figure 5.2 The gear-change lever on a mountain bike

Modern mountain bikes, like the one shown in Figure 5.1, allow the rider to climb steep hills and travel rough trails faster than by walking or running. But did you ever consider a mountain bike as a machine? A machine is any device that helps us do work.

A mountain bike is a mechanism. A **mechanism** is made up of several different types of machines that work together to perform a specific function. The bike is a complex mechanical system that is made up of many simple machines. A **simple machine** is a machine that requires the application of a single force to do work. You need only the pushing force when using an inclined plane (ramp) to move a cart into a delivery truck. Therefore, a ramp is a simple machine. Similarly, a lever uses only a single force to pry open a lid. Therefore, it is also a simple machine. Figure 5.2 shows the gear lever on a bicycle. Many different parts on the mountain bike move in different ways. Therefore, the bike consists of many simple machines.

A gear is a wheel with teeth around the edge that interacts with another toothed part of a device to change the speed, direction, or force of a transmitted motion. The sprocket or gear on the back wheel represents one of the bike's simple machines (Figure 5.3). At this location, the force and motion of the chain are transferred to the wheel. Mountain bikes allow the rider to change the distance between the chain and the axle. This is commonly called "switching gears." When the chain is mechanically moved from one sprocket to another, the mechanical advantage changes. When the rider needs to climb a steep hill, the chain is moved to a larger sprocket, increasing the mechanical advantage. When the rider needs less output force but wants to travel faster, the chain is moved to a smaller sprocket.

Simple machines (such as a ramp) and mechanisms (such as the mountain bike) both use forces to transfer energy. Machines are designed to transfer this energy as efficiently as possible. In this chapter, you will study several simple machines and their operation.

Figure 5.3 The mechanical advantage can be changed by moving the chain to different sprockets.

B23 *Quick Lab*

Locating Simple Machines on a Mountain Bike

A mountain bike is a mechanism that is made up of several simple machines. Different parts of the bike produce different kinds of motions. By analyzing where you find movement in the bike, you are identifying locations where a simple machine may exist.

Purpose

To find simple machines on a bicycle

Materials & Equipment

- bicycle
- pencil and paper

Procedure

1. As accurately as possible, make a sketch of a mountain bike.

2. On your sketch, draw circles around the locations on the bike where parts can move. These are the locations of simple machines.

3. Compare your diagram with a classmate's and discuss any differences. Using a different coloured pen or pencil, add any locations of simple machines that are different from those on your diagram.

Questions

4. How many locations of simple machines are on your diagram?

5. Were you surprised by the number of locations of simple machines on a bicycle?

6. Choose one of your simple machine locations. Describe the effect on the bike if that simple machine were not allowed to move.

Here is a summary of what you will learn in this section:

- Six types of simple machines are: lever, pulley, wheel and axle, inclined plane, screw, and wedge.
- Levers can be classified into three categories: first-class levers, second-class levers, and third-class levers.
- The ideal mechanical advantage of simple machines can be determined without measuring the input and output forces.
- Two or more simple machines that operate together form a mechanism.

The Great Pyramid of Giza, shown in Figure 5.4, was the tallest building on Earth until the 1300s. Built over 4500 years ago, the 150-m-high pyramid is still considered one of the Seven Wonders of the World. It took 20 years to assemble the 2.3 million blocks that were placed, one by one, to form this magnificent building. The granite and limestone blocks had masses between 1000 and 35 000 kilograms.

Figure 5.4 Pyramids at Giza in Egypt. The Great Pyramid is the one in the middle. Notice how tiny the people are in the lower left!

B24 *Starting Point*

Skills A C

Choose a Simple Machine

The following situations all require work to be done on an object. For each situation, suggest a tool, device, or machine that could be used to do the work.

- lifting a car to change a tire
- removing a lid from a can of paint
- undoing a tight bolt

- splitting a log for firewood
- moving a car from the lower level of a parking garage to a higher level
- raising a bucket of water in a well

Compare your list with another student's list. Did you both choose the same machine or device for each task?

The biggest question is, how did the Egyptians move these massive blocks of stone into place? Although there are no formal records, scientists believe that the early Egyptians used several simple machines. Long inclines (ramps) were built to raise the huge blocks. Some archeologists believe that the blocks were pulled up the ramps on skids (Figure 5.5). Others think that logs were placed under the blocks, like wheels under a cart, when they were pulled up the ramp. The workers set the blocks in place using long wooden and bronze levers.

Figure 5.5 The massive blocks used to build this pyramid were positioned using simple machines.

Six Simple Machines

All machines, regardless of how complex, are made up of at least one of six simple machines, which are shown in Figure 5.6

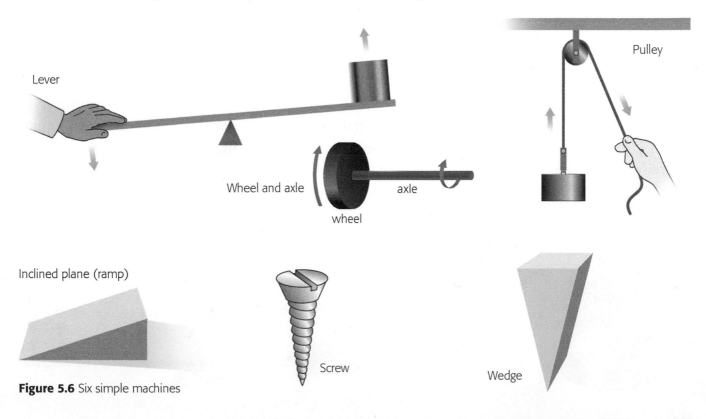

Figure 5.6 Six simple machines

To Predict or to Infer?

At the start of this chapter, you made a prediction about what you think you will learn based on what you already know. As you read, you will be able to confirm whether or not your prediction was correct.

Making an inference is related to predicting. As you read, you add what you already know to clues in the text. Making an inference, however, involves the reader using these clues to form a logical conclusion. This conclusion may not be directly confirmed until the end of the text.

Draw a three-column chart labelled "It Says," "I Say," and "And So" to help you form inferences as you read Section 5.1. What inferences can you make based on the section title? What inferences can you make about the ancient Egyptians?

Levers

If you have ever used a rake, played on a teeter-totter, or swung a baseball bat, you have used a lever. A **lever** is a rigid bar that is supported at one point. This point on the lever is called the **fulcrum**. There are three classes of levers, classified by the locations of the fulcrum, the input force, and the output force.

Three Classes of Levers

Using a pry bar to remove the lid of a paint can is an example of a first-class lever (Figure 5.7(a)). The fulcrum is the part of the pry bar that is touching the rim of the can. That part of the pry bar is stationary; it does not move. The input force is at your hand, pushing down on the pry bar handle. The output force is at the tip of the pry bar, pushing the lid of the paint can upward. A **first-class lever** always has the fulcrum between the input and output forces (Figure 5.7(b)). As well, the output force is always in the opposite direction to the input force.

Figure 5.7 When used to open a paint can, a pry bar (a) is an example of a first-class lever, which has the fulcrum between the input and output forces (b).

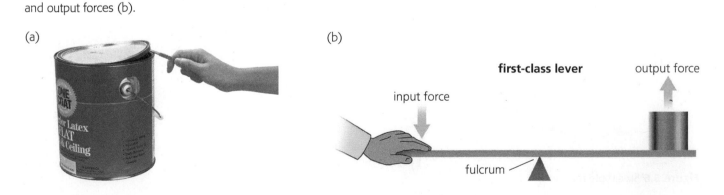

(a)

(b)

first-class lever

output force

input force

fulcrum

Removing the cap from a soft-drink bottle requires a different class of lever, called a **second-class lever** (Figure 5.8(a)). In this situation, the fulcrum is the very end of the opener that remains in contact with the bottle cap. The force used to open the cap, the output force, is between the fulcrum and the input force (Figure 5.8(b)). In a second-class lever, the input and output forces are in the same direction.

(a)

(b)

second-class lever

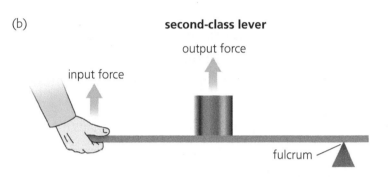

Figure 5.8 A bottle opener (a) is an example of a second-class lever, which has the output force between the fulcrum and the input force (b).

Using a garden rake or shooting a puck with a hockey stick are examples of the **third-class lever** (Figure 5.9(a)). If you hold the top of the rake stationary with your left hand (the fulcrum) and move the rake with the right, your right hand is the input force. The head of the rake applies an output force to the leaves. The third-class lever has the input force between the fulcrum and the output force, and the input and output force are in the same direction (Figure 5.9(b)).

A third-class lever always produces a mechanical advantage less than 1. That is, the output force is always less than the input force. Instead, a third-class lever is useful because the distance and speed of the output end of the lever are greater than at the input end. Swinging a baseball bat or hockey stick are all examples of creating speed with a third-class lever.

(a)

(b)

third-class lever

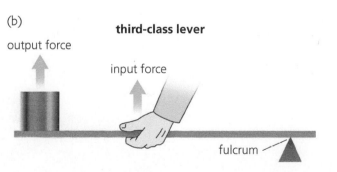

Figure 5.9 A garden rake is an example of a third-class lever, which has the input force between the fulcrum and the output force.

Ideal Mechanical Advantage of a Lever

As with all machines, the mechanical advantage can be calculated by dividing the output force by the input force. But you would have to measure these forces by conducting an experiment. Sometimes it is enough to find the ideal mechanical advantage. When the amount of friction is relatively small, calculating the ideal mechanical advantage can provide a good approximation of the machine's actual mechanical advantage. You do not have to conduct an experiment to measure the forces. Remember from Chapter 4 that the ideal mechanical advantage assumes that no friction is involved in the transfer of energy using forces.

The ideal mechanical advantage (IMA) of a lever can be calculated by dividing the length of the input arm (L_{in}) by the length of the output arm (L_{out}).

$$\text{Ideal Mechanical Advantage} = \frac{\text{length of input arm}}{\text{length of output arm}}$$

$$\text{IMA} = \frac{L_{in}}{L_{out}}$$

Suggested Activity • ·········
B27 Inquiry Activity on page 141

The length of the input arm is the distance between the location of the input force and the fulcrum. The output arm length is the distance between the fulcrum and the output force (Figure 5.10).

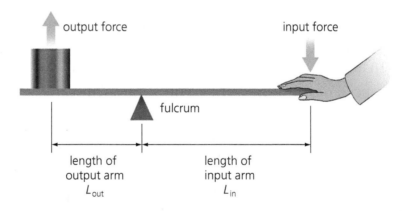

output force   input force

length of   length of
output arm   input arm
L_{out} L_{in}

Figure 5.10 The ratio of the length of the input arm (L_{in}) to the length of the output arm (L_{out}) is the ideal mechanical advantage of a lever.

For example, Jasmine tries to lift a rock using the lever shown in Figure 5.11. What is the ideal mechanical advantage of this lever?

$$\text{IMA} = \frac{L_{in}}{L_{out}}$$

$$= \frac{1.5 \text{ m}}{0.5 \text{ m}}$$

$$= 3.0$$

This lever has an ideal mechanical advantage of 3.0.

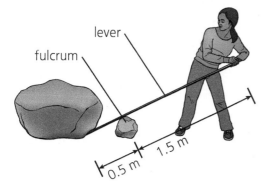

lever

fulcrum

0.5 m   1.5 m

Figure 5.11 When the length of the input arm is greater than the length of the output arm, that lever has an ideal mechanical advantage greater than 1.

Take It *Further*

Levers come in three types: first-class, second-class, and third-class. The human body contains each of these three types of lever. Give an example of a location in the human body for each of these three types of lever. Make a sketch of the fulcrum and forces for each example. Begin your search at ScienceSource.

B26 *Learning Checkpoint*

Three Classes of Levers

Figures 5.12, 5.13, and 5.14 each display a common lever. Do the following for each figure:

1. Sketch the lever involved.

2. Label the fulcrum, input force, and output force.

3. Identify the lever as a first-class, second-class, or third-class lever.

Figure 5.12

Figure 5.13

Figure 5.14

Figure 5.15 Bones and joints act as levers.

Human Levers

Many movements of the human body can be explained by comparing them with levers. For example, levers give us the ability to throw a ball (Figure 5.15). The solid rod of a lever can be compared to the bones in your forearm. When a person throws a ball overhand, the elbow acts as the fulcrum of a first-class lever and the triceps muscle applies the input force. The output force is the force that the hand applies to the ball. Since the length of the input arm (the distance between the elbow and the triceps muscle) is less than the length of the output arm (the distance from the elbow to the ball), the mechanical advantage when throwing a ball is less than 1.

The process of throwing a ball also involves other levers in the human body, such as at the shoulder and wrist.

Pulleys

If you have ever raised a flag on a flagpole or hung clothes on a clothesline, you have used a pulley. A **pulley** consists of a grooved wheel with a rope or cable looped around it (Figure 5.16). The pulley is free to spin. A pulley can change the direction of the force or increase the output force, depending on whether the pulley is fixed or movable.

Fixed pulleys change only the direction of the force. When the input force is applied downward on the rope, the output force is in the upward direction (Figure 5.17). Since the output force is the same size as the input force, a fixed pulley has an ideal mechanical advantage of 1.

If one end of the rope is fixed and the pulley is allowed to move, you have a movable pulley. The movable pulley in Figure 5.18 is supported by the rope at two locations. At each of these locations, the tension in the rope applies an upward force on the pulley. Each segment of rope that applies a force on the pulley is considered a support rope. If you pull the rope with an input force of 5 N, the rope applies this force to the movable pulley in two locations. Therefore, the output force is 10 N. This gives an ideal mechanical advantage of 2.

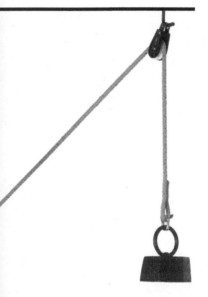

Figure 5.16 A fixed pulley

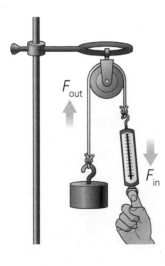

Figure 5.17 A fixed pulley showing the input and output forces

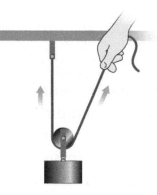

Figure 5.18 This movable pulley has two support ropes and therefore an ideal mechanical advantage of 2.

Ideal Mechanical Advantage of a Pulley System

The ideal mechanical advantage of a pulley system is equal to the number of support ropes. A combination of fixed and movable pulleys can produce various mechanical advantages. Figure 5.19 shows a pulley system with one fixed and one movable pulley. By counting the number of support ropes, you find that the ideal mechanical advantage for this pulley system is 3.

Figure 5.19 This pulley system has an ideal mechanical advantage of 3, since it has three support ropes.

Wheel and Axle

Could you tighten a screw with a screwdriver that had no handle? The screwdriver handle is part of a simple machine called a wheel and axle. The **wheel and axle** consists of a shaft or axle that is attached to a larger disk, called the wheel (Figure 5.20(a)). When you use a screwdriver to tighten a screw, the handle is the wheel and the shaft is the axle (Figure 5.20(b)). Doorknobs and the pedals on your bicycle are also examples of wheels and axles.

(a)

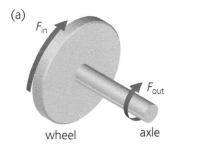

wheel   axle

(b)

axle

wheel

Figure 5.20 (a) A wheel and axle. (b) A screwdriver is an example of a wheel and axle.

Ideal Mechanical Advantage of a Wheel and Axle

Both the wheel and the axle rotate around the centre of the axle. If an input force acts on the wheel, then the output force provided by the axle produces an ideal mechanical advantage greater than 1. This is because the input force is farther from the centre of the axle than the output force is. Using a screwdriver to turn a screw is an example of using a wheel and axle to increase output force. The input force acts on the handle, and the output force is at the head of the screwdriver.

Sometimes the input force is applied to the axle. The wheels on a car or bicycle turn because of the input force applied to the axle (Figure 5.21). In this case, the mechanical advantage is less than 1 since the input force is closer to the centre of the axle than the output force is.

If the input force is applied to the axle, the ideal mechanical advantage can be calculated by dividing the radius of the axle (r_a) by the radius of the wheel (r_w).

Figure 5.21 Since the input force is applied closer to the axle than the output force on the rim, this bike wheel has an IMA less than 1.

$$\text{Ideal Mechanical Advantage} = \frac{\text{radius of the axle}}{\text{radius of the wheel}}$$

$$\text{IMA} = \frac{r_a}{r_w}$$

If the input force is applied to the wheel, the ideal mechanical advantage can be calculated by dividing the radius of the wheel (r_w) by the radius of the axle (r_a).

$$\text{Ideal Mechanical Advantage} = \frac{\text{radius of the wheel}}{\text{radius of the axle}}$$

$$\text{IMA} = \frac{r_w}{r_a}$$

For example, the handle of a garden tap of radius 3.0 cm is connected to a shaft of radius 0.50 cm (Figure 5.22). What is the ideal mechanical advantage of this wheel and axle?

$$\text{IMA} = \frac{r_w}{r_a}$$

$$= \frac{3.0 \text{ cm}}{0.50 \text{ cm}}$$

$$= 6.0$$

Figure 5.22 When you turn on the tap, you put force on the handle, which is a wheel. This turns the axle, which opens the tap.

Inclined Planes

Sometimes the force needed to lift an object up a height is greater than we can safely apply. For example, when a hill is too steep for a car to travel in a straight line, a zigzag road is built with a gentler slope (Figure 5.23). A sloping surface on which an object can move is called an **inclined plane**. A ramp (for example, a wheelchair ramp) is another name for an inclined plane. The ramp reduces the force needed to move the wheelchair, but the distance the wheelchair must travel to get to the top of the ramp has increased.

Figure 5.23 By decreasing the slope of the road, the car travels a greater distance but with less required force.

Ideal Mechanical Advantage of an Inclined Plane

If you have to lift an object a vertical height, you can use an inclined plane or ramp. While the ramp increases the distance the object must travel, as shown in Figure 5.24, the amount of force you need is less than if you lifted the object straight up. The ideal mechanical advantage of an inclined plane is the ratio of the length of the slope (l) to the height of the ramp (h).

Suggested Activity • • • • • • • •
B28 Problem-Solving Activity on page 142

$$\text{Ideal Mechanical Advantage} = \frac{\text{length of ramp}}{\text{height of ramp}}$$

$$\text{IMA} = \frac{l}{h}$$

For example, an object is raised 1.0 m (vertical distance) by pushing it along a loading ramp 6.0 m long. What is the ideal mechanical advantage of this ramp?

$$\text{IMA} = \frac{l}{h}$$

$$= \frac{6.0 \text{ m}}{1.0 \text{ m}}$$

$$= 6.0$$

Figure 5.24 An inclined plane allows you to use less force over a greater distance.

The Screw

A **screw** is simply an inclined plane wrapped around a rod (Figure 5.25). This continuous inclined plane, starting at the tip, is called the "thread." The length of the thread is much greater than the length of the screw. As with the inclined plane, this difference in length gives the screw mechanical advantage. The screw's thread allows it to penetrate into hard wood with minimal force. Many food jars have threads similar to the screw. The threads on the lid and the top part of a jar hold the lid firmly in place.

Figure 5.25 A screw is an inclined plane wrapped around a rod.

The Wedge

When we use an inclined plane, the object is pushed or pulled along the inclined plane. A **wedge** is an inclined plane that travels through the object or material. For example, a wedge can be used to split firewood (Figure 5.26). The longer and narrower the wedge, the greater its mechanical advantage. Needles, knives, and your front teeth are all examples of wedges.

Figure 5.26 A wedge is an inclined plane that moves through the object.

Mechanisms

Many of the machines that you use every day consist of several simple machines working together to perform a task. A mechanism is two or more simple machines working together. At the beginning of this unit you learned that a mechanical system is a group of physical parts that interact with each other and function as a whole in order to complete a task. Therefore, mechanisms are mechanical systems. Bicycles and cars are obvious mechanisms. Even simple scissors can be considered a mechanism since they consist of a lever and a wedge (Figure 5.27).

Figure 5.27 Scissors are a mechanism.

Measuring the Mechanical Advantage of Simple Machines

Question

What factors affect the mechanical advantage of a lever and an inclined plane?

Materials and Equipment

- spring scale
- 1.0-kg mass
- wooden board
- metre stick
- support stand
- string

Procedure

Part 1 — The Lever

1. Copy Table 5.1 into your notebook.

Table 5.1 The Lever

Trial	Length of Input Arm (cm)	Length of Output Arm (cm)	Input Force (N)	Output Force (N)	MA	IMA
1	45	25		9.8		
2	35	25		9.8		
3	25	25		9.8		
4	15	25		9.8		

2. Support a metre stick from a support stand using a string attached to the 50-cm location on the metre stick.

3. Attach a 1.0-kg mass to the 25-cm location (25 cm from fulcrum) and a spring scale to the 95-cm location (45 cm from fulcrum).

4. Measure the force required to slowly lift the mass. Record this input force in Trial 1.

5. By moving the location of the spring scale, repeat steps 3 and 4 for the remaining trials shown in the table.

6. Calculate the mechanical advantage (MA) and ideal mechanical advantage (IMA) for each trial.

Part 2 — The Inclined Plane

7. Copy Table 5.2 into your notebook, with space for four trials.

Table 5.2 The Inclined Plane

Trial	Length of Ramp	Height of Ramp	Input Force (N)	Output Force (N)	MA	IMA
1				9.8		
2				9.8		

8. Stack some books on your table. Using the wooden board, set up a ramp from your desk to the top of the stack of books. Measure the length and the vertical height of the ramp. Record these measurements in Trial 1.

9. Attach your spring scale to the mass at the base of your ramp and slowly pull the mass up the ramp. Record this input force in Trial 1.

10. Lower the height of the ramp and repeat steps 8 and 9. Repeat for a total of four trials.

11. Calculate the mechanical advantage and ideal mechanical advantage for each trial.

Analyzing and Interpreting

12. Which simple machine produced the largest mechanical advantage?

13. In general, how does the size of the ideal mechanical advantage compare to the mechanical advantage?

Skill Builder

14. For the inclined plane, which variables in the experiment did you control to ensure that this was a "fair" experiment?

Forming Conclusions

15. For each of the simple machines, explain what variables can be manipulated to change the mechanical advantage.

Best Machine for the Job

Recognize a Need

Have you ever thought of becoming an engineer? Engineering is the application of science to develop solutions and design structures that are useful to people. For example, you might need to lift a large mass to the top of a skyscraper.

Problem

Design and construct a mechanism made from simple machines that will move a 1.0-kg mass from the floor to the top of your desk using the smallest input force.

Materials & Equipment
- spring scale
- various simple machines
- string
- 1.0-kg mass

Criteria for Success
- The final design must include at least one simple machine.
- The input force must be applied by your hand.
- Your design must allow for continual measurement of the force applied by your hand.
- The mechanism must be able to move the mass from the floor to the surface of the desk in a safe manner.

Brainstorm Ideas

1. Which simple machines would be best suited for this task?

2. What variables in each machine can you control to maximize the mechanical advantage?

3. What materials will you use?

Make a Drawing

4. On a single piece of paper, start your sketch by first drawing the floor and the table. Add the starting location of the 1.0-kg mass.

5. Sketch your design for your mechanism. Label the simple machine(s) involved in your design. Your design must show the location of the spring scale used to measure your input force.

6. Be sure to show your drawing to your teacher before going any further.

Test and Evaluate

7. Construct your mechanism.

8. As you operate your mechanism to move the mass, note the maximum force measured by the spring scale. Record this value.

9. The output force required to lift a 1.0-kg mass is 9.8 N. Calculate and record your mechanism's mechanical advantage.

10. Suggest ways of improving your mechanism's mechanical advantage.

Communicate

11. Share and compare your design and mechanical advantage with your classmates' results. Did anyone have a similar design? How did their results compare with yours? What do you think is the best design for this problem?

12. Present your findings to the class or in a form suggested by your teacher.

Key Concept Review

1. Match each photograph below to one of the six simple machines.

(a)

(b)

(c)

2. State the class of lever for each of the levers in the chart. The locations are shown below the chart.

	Location 1	Location 2	Location 3
Lever A	fulcrum	input force	output force
Lever B	output force	fulcrum	input force
Lever C	fulcrum	output force	input force

①————————②————————③

3. Two ramps of different lengths are used to lift furniture into the same truck. Which ramp requires less force?

4. Explain the difference between a mechanism and a simple machine.

Connect Your Understanding

5. A metre stick is used as a lever. If the input force is applied at 0 cm and the output force is exerted at 100 cm, what is the ideal mechanical advantage if the fulcrum is at 75 cm?

6. As the mechanical advantage of a simple machine is increased, how does the distance of the input force compare to the distance of the output force?

Practise Your Skills

7. Draw a simple diagram for the lever involved in the photograph below. On the diagram, label the input force, output force, and fulcrum.

   (a) State the class of lever involved.

   (b) Is the mechanical advantage of this lever greater than 1 or less than 1?

For more questions, go to ScienceSource.

B29 *Thinking about Science, Technology, and Society*

Think Before You Buy

When shopping for a mechanism, how do you decide which one to buy? How do manufacturers try to get you to buy their product?

Consider This

Choose a mechanism that you have recently purchased.

1. What did the advertisements say and what images did they use to convince you to buy this product? How do these images attract you (or not) to buy their product?

2. List the criteria you used when deciding which mechanism to purchase.

Here is a summary of what you will learn in this section:

- The work done by a machine is less than the work put into the machine.
- The efficiency of a machine can be calculated by dividing the output work by the input work.
- A machine's efficiency can be increased by reducing the friction that produces heat.

Can you imagine a machine that runs forever without using any energy? A perpetual-motion car would run without having to be refilled with gas. Over the years, inventors have tried to invent perpetual-motion machines with no success. Such a machine would break the laws of physics.

Figure 5.28 shows a water-screw perpetual-motion machine from the 1600s. Water in the trough falls and turns the water wheel, which is connected to gears that turn a screw. The turning screw carries the water back up to the trough, and the whole process, in theory, should repeat itself. However, this machine soon comes to a grinding halt.

The gravitational potential energy of the water in the trough cannot provide enough energy to turn the screw to return the same amount of water back to the trough. Some of the water's original stored energy is transformed into other forms of energy, such as heat, that this machine cannot use to lift water.

Figure 5.28 An attempt at a perpetual-motion machine

B30 *Starting Point*   Skills Ⓐ Ⓒ

Work Can Be a Drag

When you lift an object, it gains gravitational potential energy. Regardless of what machine you use to lift the object, the output work (W_{out}) is the same.

What to Do

1. Pull a cart slowly up a ramp using a spring scale. Record the amount of force required.

2. Turn the cart over so that the wheels are not touching the incline. Repeat step 1.

Consider This

3. Which situation required a larger force? Since the length of the ramp was the same in both situations, which situation required more input work (W_{in})?

4. Both situations provided the same output work (W_{out}). Explain what happened to the extra energy needed with the larger input work (W_{in}).

Efficiency of Machines

Fuel-efficient cars and energy-efficient light bulbs are common topics in today's society. But what does it mean to be efficient? Perhaps you have been called an efficient worker. This generally means that you get jobs done without wasting time and energy. In science, the efficiency of a machine is determined by analyzing the energies involved.

The **efficiency** of a machine measures the useful work done by the machine compared to the work needed to operate it. **Useful output work** is the work that the machine is designed to perform. For example, a bicycle is designed to move forward. The bicycle's useful output work is determined by measuring the bicycle's forward motion (Figure 5.29). The input work is the work done by the person moving the pedals. For mechanisms such as the bicycle, the useful output work is always less than the input work. But where does the extra energy go?

Figure 5.29 The useful output work of the bicycle is determined by examining the forward motion.

Work Done by Friction

Whenever a machine is used to do work, parts of the machine are moving. For example, if a pulley is used to lift an object, not only does the object move, but parts of the pulley also move. A force of friction occurs where the pulley wheel rotates on its shaft. Since the force of friction is applied to a distance of motion, work is done by the friction force. Work done by the force of friction transforms input energy into heat when the pulley wheel turns (Figure 5.30). Therefore, extra work must be input into the machine to compensate for the work done by friction. For this reason, the useful output work of a machine is always less than the input work.

Highly efficient machines have less friction and therefore produce less heat from friction. More of the input work is changed into useful output work. An ideal machine would have no friction, and therefore all the input work would be converted to output work. Like the perpetual-motion machine, an ideal machine does not exist. Our current goal is to produce machines and mechanisms that are as efficient as possible, such as the solar-powered car in Figure 5.31 on the next page.

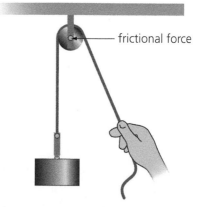

frictional force

Figure 5.30 Friction between the wheel and its shaft produces heat when the pulley is used to lift the object.

Figure 5.31 The University of Waterloo team came fourth in the North American Solar Car Challenge in 2005. The 4000-km race lasted 10 days.

Calculating Efficiency

To calculate the efficiency of a machine, the useful output work (W_{out}) is divided by the input work (W_{in}). Efficiency is usually expressed as a percentage.

$$\text{Efficiency} = \frac{\text{useful output work (joules)} \times 100\%}{\text{input work (joules)}}$$

$$\text{Efficiency} = \frac{W_{out} \times 100\%}{W_{in}}$$

For example, a machine is capable of doing 35 J of work when 50 J of work is put into the machine. What is the efficiency of this machine?

$$\begin{aligned}
\text{Efficiency} &= \frac{W_{out} \times 100\%}{W_{in}} \\
&= \frac{(35\,\text{J}) \times 100\%}{(50\,\text{J})} \\
&= 70\%
\end{aligned}$$

This means that 70% of the work put into the machine goes into doing work that the machine was designed for. The other 30% of the input work goes into other forms of energy.

The efficiency of a machine can also be calculated by measuring the forces and distances. For example, a 500-N crate is moved up a 5.0-m-long ramp (Figure 5.32). What is the efficiency of this ramp if the person pushes with a force of 400 N in order to raise the crate a vertical distance of 2.0 m?

To calculate the efficiency, we must first calculate the useful output work and the input work. Remember from Chapter 4 that $W = Fd$.

Figure 5.32 A 500-N crate is being pushed up the ramp with a force of 400 N.

5.0 m

2.0 m

Useful output work = (500 N)(2.0 m) = 1000 J

Input work = (400 N)(5.0 m) = 2000 J

Now we can use this work to calculate the efficiency.

$$\text{Efficiency} = \frac{W_{out} \times 100\%}{W_{in}}$$

$$= \frac{(1000\,J) \times 100\%}{(2000\,J)}$$

$$= 50\%$$

This inclined plane is 50% efficient.

This ramp has a mechanical advantage greater than 1, which means that less force is required to lift the crate. Even though less force is required, some of the work done by the person is transformed into heat by the friction between the crate and the ramp. Therefore, the efficiency is not 100%.

Suggested Activity •·········
B32 Inquiry Activity on page 149

Take It *Further*

In order to increase the efficiency of a machine, a lubricant can be used to reduce friction. Not all lubricants are liquids like oil. Find out which "dry" materials are used as lubricants. Find an example of a machine in which a dry lubricant is used. Begin your search at ScienceSource.

B31 *Learning Checkpoint*

Calculating Efficiency

You have to lift a mass to a higher location so that the mass gains 800 J of gravitational potential energy. You may use one of three different mechanisms given in the next column to lift the mass. Calculate the efficiency of each mechanism. Which one will you use?

1. You use an electric motor that requires 850 J of energy to lift the mass.

2. You pull the rope of a pulley, which is attached to the mass, a distance of 6.0 m with a force of 150 N.

3. You push the mass 10 m up a ramp with a force of 140 N.

Table 5.3 The Efficiencies of Some Common Mechanisms

Mechanism	Efficiency (%)
Electric generator	99
Olympic track bike	98
Mountain bike	85
Hybrid-diesel car	45
Electric car	44
Hybrid-gasoline car	36
Conventional gas-powered car	22
Solar cell	10

The Efficiency of Common Mechanisms

When a mechanism does work, its energy is transformed from one form to another or transferred from one object to another. A car transforms the chemical energy stored in its fuel into several other forms of energy, such as kinetic energy, sound energy, light energy, and thermal energy. Since the main purpose of a car is transportation, the useful output work of the car would be the work done to provide motion (kinetic energy).

We can measure the efficiency of any mechanism that transfers energy. Table 5.3 gives the efficiencies of some common mechanisms.

How to Increase Efficiency

The efficiency of any machine is not 100 % because some of the input work is used to compensate for the work done by friction. When you use a pulley, you may hear the pulley squeak (sound energy) and the pulley wheel may become warm (heat). These result from the work done by friction. If you reduce the frictional force, you increase the efficiency of a machine. The best way to reduce friction is to add a lubricant, such as grease or oil, to any surfaces that rub together. Lubricants fill the gaps between the two surfaces, making it easier for those surfaces to slide past each other. Because water is also a good lubricant, wet floors are more slippery than dry floors (Figure 5.33).

For some devices, the thermal energy produced during the energy transfer cannot be decreased by a lubricant. A good example is an incandescent lamp, which operates at 175 °C (Figure 5.34). At this temperature, only 5 % of the electrical energy is transformed into light energy. The rest becomes heat. Lubricating the filament of the lamp would not increase its efficiency. Compact fluorescent lamps (CFLs) are designed to operate at a much lower temperature, around 30 °C. At this temperature, less electrical energy is converted to heat. Therefore, the CFL has a higher efficiency than traditional incandescent lamps.

Figure 5.33 Water, like oil and grease, acts like a lubricant to decrease the amount of frictional force.

(a)   (b)

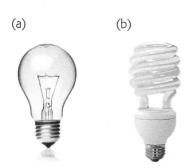

Figure 5.34 (a) Incandescent light bulb, (b) Compact fluorescent light bulb

Increasing Efficiency

No machine is 100% efficient since extra work must be input to the machine to compensate for the work done by friction. To increase the efficiency of a machine, you must decrease the amount of friction.

Question

What method will increase the efficiency of a simple machine, and by what amount is the efficiency increased?

> ### Materials & Equipment
> - spring scale
> - ruler
> - inclined plane
> - mass
> - material or process that will reduce friction

Hypothesis

Write a hypothesis about how the method you will use to reduce friction will change the efficiency of the simple machine.

Procedure

Part 1 — Measuring Efficiency

1. Copy Table 5.4 into your notebook. Give it a title.

Table 5.4

Output Force (N)	Output Distance (m)	Output Work (J)	Input Force (N)	Input Distance (m)	Input Work (J)	Efficiency (%)

2. Stack several books on your desk. Place the mass on your desk at the base of the stack. Using a spring scale, measure the force required to lift the mass straight up. Record this as the output force.

3. Using a ruler, measure the height from the desk to the top of the books. Record this distance as the output distance.

4. Calculate the work required to move the mass from the desk to the top of the stack of books. Record this value as the output work.

5. Place an inclined plane from the desk to the top of the stack of books. Using the spring scale, measure the force required to slide the mass up the incline. Record this value as the input force. Measure the length of your incline and record this as the input distance.

6. Calculate the work required to slide the mass up the incline to the top of the stack of books. Record this value as input work.

7. Calculate the efficiency of this inclined plane.

Part 2 — Increasing Efficiency

8. Suggest a process or material that you think will increase the efficiency of your inclined plane. Be sure to get your teacher's approval before going any further.

9. Copy Table 5.4 into your notebook. The values of output force, output distance, and output work are the same as in Part 1. Give this new table a title.

10. Apply your approved changes to the inclined plane and repeat steps 5–7.

Analyzing and Interpreting

11. Did your material or method increase the efficiency by as much as you expected?

12. Suggest what you might have done differently in order to increase the efficiency even more.

Skill Builder

13. Calculate the amount of heat produced in both Part 1 and Part 2.

Forming Conclusions

14. Answer the question at the beginning of this activity.

Key Concept Review

1. Explain why a machine or a mechanism cannot have an efficiency of 100%.

2. If the efficiency of a machine increases, what happens to each of the following? (Use the words "increases," "decreases," or "stays the same" to describe the changes.)

    (a) input work

    (b) useful output work

    (c) friction

    (d) mechanical advantage

3. What is the mathematical relationship between efficiency, input work, and useful output work?

4. Explain how a lubricant affects the efficiency and the frictional forces of a machine.

Connect Your Understanding

5. A student does 25 J of work on the handle of a pencil sharpener. If the pencil sharpener does 20 J of work on the pencil, what is the efficiency of the sharpener?

6. A force of 900 N pushes a wedge 0.10 m into a log. If the work done on the log is 50 J, what is the efficiency of the wedge?

Practise Your Skills

7. Use the data below to rank machines A, B, and C from:

    (a) highest to lowest mechanical advantage

    (b) highest to lowest efficiency

Machine	Input Force (N)	Input Distance (m)	Output Force (N)	Output Distance (m)
A	5.0	10	20	2.0
B	10	25	50	3.5
C	20	6.0	27	4.0

For more questions, go to ScienceSource.

B33　*Thinking about Science, Technology, and Society*　STSE

Ontario's Bright Idea

The Ontario government has decided to ban the sale of incandescent light bulbs by 2012. It is estimated that by replacing the incandescent bulbs to the more efficient compact fluorescent lights (CFLs), Ontario will save enough energy each year to power 600 000 homes.

Consider This

With a small group or the whole class, discuss statements 1 and 2. Then answer question 3 by yourself.

1. Switching to CFLs will have both an economic and an environmental impact on Ontario.

2. Switching to CFLs will have both positive and negative impacts on Ontario.

3. Do you agree or disagree with the government's decision? Give reasons for your answer.

Mechanical Engineer

Figure 5.35 Some mechanical engineers design roller coasters for a living.

Are you fascinated with building things and with taking things apart to see how they work? Do you like solving puzzles? Would you like to invent a machine that is used by people all over the world? If you answered yes to any of these questions, perhaps you should consider becoming a mechanical engineer. Mechanical engineers use science and mathematics to design mechanical systems that meet societal and consumer needs. These mechanical systems include toys, cars, roller coasters, elevators, spacecraft — basically anything that moves.

Much of a mechanical engineer's work is designing and developing new mechanical systems. This process can usually be broken into four major steps. First, mechanical engineers must fully understand the societal or consumer requirements for the system they are developing. The second step is to design and test the various components of the product. Then, the components are integrated into the final design. The final step is to evaluate the effectiveness of the complete mechanical system. This final evaluation involves cost, reliability, safety, and impact on the environment.

Once these new systems are being used, mechanical engineers often supervise their operation. This may include supervising production in factories, determining the causes of component failure, or doing tests to make sure the system is operating efficiently.

Mechanical engineers require a good background in mathematics, physics, and chemistry. Two of the units in this textbook, Systems in Action and Fluids, are important if you decide to become a mechanical engineer. After high school, you will go to university to obtain a degree in mechanical engineering, or to college to become an engineering technician.

Mechanical engineers are hired by large corporations, government agencies, and engineering companies. These companies are looking for people who are "team players." Most engineering projects require the engineers to work with groups of clients, technologists, and other engineers. For this reason, engineers must have great communication and leadership skills.

Questions

1. What is the job description of a mechanical engineer?

2. Companies that hire mechanical engineers are looking for people who will be "team players." In your opinion, what characteristics should you have to be considered a "team player"?

3. Which two units in this textbook are closely related to the study of mechanical engineering?

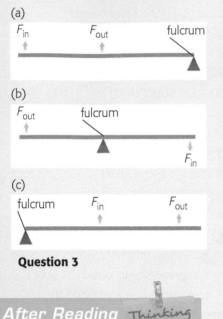

(a)

F_{in} F_{out} fulcrum

(b)

F_{out} fulcrum

F_{in}

(c)

fulcrum F_{in} F_{out}

Question 3

Key Concept Review

1. Define "simple machine." *k*

2. Give an example each of a simple machine and a mechanism. *a*

3. Classify each of the levers in the illustration on the left as first-, second-, or third-class. *k*

4. For which class(es) of lever(s) are the input force and the output force *k*

   (a) in opposite directions?

   (b) in the same direction?

5. Describe the ideal mechanical advantage and the direction of the input and output forces for a fixed pulley. *k*

6. How does the output work compare to the input work for a machine that has an efficiency *k*

   (a) equal to 100%?

   (b) less than 100%?

Connect Your Understanding

7. To increase the mechanical advantage of a lever, should you increase or decrease the length of the output arm? *a*

8. Pedro and Brittany design a mechanical device that will move desks from one classroom to another on the floor above. They measure the forces and distances and calculate the input and output work. If their calculations show that the input work equals the output work, is their calculation correct? Explain. *a*

9. If you did Activity B23, you sketched locations on a mountain bike that involved simple machines. Using that sketch, label the type of simple machine at each location. *t*

10. A mechanical system is used to pull a tarp over a grass tennis court. On a clear, sunny day, the efficiency of the system is 55%. After a rainstorm, the efficiency is measured to be 65%. Explain why there is a difference in the efficiencies. *a*

After Reading — Thinking Literacy

Making Connections

At the beginning of this chapter, you predicted what you might learn about simple machines, ideal mechanical advantage, and efficiency. How does the information you have read add to or change what you predicted about these topics?

You have also learned about making inferences. How is inferring the same as and different from predicting? Why might a writer give only essential details on a topic and expect the reader to infer meaning from this information? Share your ideas with the class.

ACHIEVEMENT CHART CATEGORIES
k Knowledge and understanding   *t* Thinking and investigation   *c* Communication   *a* Application

11. Each photograph on the right shows a common tool. Identify the type of simple machine each tool represents. ⓐ

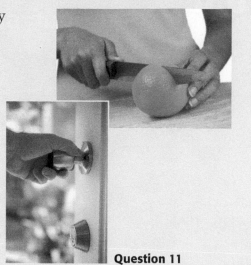

Question 11

Practise Your Skills

12. Plan an experiment to measure the ideal mechanical advantage of a three-hole punch. ⓣ

   (a) What materials would you need?

   (b) What procedure would you use?

13. Calculate the IMA of a lever whose input force is applied 3 m from the fulcrum and whose output force is 0.5 m from the fulcrum. ⓣ

14. A ramp that is 5 m long is used to raise an object 2 m vertically. Find the IMA of this ramp. ⓣ

15. Using one or two pulleys, draw a mechanical system that has: ⓣ

   (a) an IMA = 2

   (b) an IMA = 3

16. The handle of a screwdriver has a radius of 3 cm. If the shaft of the screwdriver has a radius of 0.5 cm, what is the IMA of the screwdriver when used to tighten a screw? ⓣ

17. Wei uses a pulley system to lift a box. She pulls the rope a distance of 3 m, using a force of 50 N. If the work done on the box is 120 J, what is the efficiency of the pulley system? ⓣ

Unit Task Link

In your Unit Task, you will design, construct, and test a mechanical system that uses only the energy stored in a spring-bar mousetrap. The mousetrap machine must have a function other than catching mice. What simple machines might you use in your project? How can you ensure that your design has maximum efficiency?

B34 *Thinking about Science, Technology, and Society*

Building a Modern Pyramid

The ancient Egyptian pyramids, like those shown in Figure 5.4 on page 130, were built over 4500 years ago. Archeologists believe that the workers mainly used ramps and levers when building them.

   Suppose you wanted to build a similar pyramid using modern technology.

Consider This

In small groups or as a class, discuss the following questions.

1. What modern machines do you think would be used in the construction of the pyramid?

2. What developments in science and technology have resulted in these modern machines?

Automated assembly lines build many of the cars of today.

What You Will Learn

In this chapter, you will:

- identify various non-mechanical systems and describe the components of these systems that allow them to function efficiently
- examine alternative ways of meeting current needs and assess their impact on society and the environment
- determine how society and the environment have been affected by the automation of systems

Skills You Will Use

In this chapter you will:

- investigate the information and support that is provided to the consumer to ensure that a system functions safely and efficiently
- use criteria to evaluate a system

Why This Is Important

School systems, communication systems, transit systems, and health-care systems are just a few examples of systems that have both immediate and long-term effects on your life.

Before Writing

Thinking Literacy

Problem & Solution

Writers use different organizational patterns to communicate information to readers. Knowing these patterns helps readers "see" the relationship(s) among ideas. Much of the information in this chapter is presented in a Problem & Solution pattern. Think about a problem you have had and how you solved it.

Key Terms

- automated system
- non-mechanical system
- quantitative assessment
- productivity
- criteria
- qualitative assessment

Figure 6.1 A garbage truck is a mechanism used to collect waste products.

Here in Ontario, the City of Toronto alone produces about 500 000 tonnes of garbage every year. Mechanical systems, such as levers and hydraulics, are used to lift the waste bins and dump them into the truck (Figure 6.1). On the truck, other mechanical systems compact the materials to make more room in the truck.

However, it takes more than just mechanical systems to operate an efficient waste management program that reduces and recycles waste (Figure 6.2). The staff and the procedures used to collect and dispose of waste are part of the non-mechanical system involved in waste management. **Non-mechanical systems** include the procedures, processes, and people needed to perform a task.

A complete waste management program includes both mechanical and non-mechanical systems in its task to reduce, recycle, or dispose of waste. The non-mechanical system for waste disposal consists of several components. The city hires workers and buys trucks. Some workers develop a schedule of pick-up times and publish collection calendars for delivery to the public. Residents sort their waste into garbage, recyclables, and organic material (including leaf and yard waste) and put out the bins on the appropriate collection day for pick-up. The trucks offload recyclables at a recycling plant, the organic material at a compost-processing facility, and the rest of the waste at a landfill. Other workers operate the recycling plant and compost facility and maintain the landfill site.

Like mechanical systems, each component of a non-mechanical system plays a role in the successful completion of the task. In this chapter, you will study many types of systems and their impact on both the environment and society.

Figure 6.2 The workers, along with the procedures for collecting and handling recyclable products, represent some of the non-mechanical components of a recycling program.

B35 *Quick Lab*

Your School's Waste Management

Purpose
To examine how your school community manages its garbage

Materials & Equipment
- pen and paper
- resource person such as the custodian or principal

Procedure

1. On a single piece of paper, draw a T-chart with the headings "Non-recyclable" and "Recyclable."

2. Make a list of the types of garbage in your school. Remember: recyclable materials include metal cans, plastics, cardboard, paper, and organic materials.

3. Find out what materials your school recycles and put a checkmark beside those materials on your list.

Questions

4. Choose one item from your non-recyclable list. Describe what you think happens to this piece of garbage after you throw it away.

5. Choose one item from your recyclable list. Describe what you think happens to this item after you throw it away.

6. Suggest one change that you believe would improve the current system of waste management in your school.

Non-mechanical Systems in Society

Here is a summary of what you will learn in this section:

- As in mechanical systems, the components of a non-mechanical system interact to perform a task.
- Many non-mechanical systems are designed because of the needs of society.
- Information and support are required to keep a system working efficiently.

Figure 6.3 Students, desks, and books are just a few of the components that make up a school system.

In Chapters 4 and 5, you learned that mechanical systems use forces to do work and transfer energy. In this chapter, we will look at non-mechanical systems, which perform tasks without transferring forces. A non-mechanical system that you are familiar with is the school system (Figure 6.3). The school system involves more than just students and teachers. Principals, custodians, administrative staff, bus drivers, and school boards are all part of the system. The school system is not just people. It is also all of the objects such as books, desks, buildings, playgrounds, and equipment. Subjects (such as science), timetables, and even the rules are part of the school system.

In order for any system to perform its task successfully, the **components** of the system must interact. The components are the parts of the system. Most non-mechanical systems have an overall plan so that each component of the system has a purpose or role. For example, teachers, timetables, and books each have very different roles in the system, but each contributes to the overall success.

The school system is just one example of a non-mechanical system. Many other non-mechanical systems provide services to you, your community, your province, and your country.

B36 *Starting Point*   Skills **P C**

Non-mechanical Systems in Society

Non-mechanical systems usually include an organizational system that provides a service to some part of society. Work with a partner and brainstorm as many non-mechanical systems as you can think of. Keep this list for a future activity.

A Problem, Its Causes, and Some Solutions

Society has many systems that improve our lives, but some may also cause problems. As you read, identify a problem in our society. What causes this problem? What solutions do we use to solve this problem? Develop a graphic organizer and record this problem, its cause, and its possible solutions.

Can you find any signal words on this page that tell you the writers used a "Problem & Solution" pattern to organize their ideas?

Systems Require Organization

In order for a non-mechanical system to function properly, the components of the system must work together in an organized manner. This organization is usually done by a person, a company, or a government, who oversees the operation of the system. Once all of the procedures and components are put in place, the system can perform the desired task.

Figure 6.4 A transportation system involves both mechanical and non-mechanical systems.

Suppose the desired task is helping people travel without taking their own vehicles. Most cities in Ontario have organized a transportation system to perform such a task. Both mechanical and non-mechanical systems make up such a system (Figure 6.4). The mechanical components are the buses, trains, or subways. The non-mechanical components include the drivers, routes, and schedules (Figure 6.5). By themselves, none of these components could provide an adequate transportation system. Instead, the components interact in such a way that people are moved from one location to another efficiently and safely. If you were in charge, how would you organize such a transportation system?

One method may be to organize the non-mechanical components of the system first. You would design the bus routes that best meet the needs of the riders. A schedule of when the bus will arrive at each stop is next. Bus drivers must be informed of their routes and time lines. Finally, the mechanical system (the bus) is used to complete the task.

Figure 6.5 Bus routes and schedules represent a non-mechanical component of a transportation system.

A transportation system is just one example of a non-mechanical system that is used to organize our society. The same analysis can be done with any system.

Figure 6.6 Day-care facilities like this are one component of the child care system.

Take It Further

As new products are developed to meet the needs of society, a system is needed to evaluate the safety of these products. The Canadian Standards Association (CSA) is a non-government association that tests and approves new products to make sure that they are safe for the consumer and the environment. Find out how the CSA evaluates consumer products. Begin your search at ScienceSource.

RefWorks User Quick Start Guide
VERSION 5.0

LOGGING IN

• Access www.xxxxxxxxxxxxx and then enter your personal Login Name and Password. (First-time users need to sign up for an individual account following the screen prompts.)
• NOTE: Remote users, accessing RefWorks from off-site or from a non-registered IP address, must either enter the "Group Code" prior to the personal Login Name and Password or log-in via the organization's proxy server.

RefWorks
Technical Services

Systems Develop from a Need

Our society has many systems that improve our standard of living. You might wonder how non-mechanical systems become part of our society. Most are the result of a need.

A transportation system is just one example of a system that was developed in response to a need. Another example is child care. Over the past 40 years, the number of families with both parents working away from the home has increased. This meant that society had a need for a system that could take care of these parents' children. To meet this need, a child care system was developed (Figure 6.6).

In 2004, Ontario initiated its Best Start child care program. The demand for child care has continued to increase, and in 2007, the Ontario government added an extra $142.5 million to meet the demands of the child care system. In order for a system to continue to meet the needs of society, it must be evaluated and upgraded continuously.

Keeping the System Working Efficiently

Once a system is in place, it needs to be monitored frequently to make sure that it is meeting the needs of its consumers. A **consumer** is an individual who uses the goods or services provided by a system. In order for the system to work efficiently, the consumer must be provided with information and support on how to use it.

Suppose that you recently purchased a new computer system. The manufacturers of that computer system need to communicate to you, the consumer, how you can use that system. Often, the manufacturer provides an instruction manual (Figure 6.7), either as a booklet or on-line.

Not all systems work continuously without developing problems. When a problem arises, the consumer may need to get help. Most systems have a service component that deals with such problems. In the school system, your school counsellor might be one component that can help when you are having problems in school. Most companies offer "tech support" to make sure that you can get help if their product needs service.

Figure 6.7 Instruction manuals like this provide information to the consumer.

Assembly Not Included

Instruction manuals are one type of support that a manufacturer might provide to a consumer. In order for a manual to be useful, it must convey the information clearly and accurately.

Purpose

To evaluate assembly instructions

Materials & Equipment

- paper and pencils

Procedure

1. You have just bought a bookshelf at a furniture store. It came with the directions shown in the box at the right and a diagram to show you how it should be assembled (Figure 6.8).

2. Copy Table 6.1 into your notebook. Use it to record your evaluation of the instructions. Rate the Construction Steps as follows:

   - 4 = very good
   - 3 = good
   - 2 = satisfactory
   - 1 = unsatisfactory

3. In the Comments column, provide a reason for your rating. Include a least two suggestions for improving the directions.

Questions

4. Most instruction manuals contain both diagrams and written instructions. Explain why you think it is important to include both.

5. You used three categories when evaluating these assembly instructions. Which of these three categories do you think is most important to the consumer? Suggest another category that could be used in the evaluation.

Construction Steps

Assembling the bookcase

1. Locate the holes for insert A.

2. Screw connector B into insert A. There are 2 for each side.

3. Do the same for the other side.

Table 6.1

Category	4	3	2	1	Comments
Clarity of directions					
Thoroughness					
User-friendliness					

Figure 6.8 Bookcase assembly

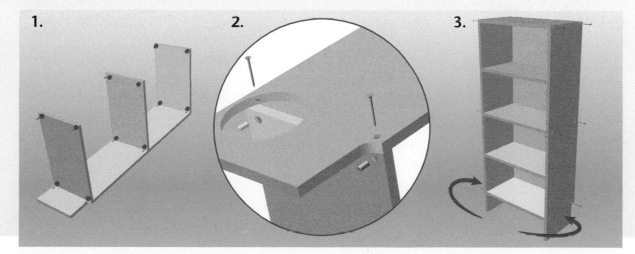

Providing a Service to Society

Similar to mechanical systems, non-mechanical systems consist of several components that work together to perform a task or function. Often these components perform several tasks. At the beginning of this chapter, you created a list of different types of non-mechanical systems. In this activity, you will examine one system from your list.

Purpose

To examine a non-mechanical system that provides a service to society

> **Materials & Equipment**
> - paper and pencils

Procedure

1. With a partner, choose a non-mechanical system from the list you made earlier.

2. Write the name of your system at the top of a blank piece of paper.

3. Identify all of the components of this system that you can think of. Write the names of these components anywhere on the paper.

4. Draw lines between components that interact with each other. On each line, write a short description of how those components interact. Figure 6.9 shows a small example.

Questions

5. What societal need does the system you chose fulfill?

6. Some of your components may interact with more than one other component. Which component had the largest number of interactions?

7. If you removed the component that you identified in question 6 from the system, what might happen to the system?

8. Describe one part of the system that you believe is responsible for making sure the system works efficiently.

9. Suggest one improvement that you think would increase the effectiveness of this system.

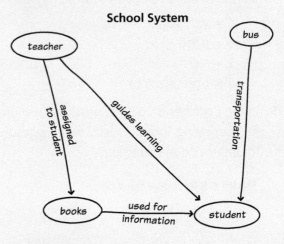

School System

Figure 6.9

Key Concept Review

1. In Canada, our government is considered a "democratic system." Is this a mechanical or a non-mechanical system? Explain.

2. Identify three components of the school system.

3. Explain what the concept "systems need organization" means to you.

4. What is the relationship between a need in society and a system?

5. Define "consumer."

6. In order for a system to work efficiently, what two services should be provided to the consumer?

Connect Your Understanding

7. Your company has been hired to install an automatic sprinkler system for a large park. The mechanical and non-mechanical components of the job are listed in random order below. Organize the components in the correct sequence.

   - Dig trenches to bury the water pipes.
   - Set the timer for the watering times.
   - Identify the areas that need watering.
   - Sketch a plan of the locations of the water pipes and sprinkler heads.
   - Connect the pipes to the water supply.
   - Connect the pipes to the sprinkler heads and bury them in the trenches.

8. What societal needs do you believe each of the following systems fulfills?

   (a) merchandise distribution system

   (b) provincial electrical system

Practise Your Skills

9. The photograph below shows part of a library system.

   (a) What socictal need does a library system fulfill?

   (b) Identify the components of this library system.

   (c) Describe the interaction between any two components you have identified.

   (d) Describe one aspect of this system that keeps it working efficiently.

For more questions, go to ScienceSource.

B40 *Thinking about Science, Technology, and Society* **STSE**

You: The Consumer

A consumer is a person who purchases the goods or services provided by a system. Many companies advertise their products to specifically attract teenage consumers.

With a group or the whole class, make a list of products that you think are intended for teenage consumers. Discuss the methods of advertising that companies use to make their products more attractive to teenagers.

Here is a summary of what you will learn in this section:

- Increasing productivity allows a task to be accomplished faster or allows more tasks to be done at the same time.
- An automated system replaces human workers with machines that operate without human intervention.
- Automation has had an impact on our society, the environment, and our economy.
- The criteria for assessing a system include efficiency, safety, cost, and impact on the environment.
- When considering alternative ways of meeting the needs of society, we must assess both the current system and the proposed system.

Today you finally buy those shoes that you have been saving for. You may begin your search at the mall, involving many stores, styles, and prices (Figure 6.10). For some people, shopping is a dream come true, but others see it as a huge waste of time. If the only purpose for going to a mall is to buy shoes, then walking from store to store and trying on several styles seems very inefficient. There must be a way to be more productive.

Figure 6.10 A mall provides many options to the shopper.

B41 *Starting Point*   Skills Ⓐ Ⓒ

To Mall or Not to Mall: That Is the Question

Working with a partner or as a whole class, create a "Pros" and "Cons" list for shopping on-line versus shopping at a mall. Once the list is completed, classify each of the items as being:

- economic: deals with money issues
- environmental: has an impact on the environment (e.g., pollution)
- social: deals with the interaction of people

Organizing Writing Ideas

The automation of the car industry has changed the way we live. The freedom of movement that comes with widespread use of the car has both positive and negative consequences.

Copy Table 6.2, leaving lots of room to add information. As you read this section, think about and record some of the positive and negative impacts of the increasing use of the car. For each negative impact, suggest a possible solution. Use this information to write a few paragraphs about the impact of the car. Use a Problem & Solution pattern for your writing.

Table 6.2 The Impact of the Car

Type of Impact	Positive Impacts	Negative Impacts	Solutions for Negative Impacts
Social			
Economic			
Environmental			

Productivity

Productivity is the amount of output that is produced per unit of time. If you can increase productivity, you can accomplish a task faster or do more tasks in the same amount of time. So how can you make the task of buying shoes more productive? One way would be to shop on-line (Figure 6.11), where you can search for different styles and even pay for your purchase. On-line shopping is much more productive because you do not waste time getting to the mall and walking from store to store.

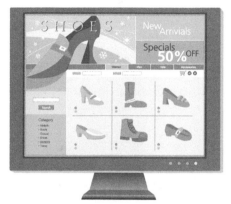

Figure 6.11 On-line shopping may increase the productivity of shopping.

Increasing Productivity

In this unit we have studied how both mechanical and non-mechanical systems are used to do work or complete a task. Well-designed systems can improve productivity, allowing the work to be done faster or more tasks to be done at the same time.

Consider the amount of work required to dig a tunnel under a river or through a mountain. In 1854, construction of the Brockville Tunnel began under the City of Brockville, Ontario (Figure 6.12, next page). Workers used simple machines, such as shovels, picks, and ramps, to construct this 527-m-long railway tunnel.

Figure 6.12 The Brockville Tunnel, Canada's first railway tunnel, took more than six years to construct.

Figure 6.13 Modern tunnel-boring machines allow tunnels to be dug much faster than in the past.

In 2005, 150 years later, construction of the Niagara Tunnel began. This tunnel channels water under the City of Niagara Falls. Today, mechanisms such as the tunnel-boring machine (TBM) (Figure 6.13) have replaced the simple machines used on the Brockville Tunnel. If the Brockville Tunnel had been dug by the TBM used under Niagara Falls, it would have been completed in just over a month.

The building of the Brockville Tunnel employed hundreds of people for several years. Modern methods of tunnelling do not require the same number of workers. In situations like this, increased productivity has decreased the number of jobs available.

Often it is a combination of mechanical and non-mechanical systems that increase productivity. For example, some libraries now have self-checkout machines (Figure 6.14). These machines allow the consumer to scan the bar code to check out the items without waiting for a librarian. The mechanical system includes a scanner that is connected to a computer. By passing a laser light across the bar code, the scanner records the information on the computer's hard drive and a receipt is printed.

Figure 6.14 Consumers can check out their own books using this machine.

The non-mechanical part of the system includes the instruction sheet posted at each machine. The instructions help the library patrons use the machine to check out their books. These machines increase productivity because more books can be checked out in a given amount of time. Does this mean that we no longer need librarians? Librarians provide many services that are vital to the operation of a library, other than checking out books. However, when a system is implemented to increase productivity, there is always a danger that the quality of service will decrease.

Mass Production

In the past, many consumer goods were made by hand. For example, a small group of employees would build an entire car. Today, some high-quality furniture and musical instruments are still hand crafted (Figure 6.15).

Nowadays, many consumer goods are produced by a system called mass production, in which each employee repeatedly performs a small task as the item moves past on a conveyor belt (Figure 6.16). The system — from raw materials to final product — is called an assembly line. Each item is made faster and for less cost, and is very similar in design and quality.

Increasing productivity by mass production may also have negative consequences. Goods manufactured on an assembly line are often of a lower quality than hand-crafted items are.

Figure 6.15 Hand-made products require many hours to complete.

Automated Systems

Another way to increase productivity is to replace the current system with an automated system. An **automated system** replaces human workers with machines that are controlled by a computer. Once the automated system is set up, the machines monitor and react to situations without human intervention. An automated system can be as simple as the thermostat that controls the heat in your home. Once it is set, the thermostat monitors the room temperature and reacts to control the temperature by turning the furnace on and off.

Automation is used for both simple tasks, like baking bread with a bread machine, and complex ones like assembling cars (see the chapter opener photo on page 154). Even professions such as farming have been automated. On modern poultry farms, thousands of chickens or turkeys are fed and watered by automated systems (Figure 6.17).

Figure 6.16 Many consumer goods are processed on an assembly line.

Figure 6.17 Many farms use automated feeding and watering systems.

WORDS MATTER

The prefix "auto-" means self-operating. For example, "automobiles" are self-operating vehicles. "Automatic" means "working by itself," and an "automaton" is a human-like robot.

The Impact of Automation

Over the past 20 years of computer development, many tasks traditionally done by workers have become fully automated. As with any change, this can be viewed both positively and negatively. To make up your own mind, you need to consider the social, economic, and environmental impacts that automation has on society. A social impact is how automation helps people live, work, and interact with each other in a society. Economic impacts of automation deal with the money aspects. Finally, environmental impacts include how automation affects both the biotic and abiotic elements of our ecosystems.

Socially, many traditional jobs have been replaced by automated systems. Some people have lost their jobs to automation. However, automated systems have also been responsible for creating many new types of occupations. Thus, automated systems have changed the types of work that people do. Automated systems have definitely changed how society lives and works.

Economically, automating a system usually increases productivity. This means that the business can make the product at less expense and therefore can sell it at a lower cost. If automating a system reduces the number of employees required, this affects the economy of both the company and the community.

Environmentally, automating an assembly line may require an increase in the amount of energy used by the machines (Figure 6.18), which might have a negative environmental effect. Car manufacturers install an automated pollution control system in each car that decreases harmful emissions. This automated system has a positive environmental effect.

Figure 6.18 A fully automated bottling system.

Take It *Further*

Automated teller machines (ATMs) replace some of the work done by a bank teller. A bank teller counts money visually. How do ATMs know the difference between a $10 bill and $20 bill? How do they count the correct amount of money? Begin your search at ScienceSource.

Assessing a System

When the needs of society change, the existing systems may no longer meet those needs. Either the existing systems must be changed or new systems must be developed. Before the changed system or the new system is put in place, the developers must evaluate the impact it will have on individuals, society, and the environment.

Using Criteria to Evaluate a System

Criteria (singular: criterion) are standard rules or tests on which a decision or judgement can be based. To assess systems, the developers often use the following criteria:

- efficiency
- cost
- safety
- environmental impact

Each of these criteria can be assessed quantitatively or qualitatively. A **quantitative assessment** involves analysis of numerical data. As we saw in Chapter 5 for a mechanical system, the quantitative efficiency is determined by:

Efficiency = (useful output work)/(input work)

Qualitative assessments are often made by observations. For example, "My car gets great gas mileage" is a qualitative assessment. Compare this qualitative assessment of the car's fuel efficiency with the quantitative assessment, "My car travels 10 km per litre of gas."

Assessing Systems for Transporting Groceries

Thousands of years ago, people grew or caught their food. They needed containers to transport the food to their villages and to store the food. Early containers were made from woven grass or twigs, animal skins, clay, and even animal organs (Figure 6.19). If we use the criteria listed above to assess these early containers, we might come to the following conclusions.

- Efficiency: Low since large amounts of time and effort were required to produce one container. It was also inconvenient to have to take the empty containers to the field.
- Safety: These containers were difficult to keep clean. As well, they did not provide protection against insects and rodents.
- Cost: Low since the materials were readily available in nature.
- Environmental impact: Low since the containers were made from natural materials and would decompose easily when discarded.

Figure 6.19 Sacks and baskets were used by our ancestors to carry things.

From Paper to Plastic Bags

Society assessed these early containers as being inefficient, hard to store, and hard to keep clean. An efficiently produced, disposable bag was deemed a societal need. By the early 1900s, the system of making paper from wood products was well developed. Paper shopping bags soon replaced traditional methods of carrying groceries (Figure 6.20).

Applying the criteria to the paper bag, we find that paper bags were expensive to produce and not very strong. Since they were considered disposable, they were safe to use. Their environmental impact is questionable: the bags decompose easily, but paper is made from trees. For cost and efficiency, society wanted a cheaper bag that was light and strong, and could be given free to shoppers.

By the late 1970s, plastic shopping bags had almost totally replaced paper bags (Figure 6.21). It is estimated that Canada uses and discards about six billion plastic bags annually. Plastic bags are inexpensive to produce and can be re-used and recycled. However, they decompose extremely slowly.

Beyond Plastic Bags

The high efficiency of producing plastic bags and their low cost have made their use very appealing. Their safety is a concern, however, because of their potential to suffocate babies who play with them. Currently, society is again assessing our system for carrying groceries, mainly because of the impact of plastic bags on the environment. Most plastic bags are made of polyethylene, which is a type of plastic derived from oil. It is estimated that only about 1 percent of all plastic bags are recycled. The production, disposal, and environmental impact of plastic shopping bags must be considered when assessing our current system of transporting groceries.

Many shoppers are now bringing their own reusable bags every time they go to the store. The system for transporting groceries has gone full circle — from reusable containers, to disposable paper, to usually discarded plastic, and back to reusable containers.

Figure 6.20 Paper grocery bags were used for many years.

Figure 6.21 Most stores use plastic bags now.

My Opinion of Automation

Issue

Many jobs and tasks that used to be done by people are now being done by automated systems. Choose a job or task that has been automated and decide if this automation has had a positive or negative effect on society.

Background Information

The number of jobs that have become automated continues to grow. Jobs that have been automated include:

- phone-answering systems
- automated teller machine (ATM) (Figure 6.22)
- assembly lines (in manufacturing)
- autopilot on commercial airplanes
- checkouts at libraries or stores
- ticket-dispensing machines at movie theatres (Figure 6.22)
- farming (poultry, dairy, hydroponics)

Analyze and Evaluate

Choose any job that has been automated. Your task is to look at the positive or negative impacts the automation of that job has had on society, and decide whether the automation was positive or negative on the whole. Research evidence to support your argument. You will present your findings as either a report or a class presentation. Your teacher will provide more details about how to present your information.

As you research, answer the following questions.

- How was this task accomplished before it was automated?
- How is this task accomplished with automation?
- What is the social impact of this automation?
- What is the economic impact of this automation?
- What is the environmental impact of this automation?

1. Use the following resources for your research.

   - Go to ScienceSource to begin your search for information.
   - Look in print materials such as magazines, newspapers, and books for information on the automated job you have chosen.

2. Summarize the information you find in a short report for presentation. Be sure to include only information that supports your viewpoint or refutes the opposite view.

Figure 6.22 It seems like everything is automated these days!

Key Concept Review

1. How does increased productivity change:

   (a) the time it takes to complete a task?

   (b) the number of tasks performed in a certain amount of time?

2. Explain what is meant by an automated system. Give two examples of automated systems.

3. What four criteria are often used when assessing a system?

4. Indicate which of the following is a qualitative assessment and which is a quantitative assessment.

   (a) 45 percent efficient

   (b) makes your clothes whiter

Connect Your Understanding

5. Baking bread at home can now be automated. Just add the ingredients to a bread machine and press a button (photo at right). Identify the mechanical and non-mechanical systems involved in this automation.

6. Use an example to explain how automating a system can have both positive and negative effects on society.

7. Explain how increasing the efficiency of a system can have a positive effect on society.

8. Give two reasons why people look for alternative ways of meeting the current needs of society.

9. Suppose the government passed a law saying, "Everyone must use an electric toothbrush." Use the four criteria to assess this change in the system of brushing your teeth.

Practise Your Skills

10. Explain why you think the figure below displays an automated system. List some positive and negative aspects of automating how we wash and dry our clothes.

For more questions, go to ScienceSource.

B44 *Thinking about Science, Technology, and Society*

Automating Your School's Recycling Program

At the beginning of this chapter, you examined the recycling program in your school. Suggest one component of this system that could be automated. Predict what effect this automation might have on your school community. If possible, predict the social, economic, and environmental impacts.

Making Connections

Jay Ingram

Jay Ingram is an experienced science journalist and is the host of *Daily Planet* on Discovery Channel Canada.

The Trebuchet

Imagine it is 1304. You are a Scottish soldier defending Stirling Castle against the English. You've hung in for months as the English siege machines battered the castle walls with balls made of stone and lead. You are completely surrounded and you're running out of food. If all that weren't bad enough, the King of England, Edward I, has just ordered his chief engineer to build a massive trebuchet, called the Warwolf.

A trebuchet (pronounced treb-you-shay) is a mechanism, but its heart is a strange lever with one arm longer than the other. The short arm has a gigantic weight at the end. The long arm is pulled down to the ground and held there. Imagine a teeter-totter with a very large man sitting on the short end and a gang of kids holding down the long end. When they let go, the man comes crashing to the ground. The trebuchet is like that, except that the large man is replaced by a giant weight and the kids by a trigger.

There is one more thing. The long arm has a sling attached to it: a long cord with a stone ball cradled in a net at the end. When the trigger is released, the weight falls. The long arm of the lever swings up like lightning, whipping the sling and its ball overhead. At just the right moment, the sling releases the stone ball and it goes flying toward the target.

What's most amazing about trebuchets is this: they're ancient machines, yet they were capable of amazing power and accuracy. They could throw weights of up to 1000 kg more than 200 m. They were also much more accurate than other launching devices, such as catapults.

Fifty men took three months to build the Warwolf, but in the end, it didn't play a part in the English victory. The Scots surrendered before it was even used. However, King Edward refused to accept their surrender until the Warwolf had flung a few of its 140-kg weights at the castle wall and bashed it in. That was the trebuchet's specialty: breaking down walls.

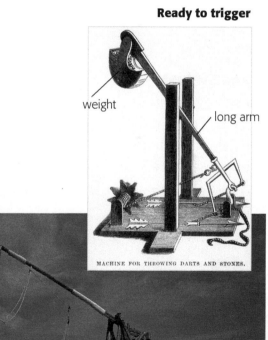

Figure 6.23 An old diagram of a trebuchet and a recently built one.

Key Concept Review

1. List three non-mechanical components of the school system.

2. The postal service is a system for delivering mail. Who are the "consumers" of this system?

3. What are two methods of support used to keep a system operating safely and efficiently?

4. Explain how an automated system is different from a non-automated system.

5. A bakery bakes 35 loaves of bread every hour. If the productivity of the bakery increases, how does the time to bake 35 loaves change?

6. Identify each of the following as a qualitative measurement or a quantitative measurement.

   (a) The water is at 66°C.

   (b) The creek had a strong current.

Connect Your Understanding

7. Your younger brother is given a toy that requires some assembly. Are the instructions for assembly a mechanical or a non-mechanical component of the toy system? Explain.

8. Often, a system is developed to meet a need of society. Identify the needs that resulted in the development of the following systems:

   (a) home alarm system

   (b) irrigation system

9. One year ago, a company stated: "We make 100 widgets every day." If the productivity of the company has increased in the past year, what statement(s) might the company make now?

After Writing Thinking Literacy

Reflect and Evaluate

Exchange your "Problem & Solution" writing piece with a classmate. Take some time to read your classmate's work. Provide each other with descriptive feedback, such as, what two things did he or she do well?

   Did you learn something new about the impact of cars? Did you find new solutions to the negative impacts? Finally, share tips for writing a good "Problem & Solution" piece with the class.

ACHIEVEMENT CHART CATEGORIES
Ⓚ Knowledge and understanding   Ⓣ Thinking and investigation   Ⓒ Communication   Ⓐ Application

10. The Sweet Tooth chocolate company produces one-of-a-kind handmade chocolates. To increase productivity, they decide to automate chocolate making. Suggest two positive and two negative impacts that might result from the automation of this company. ⓣ

11. Explain how the furnace thermostat in your home or school is an example of an automated system. ⓐ

Practise Your Skills

12. You have just purchased a new DVD player. You also received an owner's manual, shown at the right. Identify at least two properties of this owner's manual that are designed to help you operate this DVD player efficiently. ⓣ

Question 12

13. The histogram to the right displays a company's productivity and the number of employees during a 10-year period. Use the histogram to answer the following. ⓣ

(a) Describe the changes from 1995 to 2005:

(i) in productivity

(ii) in the number of employees

(b) What is the relationship between productivity and the number of employees?

(c) Suggest a possible reason for these changes.

Unit Task Link

In your Unit Task, you will design, construct, and test a mechanical system that uses only the energy stored in a spring-bar mousetrap. The mousetrap machine you design must have a function other than catching mice. What is the need being met by your device? Using the four criteria, assess your mechanical system.

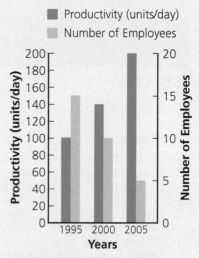

Question 13 Productivity and number of employees in 1995, 2000, and 2005

B45 *Thinking about Science, Technology, and Society*

Assessing the Change

Pollution caused by motor vehicles is a problem in all parts of the world. To address this problem, your local government decides to ban the use of any vehicle with a motor in your city or town.

Consider This

With a classmate or as a whole class, use the four criteria on page 169 to assess this new system of transportation.

4.0 Mechanical systems use forces to transfer energy.

KEY CONCEPTS

- A force is a push or a pull on an object
- $W = F \times d$
- A machine is a mechanical system that makes doing work easier.
- $MA = \dfrac{F_{out}}{F_{in}}$
- Ideal mechanical advantage (IMA) assumes that the machine has zero friction.

CHAPTER SUMMARY

- The force of gravity (weight) is the product of the object's mass and the Earth's gravitational field.
- Work is done when a force causes something to move and energy is transferred.
- Machines make work easier by increasing the force applied to the object, by increasing the distance over which the force is applied, or by changing the direction of the force.
- The amount by which a machine can multiply the input force is called its mechanical advantage (MA).

5.0 Mechanical systems involve machines that are designed to do work efficiently.

KEY CONCEPTS

- A simple machine requires the application of a single force to do the work.
- Two or more simple machines that operate together form a mechanism.
- $\text{Efficiency} = \dfrac{W_{out}}{W_{in}}$
- Machines can be made more efficient by reducing friction.

CHAPTER SUMMARY

- The six types of simple machines are the lever, pulley, wheel and axle, inclined plane, screw, and wedge.
- The IMA of simple machines can be calculated as the ratio of lengths, the ratio of radii, or the number of support strings.
- The efficiency of a machine measures the useful work done by the machine compared to the work needed to operate the machine.
- Friction causes the input work to be transformed into heat, thus decreasing the efficiency of the machine.

6.0 Systems have an impact on our society.

KEY CONCEPTS

- A non-mechanical system is a procedure or process designed to perform a task.
- Systems develop from a need.
- Automating a system may have social, economic, and environmental effects.

CHAPTER SUMMARY

- Information and support are required to keep a non-mechanical system working efficiently.
- Productivity is the amount of output that is produced per unit of time.
- Automated systems replace human workers with machines that react without human intervention.
- The criteria for evaluating a system include efficiency, safety, cost, and environmental impact.

Mousetrap Machines

Getting Started

Successful machines carry out their functions consistently and efficiently. The best mechanical systems use the minimum component materials and are surprisingly simple in design.

The humble mousetrap evolved from an idea that was patented well over 100 years ago. Its job is simple: the instantaneous, painless, and humane dispatch of small rodents. The design that you can buy in any housewares store is virtually unchanged from the first working prototype.

Can you identify the components of this system? What is the role of each component? How do these parts work together to accomplish the desired result?

Your Goal

A spring-bar mousetrap will be your only source of power. You will design, construct, and test a mechanical system that uses the energy stored in the spring, to perform a task other than killing mice.

What You Need to Know

You have learned that systems are designed for specific functions. In this task, the mousetrap will power a system with a different function. How will you design your system so that the components work together to accomplish your new function? Check online at ScienceSource for mousetrap machine ideas or construction tips.

Review your notes dealing with mechanical advantage. Your chapter investigations will help you study the input and output forces acting on your system. Consider efficiency and friction in order to improve your initial prototype.

Steps to Success

1. As a class and under the strict guidance of your teacher, review the safe handling of a mousetrap.

2. Give your teacher a plan of your intended system (either CAD or technical drawing). Your teacher will give you the "proceed order" on your job.

3. Decide on the performance criteria that will determine if you have succeeded in your quest.

4. Construct your prototype. Keep an inventory of all materials used (including amounts) in a fabrication log.

5. Record in the log any problems or changes in plans as they occur.

6. Test your prototype's performance. Record your findings in your log. Modify components to determine the effect upon the system. Can you improve on the performance by changing one or more features? (Be sure to change only a single component each time.)

7. Present your final prototype, along with the design plans and fabrication log, in a gallery tour format. Be prepared to show the system in action.

How Did It Go?

8. Did your machine accomplish its stated function? Defend your answer using your results.

9. When you tested your machine, what component(s) worked as intended? Which did not?

10. Can you explain the problems that arose? Could they have been avoided?

11. Which component, when modified, caused the greatest change in performance of the system?

12. If possible, calculate the efficiency of your system.

Key Terms Review

1. Create a concept map that illustrates your understanding of the following terms. Begin with the term "Systems." *(k)*

   - automated system
   - efficiency
   - energy
   - force
   - ideal mechanical advantage
   - inclined plane
   - lever
   - mass
   - mechanical advantage
   - mechanical system
   - mechanism
   - non-mechanical system
   - productivity
   - pulley
   - simple machine
   - weight
   - work

Key Concept Review

4.0

2. What is a mechanical system? *(k)*

3. Give an example of a force that is classified as a: *(k)*
   (a) contact force
   (b) action-at-a-distance force

4. Your friend steps on a bathroom scale and states, "I weigh 40 kg." Explain why this statement is incorrect. *(k)*

5. What is the difference between force and work? *(k)*

6. State the two classifications of energy. *(k)*

7. In what three ways can a machine make work easier? *(k)*

8. Describe the difference between mechanical advantage (MA) and ideal mechanical advantage (IMA). *(k)*

5.0

9. What is the difference between a simple machine and a mechanism? *(k)*

10. Identify six simple machines. *(k)*

11. Make sketches of a first-class, second-class, and third-class lever. Be sure to label the input force, output force, and fulcrum on each diagram. *(k)*

12. What type of simple machine is each item below? *(a)*
    (a) inline skates
    (b) your jaw
    (c) screwdriver
    (d) hammer

13. Explain why machines are not 100 percent efficient. *(k)*

14. What is one method of increasing the efficiency of a machine? *(k)*

6.0

15. You just purchased a new stereo system. What two services might the stereo company provide to ensure that the system works safely and efficiently? *(k)*

16. Define "increased productivity" in terms of the number of tasks and the amount of time. *(k)*

17. Explain how a telephone answering machine could be considered an automated system. *(a)*

18. What is the difference between a qualitative and a quantitative assessment? *(k)*

ACHIEVEMENT CHART CATEGORIES
(k) Knowledge and understanding   *(t)* Thinking and investigation   *(c)* Communication   *(a)* Application

19. What four criteria are often used when assessing a system? *k*

Connect Your Understanding

20. A person travels to a distant planet that has a greater gravitational field than Earth. Describe the person's change in weight and mass. *a*

21. Fouad pushes on a wall with a force of 75 N for one hour. Is he doing any work on the wall? Explain. *a*

22. In a short paragraph and using examples, compare the scientific definitions with the everyday uses of the terms "work," "energy," and "efficiency." *t*

23. If you increase the efficiency of a simple machine, does the: *a*

(a) MA increase, decrease, or remain the same?

(b) IMA increase, decrease, or remain the same?

24. An Olympic track bike has an efficiency of 98 percent. By comparison a mountain bike has an efficiency of 85 percent. Suggest reasons for the Olympic bike's greater efficiency. *a*

25. You need to lift a box 1 m to put it in a truck. Lifting the box straight up requires a force of 100 N. On the other hand, you could push the box up a 5-m-long ramp. This requires a force of 30 N. *a*

(a) Which method of raising the box requires more work?

(b) Which method do you think would be easier? Why?

26. A cafeteria is a system designed to allow people to purchase a meal.

(a) List five components of a cafeteria system. *a*

(b) Explain how each of the five components contributes to the system. *a*

(c) List one factor that contributes to the system operating safely and one factor that contributes to the system working efficiently. *a*

(d) Suggest how automation could be used to provide the same service. *t*

27. What part of this unit did you find most difficult? What could you do to improve your understanding of that part? *c*

Practise Your Skills

28. If the Earth's gravitational field is 9.8 N/kg, what is the force of gravity on a 5-kg mass? *t*

29. Michelle uses a force of 50 N to push a table 2.5 m across the floor. How much work did Michelle do on the table? *t*

30. Calculate the mechanical advantage (MA) for each situation in the chart below. *t*

	Input Force (N)	Output Force (N)	Mechanical Advantage (MA)
(a)	5	25	
(b)	15	5	
(c)	12	12	

31. Calculate the ideal mechanical advantage (IMA) of the lever shown below. *t*

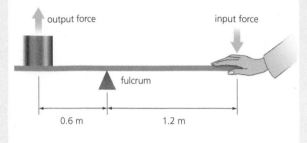

output force

input force

fulcrum

0.6 m   1.2 m

Question 31

32. A pulley system lifts a 500-N weight a distance of 1.5 m. Marina pulls the rope a distance of 9.0 m, exerting a force of 100 N. *t*

(a) What is the MA of this pulley system?

(b) What input work did Marina do on the rope?

(c) What useful output work did the rope do on the weight?

(d) What is the efficiency of the pulley system?

Question 34

33. A box weighs 20 N. Sketch a pulley system that will lift this box using an input force of 10 N or less. *t*

Revisit the Big Ideas

34. A family currently uses a gas-powered lawnmower to cut their grass. They are thinking about switching to a human-powered push mower, like the one shown below left. Use the four criteria on page 169 for assessing a system to evaluate the new lawn-cutting system. *a*

35. Explain the difference between a mechanical system and a non-mechanical system. *k*

36. What does "Systems develop from a need" mean? *k*

37. Using the illustration below, make a sketch of the lever.

(a) On your sketch, label the input force, the output force, and the fulcrum. *k*

(b) How could you move the smaller rock to increase the mechanical advantage of the lever? *t*

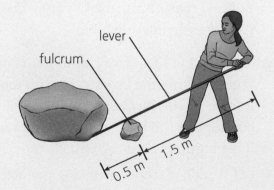

lever

fulcrum

0.5 m   1.5 m

Question 37

ACHIEVEMENT CHART CATEGORIES
k Knowledge and understanding   *t* Thinking and investigation   *c* Communication   *a* Application

38. The following are components of a school system. Identify each component as either mechanical or non-mechanical. *ⓐ*

   (a) timetables

   (b) staplers

   (c) water fountains

   (d) fire drill procedures

39. Suggest one positive and one negative outcome of increasing productivity. *ⓒ*

40. A box lifted from the floor to a desk gains 300 J of gravitational potential energy. Calculate the efficiency of each machine used to move the box. *ⓒ*

   (a) An electric motor uses 400 J to lift the box.

   (b) The rope on a pulley, attached to the box, is pulled a distance of 3 m using a force of 150 N.

   (c) You push the box 5 m up a ramp using a force of 90 N.

B46 *Thinking about Science, Technology, Society, and the Environment*

ST S E

Rethinking the Engine

Imagine that you are listening to a group of inventors in the 1880s describing their development of the internal combustion engine. This is the type of engine used in most cars today. During the discussion, you realize that they have not considered any of the social or environmental issues associated with the engine.

Consider This

With a classmate or as a whole class, discuss the following questions.

1. What need of society does the engine fulfill?

2. What are the social impacts of producing an internal combustion engine?

3. What are the environmental impacts of producing an internal combustion engine?

4. Why do you think the inventors in the 1880s ignored the social and environmental aspects of their invention?

Fluids

Fundamental Concepts

In Science and Technology for grades 7 and 8, six fundamental concepts occur throughout. This unit addresses the following two:

- Matter
- Systems and Interactions

Big Ideas

As you work through this unit, you will develop a deeper understanding of the following big ideas:

- Fluids are an important component of many systems.
- Fluids have different properties that determine how they can be used.
- Fluids are essential to life.

Overall Expectations

By the end of this unit, you will be expected to:

1. analyze how the properties of fluids are used in various technologies and assess the impact of these technologies on society and the environment
2. investigate the properties of fluids
3. demonstrate an understanding of the properties and uses of fluids

An industrial pipeline system transports fluids.

Exploring

A child in Malaysia uses a Canadian invention.

When you want a drink of water, you simply need to turn on a tap and use the water pumped to your home from a well, lake, or reservoir. But for many people in the world, access to clean, safe water is a daily challenge. That challenge has been made easier in some developing countries, thanks to an invention by researchers at the University of Waterloo, in Ontario. Their invention is a low-cost, shallow-well hand pump that has the following advantages:

- The pump is durable enough to work continuously for 18 hours a day.

- The pump is inexpensive enough for people in developing countries to afford.

- The pump is simple enough that villagers can maintain and repair it themselves.

- The pump can be manufactured within developing countries, creating jobs and ensuring that spare parts are available.

New Technology from Old

When the inventors were researching pump designs, they noticed a pump at a Mennonite community in southern Ontario that had been used for many years. With this pump as a model, they designed a hand pump with tubing made out of a plastic called polyvinyl chloride (PVC). In the past, pumps were made of iron and steel, materials that are scarce and costly in many developing countries. PVC is inexpensive, available everywhere around the world, and does not rust. The PVC hand pump is light, sturdy, cheap to build, and easy to install and maintain.

Adapting the Technology

Over 11 000 PVC hand pumps are now in use in 13 developing nations. The pumps are modified for local conditions. For example, in Sri Lanka, a leather washer is used instead of a plastic one. The advantage of the leather washer is that it can be made locally. In Malawi, the spigot on the pump is now made out of black metal instead of the original white plastic. The white spigots looked somewhat like bones, and the local hyenas kept chewing them off the pump.

The new PVC hand pump is based on a metal pump like this one.

The PVC hand pump is a good example of the importance of understanding a concept and then applying that understanding to different situations. In this case, the inventors knew about the properties of fluids and how a water pump operates. They applied this knowledge to develop a better pump that could be made locally, work reliably for long hours, and be easy to fix.

In this unit, you will learn about the properties of fluids and discover how fluids can be used to solve a variety of practical problems. You will learn that fluids include both liquids and gases, and that you put fluids to work for you every day.

...MORE TO EXPLORE

Pump Up the Volume

Many people of the world obtain the water they use from a well. The device used to transfer this water must be reliable, efficient, and sanitary.

Purpose

To test and evaluate several methods of transferring water from a low elevation to a high elevation

Materials & Equipment

- large plastic container
- 5 disposable cups
- felt pen
- water
- stopwatch
- plastic straw
- spoon straw
- small sponge
- spoon
- cardboard tube

Procedure

1. Place a large container of water (the well) on the floor at the base of your table.

2. Label the five disposable cups A, B, C, D, and E. Place them in a row on your table.

3. Predict which "pump" will transfer the most water in 30 s. Your "pumps" are the straws, sponge, spoon, and cardboard tube.

4. Have a partner time 30 s while you use plastic straw A to transfer as much water from the well into cup A. Do not put any of the devices in your mouth. Be careful not to spill any water. Clean up any spills immediately.

5. Repeat step 4 for the remaining pumps, using pump B for cup B, and so on.

6. Determine which cup contains the most water.

Questions

7. Which pump transferred the most water in 30 s? How did this result compare to your original prediction?

8. The best pump is the one that transfers lots of water, lasts a long time, and is the most sanitary. Use these criteria to explain which of the five pumps is the best.

C2 **Thinking about Science, Technology, Society, and the Environment**

Fluids on the Move

Suppose you were in charge of designing a pipeline to bring fresh water from a lake to a village at the top of a hill 20 km away.

1. How would you decide what materials to use to build the pipeline?

2. How would you decide which route the pipeline should follow?

3. How would you raise the water from the low level of the lake to the high level of the hill?

4. Who should pay for the pipeline? The villagers desperately need the water, but are unable to pay the full cost.

UNIT C

Contents

Unit Task

Pipelines transport fluids across Canada. Our understanding of the properties of fluids helps us design pipelines to function without spills or problems. In your Unit Task, you will investigate the effect of changing a variable on the movement of fluid in a pipeline that you design.

Essential Question

How do the properties of fluids explain the factors that influence the movement of fluids through a pipeline?

Getting Ready to Read

Thinking Literacy

Probable Passage

You will encounter the following terms in this unit: "fluids," "solid," "liquid," "gas," "volume," "particle theory of matter," and "thermal expansion." Which of these terms can you already define? Which are you unsure of? Write your prediction of what you will learn in this unit.

A firefighter relies on an air tank and a powerful water system to battle a blaze.

What You Will Learn

In this chapter, you will:

- explain the difference between solids, liquids, and gases using the particle theory of matter
- recognize a variety of uses for fluid technologies

Skills You Will Use

In this chapter, you will:

- follow safety practices for using apparatus, tools, and materials
- use appropriate science and technology vocabulary
- use a variety of forms to communicate with different audiences and for a variety of purposes

Why This Is Important

When you understand how fluids can change and move, you can more easily put fluids to work for you. Fluids are an important part of many devices and systems.

Before Reading

Thinking Literacy

Making Predictions

This chapter builds on your learning in science in previous years and your everyday life. As you consider the title for this chapter, "Fluids are used in technological devices and everyday materials" and scan the photographs, use your prior knowledge to make a prediction about what you will learn.

Key Terms

- mass
- volume
- matter
- thermal expansion
- particle theory of matter
- fluid

Figure 7.1 HMCS *Victoria* is one of Canada's four diesel-electric patrol submarines. Each submarine of its class is over 70 m long and can dive to a depth of more than 200 m.

How is a submarine able to dive, travel along at a constant depth, and then rise to the surface of the water? Why does a submarine not simply float, like a boat, or sink, like a huge piece of metal? The answer is related to the weight of the water a submarine takes the place of, or displaces. For example, when HMCS *Victoria* is at the surface, it displaces over 2100 tonnes of water (Figure 7.1). When HMCS *Victoria* is below the surface, it displaces over 2400 tonnes.

In order for a submarine to sink from the surface to the depths, its weight must be more than the weight of the water it displaces. When the submarine rises back to the surface, its weight must be less than the weight of the water it displaces. The weight of a submarine changes depending on whether seawater or compressed air fills its ballast tanks.

When the ballast tanks are filled with seawater, the weight of the submarine is greater than the weight of the water it displaces, and so the submarine sinks (Figure 7.2). When seawater is pumped out of the ballast tanks and is replaced by compressed air, the submarine becomes lighter than the water it displaces and rises to the surface. A balance of seawater and compressed air in the ballast tanks allows the submarine to stay at a constant depth.

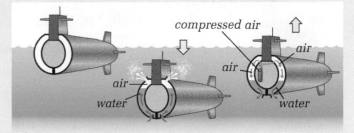

Figure 7.2 The ballast tanks are located between the inner and outer hulls of the submarine.

The technology that allows a submarine to rise, sink, or stay at a constant level is similar to a technology used by fish. A fish has an internal organ under its backbone called a gas bladder. By making changes to the volume of gases in the bladder, a fish can control whether it stays at a constant depth, rises, or sinks.

C3 Quick Lab

Cartesian Diver

This type of diver is named after Rene Descartes, a French scientist, mathematician, and philosopher who lived about 400 years ago.

Purpose

To model the movement of a submarine by making a Cartesian diver

Materials & Equipment

- 2-L plastic bottle with cap
- medicine dropper
- water

Procedure

1. Completely fill the 2-L plastic bottle with water.

2. Fill the medicine dropper about two-thirds full of water and place it in the bottle. The medicine dropper should float at the top of the 2-L bottle.

3. Continue to increase the amount of water in the medicine dropper until it floats at the top but is almost completely submerged.

4. Put the cap on the bottle and tighten securely.

5. Squeeze the sides of the bottle. Observe what happens.

6. Release the sides of the bottle. Observe what happens.

Questions

7. State what happened to the diver when you:

   (a) squeezed the sides of the bottle

   (b) released the sides of the bottle

8. Did the weight of the diver increase or decrease when you squeezed the bottle? Explain.

9. Suggest a possible explanation for why the weight of the diver changed.

The Many Uses of Fluids

Here is a summary of what you will learn in this section:

- A fluid is any substance that flows.
- Fluids have many uses, including holding and transporting other materials.
- Substances in their fluid form can be shaped and then cooled to become solids.

Every time you brush your teeth with toothpaste, take a drink of juice, or draw in a breath of air, you are using a fluid. A **fluid** is any substance that flows. The blood flowing through your blood vessels is a fluid. Lava flowing from a volcano and honey flowing from a spoon onto your toast are also fluids. Other fluids include gases, such as oxygen and carbon dioxide, and liquids, such as shampoo, salad dressing, window cleaner, and engine oil. We use the properties of fluids in many different devices and systems to improve our lives.

C4 *Starting Point*

Skills **P** **C**

Finding Flowing Fluids

Whether it is a race car or a family car, an automobile needs fluids and fluid technologies to run smoothly, safely, and efficiently (Figure 7.3).

1. With a partner, make a list of all of the different fluids you can think of that are used in an automobile. You can include uses by people who drive and ride in automobiles as well.

2. Group your examples into four different categories. Label each category with a title.

Figure 7.3 There are many uses for fluids in transportation.

Putting Fluids to Work

One of the reasons why fluids are so important is that they make it easier to transport, process, and use different kinds of materials, even if these materials are solids (Figure 7.4).

Fluids Can Transport Solids

A mixture of water and solids is called a **slurry**. Slurry technology — the transport of solids in water — is important in many applications. The paper you write on was once a slurry of wood pulp and water. Hydroseeding is the process of spraying a slurry of seeds, fertilizer, and sawdust to plant difficult-to-reach areas (Figure 7.5). Mines, such as the Campbell Gold Mine in northwestern Ontario, use slurry technology to process the minerals. Some mineral ores are converted to liquids in a method called *froth flotation* so that they can be transported more easily.

Fluids Can Hold Other Materials

The ability of fluids to hold or carry other materials makes them useful in many applications (Figure 7.6). For example, the watery cytoplasm in your cells holds the organelles that allow a cell to expand, grow, and replicate. Fluids can hold abrasive particles to clean other surfaces, such as marble, metal, and your teeth (Figure 7.7).

Figure 7.4 You can use air to move solids, such as leaves and paper.

Figure 7.5 A slurry of seeds and nutrients can be used to replant an area.

Figure 7.6 An airplane drops a load of fluid containing fire retardant on a forest fire.

Figure 7.7 Toothpaste is a fluid that holds materials to clean, polish, and protect your teeth

Fluids Become Solids

Fluids are easy to move, and they take the shape of their containers. Because of these properties, many of the solid objects we see and use were originally prepared as fluids.

A slurry of water and cement is easy to transport. As it hardens, the cement can be shaped to become a smooth and level concrete sidewalk (Figure 7.8).

Steel is an example of the use of fluids in processing materials. Steel consists of a mixture of iron, carbon, and small quantities of other substances. This mixture is heated to 1650°C to melt everything together so that more materials can be added. The fluid steel is then shaped into the desired forms and allowed to cool (Figure 7.9).

Figure 7.8 Cement is a mixture of materials, such as limestone, clay, and gypsum.

Figure 7.9 Molten steel on a rolling mill

C5 *During Reading*

Thinking Literacy

POE (Predict, Observe, Explain)

Readers often make an "educated guess" about what will happen as they approach new or unfamiliar text or topics. This same strategy can help us in science. This chapter contains several Quick Labs and an Inquiry Activity. Set up a three-column chart in your notes with the headings: Predict, Observe, and Explain.

Read through C6 Quick Lab, Functions of Fluids, on page 195. Notice the title, purpose, and procedure. How can you connect them to other learning or experiences you have had? Use this background knowledge to predict what you think will happen when you do the lab. Record and explain your prediction in the first column of your chart. You have now formed a hypothesis about what you think will happen!

As you do the lab, record what did happen in the Observe column. The Explain column is a place for you to connect to your learning in this chapter and explain the results of the Quick Lab.

Other Uses for Fluids

Fluids have many other uses. For example, oil is added to the engine of a car to decrease friction, and to reduce noise, heat, and wear. Paint is applied to iron to create a barrier that prevents rust from forming. A fluid circulating in the back of a refrigerator keeps the temperature cool, and a fluid circulating in a radiator can warm a room. Some fluids, such as gases, can be forced into a smaller volume, such as the air that pumps up a bicycle tire or the air in a breathing apparatus for scuba divers (Figure 7.10).

Take It Further

Plasma is considered to be a fourth state of matter. How is plasma different from a gas? Begin your search at ScienceSource.

Figure 7.10 Scuba tanks are sometimes filled with a mixture of gases that includes slightly more oxygen than what is found in ordinary samples of air.

C6 Quick Lab

Functions of Fluids

You are at a birthday party and all around you are colourful balloons. Helium balloons are floating near the ceiling and air-filled balloons cover the walls. A balloon is an example of an everyday object that requires a fluid to function properly.

Purpose

To identify, describe, and explain a variety of everyday common devices that require a fluid to function

Materials & Equipment

- chart paper
- felt pens
- fluid-operated device supplied by your teacher

Procedure

1. Brainstorm with your partner objects or devices that require the use of a fluid to operate. List your ideas on the chart paper.

2. From your list, identify 10 objects or devices that use a variety of different fluids.

3. Create a chart that explains how each object or device functions. You may want to use a chart like Table 7.1.

Table 7.1 Functions of Fluids

Object or Device	Type of fluid used to operate object or device	How the fluid helps the object or device to function

4. Your teacher will provide you with a device that requires a fluid to operate. Add the name of this device to your chart and complete the chart.

5. Present your chart to the class.

Questions

6. (a) List the different fluids that you and your classmates identified.

   (b) Explain how the fluids were used in various objects and devices.

7. What was the most common state of matter for the fluids you identified?

8. Choose one object or device. How could it operate if another fluid were used in place of the one usually used?

Key Concept Review

1. Name two fluid technologies that make use of air.

2. Name two fluid technologies that make use of water.

3. Describe an example where materials are prepared as fluids so that they can be moved more easily.

4. Explain why it is important for steel to go through a fluid phase as it is being produced.

Connect Your Understanding

5. Review the list of fluids and their uses that you made for Figure 7.3 on page 192. What changes would you make based on what you have learned?

6. Add at least three other examples of fluids to your list in question 5. Make one new category for your list.

Practise Your Skills

7. Describe how different fluids are used to operate the can of spray paint shown below.

For more questions, go to ScienceSource.

C7 Thinking about Science and Technology

Useful Properties of Fluids

Each of these photographs shows fluids in use.

1. How are our lives improved by each of the uses shown?

2. How have advances in technology contributed to each use?

3. What are environmental issues raised by each use?

(a)

(b)

(c)

7.2 Fluids and the Particle Theory of Matter

Here is a summary of what you will learn in this section:

- Matter is anything that has mass and volume.
- The particle theory of matter is a way of explaining the behaviour of matter.
- Solids hold a definite shape because their particles are packed closely together and vibrate in one place.
- Liquids can flow and take the shape of their container because their particles have partly overcome their attraction for each other.
- Gases can flow and spread out because their particles are far apart and have overcome their attraction for each other.

In how many different states is water shown in Figure 7.11? There is liquid water around the kayak, water in its solid state in the iceberg, and water in its gaseous state in the air. The water, the iceberg, and the clouds are all examples of matter. The kayak, the person, and the paddle are also matter. **Matter** is anything that has mass and volume. **Mass** is a measure of how much matter there is in a substance. **Volume** is a measure of how much space a substance takes up.

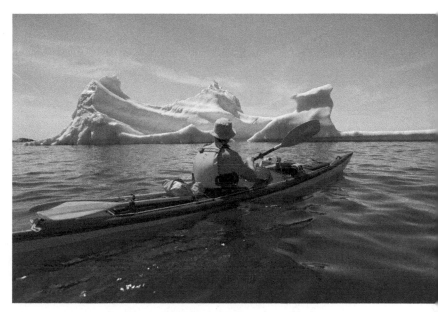

Figure 7.11 Three states of matter are shown in this photograph.

C8 *Starting Point*

Skills A C

Colourful Crystal

A crystal of potassium permanganate was carefully added to the still water in Figure 7.12(a). The photograph in Figure 7.12(b) shows the potassium permanganate after 5 min. What do you think happened? How do you think this happened?

(a) (b)

Figure 7.12 Potassium permanganate in water

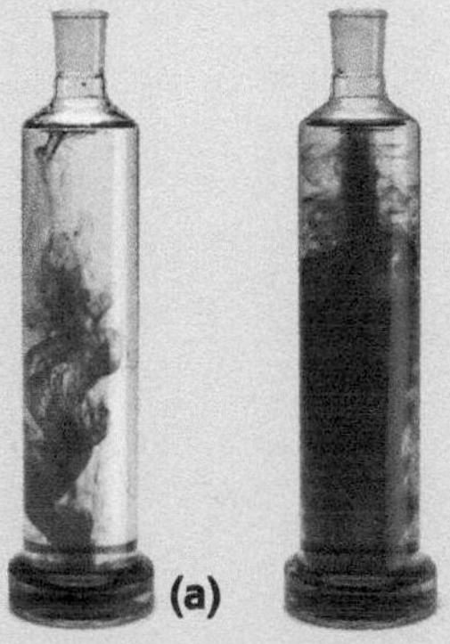

The Particle Theory of Matter

In earlier grades, you may have learned about the particle theory of matter. The **particle theory of matter** is a simple way of describing matter and its behaviour. You can use the particle theory of matter to help you understand how matter behaves in each state. The particle theory has six main points that describe the structure of matter.

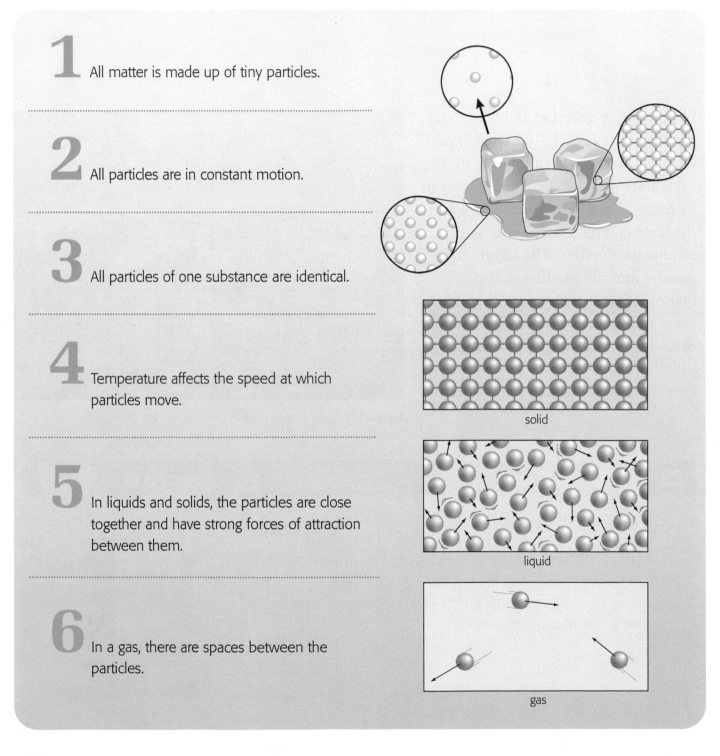

1 All matter is made up of tiny particles.

2 All particles are in constant motion.

3 All particles of one substance are identical.

4 Temperature affects the speed at which particles move.

5 In liquids and solids, the particles are close together and have strong forces of attraction between them.

6 In a gas, there are spaces between the particles.

solid

liquid

gas

Understand the Text

Answer the following questions. You can check your answers by looking back through the previous two pages.

1. Which has more particles in the same volume, liquid water or water vapour?

2. In which state of matter do particles stay in more or less the same position?

3. In which state of matter is there the greatest space between particles?

How the Particle Theory Explains Properties of Fluids

The particle theory states that particles are attracted to each other. However, particles in some substances may be more attracted to particles in other substances than they are to each other. For example, when potassium permanganate is placed in water, its particles are more attracted to the water particles than to other potassium permanganate particles. Since the water particles are continually moving, the potassium permanganate particles are moved farther apart. This is the process we call dissolving.

Liquids Can Flow

Particles in a liquid can overcome some of their attraction to each other and slide past each other. This is why liquids flow and take the shape of their container. For example, water takes a different shape in a vase compared to in a bowl.

Gases Can Flow

Gas particles move so quickly and are so far apart that they overcome almost all of their attraction to each other. This is why gases flow and spread out to all parts of their container. For example, if you spray some air freshener in one part of a room, you can soon smell it in other parts of the room.

Suggested Activities •·······
C10 Quick Lab on page 200
C11 Inquiry Activity on page 201

Thermal Expansion and Contraction

When the temperature of a solid, liquid, or gas increases, its particles move faster and farther apart. As a result, the substance expands. **Thermal expansion** is an increase in the volume of a substance in response to an increase in its temperature.

When the temperature of a solid, liquid, or gas decreases, its particles move more slowly and closer together. As a result, the substance shrinks, or contracts. Substances expand or contract with changing temperature at their own particular rate.

A thermometer shows the temperature by the expansion or contraction of a liquid in a narrow tube (Figure 7.13). When the temperature rises, the particles in the tube move farther apart as their motion increases. Even a slight expansion results in a large change on the temperature scale.

Figure 7.13 When the temperature drops, the particles in the tube move closer together and the level of liquid falls.

Take It **Further**

You have probably heard about atoms. How are atoms related to particles? Find out about atomic structure at ScienceSource.

C10 *Quick Lab*

Balloon Tricks

Purpose

To observe evidence of the particle theory of matter

Materials & Equipment

- 2 round balloons
- measuring tape
- heat lamp
- felt pen
- bowl of ice water

Procedure

1. Make a table to record your data.

2. Blow up the two balloons about three-quarters full, and tie them off.

3. Use the felt pen to label one balloon "cool" and the other balloon "warm."

4. Measure and record the circumference of the largest part of each balloon.

5. Place the balloon labelled "cool" in a bowl of ice water until you observe a change in its size.

6. Place the balloon, labelled "warm" near a heat lamp until you observe a change in its size.

7. Measure and record the circumference of the largest part of each balloon.

Questions

8. (a) How did the balloon change when it was cooled?

   (b) How did the balloon change when it was warmed?

9. How would you explain your observations using the particle theory of matter?

C11 *Inquiry Activity* Toolkit 2

SKILLS YOU WILL USE
- Measuring
- Drawing conclusions

Mixtures of Matter

Question

How does the particle theory of matter explain what happens when substances are combined?

Materials & Equipment

- 50 mL of small marbles in a 250-mL beaker or graduated cylinder
- 50 mL of sand
- 50 mL of water

Procedure

Part 1 – Predict and Measure

1. Copy the following table into your notebook. Give your table a title.

Table 7.2 Data Table

	Predicted Volume (mL)	Actual Volume (mL)
50 mL of marbles + 50 mL of sand		
50 mL of marbles and 50 mL of sand + 50 mL of water		

2. Predict and record the volume that will result when you add 50 mL of sand to 50 mL of marbles.
3. Slowly pour the 50 mL of sand into the container of marbles. Measure and record the total volume.
4. Predict and record the volume that will result when you add 50 mL of water to the mixture.
5. Slowly pour the 50 mL of water into the container of marbles and sand. Measure and record the total volume. Be sure to wipe up any spills immediately.

Part 2 – Combining Two Liquids

6. A lab technician measured 20 mL of rubbing alcohol into one graduated cylinder and 20 mL of water into a second graduated cylinder as shown in Figure 7.14(a). She then combined the two liquids. The combined liquid filled the graduated cylinder to a level of 39 mL in Figure 7.14(b).

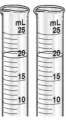

Figure 7.14(a) 20 mL of rubbing alcohol and 20 mL of water in separate 25-mL graduated cylinders

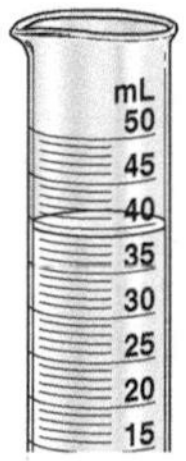

Figure 7.14(b) The two liquids combined in one graduated cylinder

Analyzing and Interpreting

7. (a) Would the end total volume in Part 1 be the same if you added the marbles to the sand instead of vice versa?

   (b) Why or why not?

8. (a) Would it make a difference to the total volume if you added the water to the marbles before the sand in Part 1?

   (b) Why or why not?

Skill Builder

9. What are possible sources of error when the technician combined the liquids in Part 2?

Forming Conclusions

10. If no error occurred in Part 2, why was the sum of the volumes of the liquids less than 40 mL?

Key Concept Review

1. (a) What does "mass" mean?

   (b) What does "volume" mean?

2. According to the particle theory of matter:

   (a) How is the motion of particles in a liquid different from the motion of particles in a solid?

   (b) How is the motion of particles in a gas different from the motion of particles in a liquid?

3. (a) What determines a liquid's shape?

   (b) What determines a gas's volume?

4. Which two states of matter can flow?

Connect Your Understanding

5. Why did the potassium permanganate crystals in Figure 7.12 on page 197 start to dissolve in water without being stirred or shaken?

Practise Your Skills

6. Explain why highways and bridges must be built with gaps, as shown in the photograph below.

For more questions, go to ScienceSource.

C12 Thinking about Science and Technology

When Water Freezes

The volume of most fluids decreases when they cool from a liquid to a solid. Water is an exception. When water freezes, the resulting ice takes up more volume than the liquid water did. The repeated freezing and thawing of water in cracks damages roads by causing potholes, bumps, and cracking.

What to Do

With a partner or in a group, discuss and record your ideas about the following questions.

1. What are the safety issues of water that freezes and thaws?

2. Suggest a method that could be used to prevent damage to roads caused by water freezing and thawing.

3. What are the costs associated with water freezing and thawing? Who pays? Who should pay if there is an accident?

Glowing Glass

Figure 7.15 Blowing molten glass with a blowpipe

The art and technology of making beautiful glass sculptures began over 3500 years ago. In the early days of glass making, silica sand was heated to more than 1700°C. At this temperature, the sand melts and becomes a fluid, resembling syrup on a cold day. When the fluid slowly cools, the hardened material becomes glass, similar to that in windows.

Coloured glass was created by adding other compounds to the silica sand. For example, green-brown glass was created by adding iron oxide. Light blue and red glass needed copper compounds to be added.

Today, there are several different techniques for creating glass art that involve the glass being heated to different temperatures.

- *Slumping* involves heating the glass to temperatures around 600°C so it can be shaped in a mould. Slumping is sometimes used to make objects such as glass bowls.

- When glass is heated to between 700°C and 800°C, it starts to become "sticky." *Glass fusing* involves placing various pieces of glass on a surface so that they are in contact. When the assembled pieces are heated, they adhere and become one solid piece. Mosaic tiles and some stained glass windows are made this way.

- *Glass blowing* involves using air to shape the fluid glass, much like blowing a bubble with bubblegum. Glass blowing involves temperatures around 1000°C. At these temperatures, the liquid glass flows much more easily than at lower temperatures. A hollow blowpipe is dipped in the molten glass so that the end of the blowpipe is covered in glass, much like dipping a straw in liquid honey. The artisan then blows through the blowpipe to create the hollow bubble of glass. By using different tools and techniques, this bubble can be shaped and sculpted.

Figure 7.16 Glass can be sculpted into many colourful shapes and forms.

Questions

1. Explain what happens to how glass flows as it is heated.

2. Which of the three methods do you think would be used to create the glass in a light bulb? Explain.

3. In your opinion, is it more important for a glass sculpture to be beautiful or to be practical? Explain.

Key Concept Review

1. Describe the process for getting rid of broken glass in your class. ⓚ

2. What are the safety procedures for tasting and smelling substances in the science room? ⓚ

3. What are the six main points of the particle theory of matter? ⓚ

4. Make a particle sketch showing how the volume of a liquid changes when heat is added. ⓚ

5. Explain how a fluid is different from a solid in terms of its shape. ⓚ

6. Describe an example where materials are prepared as fluids to make it easier to use them. ⓚ

Connect Your Understanding

7. What symbols would you expect to find on containers of the following fluids? ⓚ

   - oven cleaner in a spray can
   - bleach

8. What is an example of thermal expansion that you have observed in your daily life? ⓐ

9. How does applying oil to a bicycle help the bicycle to work better? ⓐ

After Reading Thinking Literacy

Reflect and Evaluate

Revisit the prediction you made at the start of this chapter. Was your prediction correct? How did what you already know (your prior knowledge) help you make a prediction? Did making a prediction before a Quick Lab or Inquiry Activity help you? Share your ideas with a partner.

ACHIEVEMENT CHART CATEGORIES
ⓚ Knowledge and understanding   ⓣ Thinking and investigation   ⓒ Communication   ⓐ Application

10. Arrange the following list into two columns titled "Fluids" and "Non-fluids." ⓐ

- sunscreen
- baby powder
- hand lotion
- helium
- carbon dioxide
- syrup
- ketchup
- mustard
- flour
- sugar
- orange juice
- soy sauce

11. Use the particle model to explain the difference in appearance between steam and liquid water. ⓣ

12. Why does a liquid take the shape of the container but not expand to completely fill the container? ⓣ

13. Suppose you had to remove a tight-fitting lid from a jar. Would it be a good idea to heat the lid or cool it before trying to remove it? Explain your answer. ⓐ

14. If you pour sand into a container, it appears to take the shape of the container. How could you prove that sand is not a fluid? ⓣ

Practise Your Skills

15. Identify a fluid technology you have recently used to make your life easier or better. Draw a chain of events that shows the fluid, how you used it, and how it improved your life. ⓐ

Unit Task Link

In your Unit Task, you will investigate the effect of a variable, such as temperature, on the movement of fluid in a pipeline. The fluid in this task will be a liquid. Use the particle model to explain how temperature will affect the liquid in your pipeline.

C13 *Thinking about Science and Technology*

Technology Tools

The goal of technology is to provide solutions to practical problems. With a classmate or as a whole class, discuss the following questions.

1. What are three problems that fluid technology helps to solve?

2. How does a fluid help to solve each of the problems?

Neon tubes are a fluid technology that makes use of the properties of neon gases. The gases in the tubes are kept at a low pressure. Adding energy makes the gases glow brightly.

What You Will Learn

In this chapter, you will:

- compare the viscosity of various fluids
- explain the difference between liquids and gases in terms of their compressibility
- determine the buoyancy of an object
- explain the relationship between pressure, volume, and temperature
- describe the relationship between mass, volume, and density

Skills You Will Use

In this chapter, you will:

- determine the mass-to-volume ratios of different amounts of the same substance
- identify factors that affect the flow rate of fluids
- design an experiment to measure the flow rate of fluids
- investigate and compare the densities of a variety of fluids
- construct and calibrate a hydrometer

Why This Is Important

Fluids can change when their temperature or pressure changes. Understanding density can help you determine whether a fluid and other substance will float or sink.

Before Reading

Thinking Literacy

Activate Prior Knowledge

Create a KTW chart with headings "What I Know," "What I Think I Know" and "What I Want to Know." Complete the chart using the key terms below.

Key Terms

- buoyancy
- density
- flow rate
- friction
- pressure
- compressibility
- viscosity

(a)

Figure 8.1 Modern hot air balloons (a) and ancient Chinese floating lanterns (left, b) both rise because of hot fluids.

(b) Chinese lanterns

The scientific principle used to float Chinese lanterns 1500 years ago is the same principle at work in today's hot air balloons (Figure 8.1).

The first successful "modern" hot air balloon was invented by a French scientist in 1783. The passengers of this experimental balloon were a duck, a rooster, and a sheep. These barnyard passengers stayed airborne for 15 minutes. Two months later, the first human flight took place. Balloon technology increased at a quick pace, and within two years a hot air balloon and its two human passengers crossed the English Channel.

The largest part of a hot air balloon is the gas bag or envelope, which is made from strong, lightweight fabrics such as nylon. A basket for carrying passengers is attached to the envelope.

Mounted above the basket is a burner that injects a flame into the mouth of the envelope to heat the air (Figure 8.2). At the very top of the balloon's envelope are vents which are used to release the air from the balloon during a quick descent or once the balloon has landed.

What scientific principle is at work in hot air balloons? When the air inside the envelope of the balloon is heated, the air particles move faster and take up more space compared to the particles outside the envelope. The hot air balloon rises.

When the balloon pilot allows the warm air inside the balloon to cool down, the air particles move more slowly and take up less space. The balloon sinks back down to Earth.

Figure 8.2 A balloonist fires the burner to heat the air.

C14 *Quick Lab*

Full of Hot Air — Teacher Demonstration

Purpose

To model a hot air balloon

Materials & Equipment

- clear adhesive tape
- dry cleaner plastic film bag
- heat source, such as hairdryer or electric popcorn maker
- paper clips

Procedure

1. Use a small amount of clear adhesive tape to seal any openings in the upper end of the bag.

2. Attach several paper clips to the bag around the lower opening. You will need to experiment to decide how many paper clips to add.

3. With a partner, hold the opening of the bag over the heat source to capture the hot air.

4. Let go of the bag. If the bag rises, observe its motion. If it does not rise, continue heating it for a little while longer. If it still does not rise, remove a few paper clips and then heat it again.

5. If the rising bag tips over before it reaches the ceiling, add a few more paper clips to the bottom of the bag. Then, heat and release the bag again.

Questions

6. Explain what causes the bag to rise.

7. Explain what causes the bag to eventually return to the floor.

8. Suggest possible changes you could make to your design that would allow the bag to remain aloft for a longer period of time.

Here is a summary of what you will learn in this section:

- Viscosity is the resistance of a fluid to flow. Different fluids have different viscosities.
- As the temperature of a liquid decreases, the viscosity increases. As the temperature of a gas decreases, the viscosity decreases.
- Flow rate is a measure of the speed at which a fluid flows from one point to another. The higher the flow rate, the lower the viscosity.

Figure 8.3 Ketchup has a higher viscosity than fluids like milk and water.

Ketchup, like all fluids, will flow. However, ketchup is designed to flow slowly so that it will stay on foods, as shown in Figure 8.3. Thin fluids, like milk and water, flow much more quickly and easily than ketchup.

The thickness or thinness of a fluid is a property called viscosity. **Viscosity** is the resistance of a fluid to flow. Fluids with high viscosity do not flow as easily as fluids with a low viscosity.

C15   *Starting Point*   Skills

Thick or Thin?

One property of fluids is how they move or flow. Think about the fluids you have used in the past few days. What would happen if they did not flow the way they usually do? For example, what would happen if water flowed like a thick syrup or ketchup flowed like oil?

1. Make a chart like the one shown in Table 8.1 to record your descriptions.

2. With your partner, identify five fluids that you have used recently.

3. Describe what the fluids would be like if they were thicker or thinner. Here is an example.

Table 8.1 Five Fluids

Fluid	Thicker	Thinner
Shampoo	Hard to get out of the bottle	I would probably use more to wash my hair

Viscosity and Temperature

Suppose you wanted ketchup to flow faster. What could you do to change its viscosity?

Temperature is one factor that can have a big effect on viscosity. The viscosity of a fluid can change as the fluid is heated up or cooled down. Notice in Figure 8.4 how the viscosity of each liquid changes.

Figure 8.4(a) Olive oil placed in a refrigerator becomes more viscous as it cools.

Figure 8.4(b) Cold maple syrup poured on hot pancakes becomes less viscous as it heats up.

Figure 8.4(c) Hot tar, ready to spread on a road, becomes more viscous as it cools.

Temperature Changes in Liquids

Why does ketchup flow faster if you heat it? Recall that in the particle theory, a liquid is made of particles that can move past each other. When heat is added to the liquid, the particles move faster and spread farther apart. Since the distance between particles has increased, there is less attraction between the particles. This allows the particles to move past each other more freely.

As the temperature of a liquid increases, its viscosity decreases. As a result, the fluid flows more easily. The warmer the liquid, the faster it flows.

As the temperature of a liquid decreases, the particles slow down. The result is that the viscosity increases. The cooler the liquid, the slower it flows.

Figure 8.4(d) Room temperature engine oil poured into a hot engine becomes less viscous as it heats up.

Viscosity, density, and compressibility are all properties of fluids.   **211**

Temperature Changes in Gases

Temperature affects the viscosity of gases differently from how it affects the viscosity of liquids. According to the particle theory, a gas is made of particles that are very far apart. When heat is added to the gas, the particles move faster and collide more often, resulting in greater resistance, or friction. **Friction** is a force that works to slow down motion as a result of surfaces rubbing against each other. The greater the friction, or rubbing, between particles in any fluid, the higher the viscosity. A fluid with a high viscosity has a large amount of internal friction.

As the temperature of a gas increases, friction increases, and so the viscosity of the gas increases (Figure 8.5). The warmer the gas, the slower it flows.

As the temperature of the gas decreases, the particles slow down and collide less often, so there is less friction. The result is that the viscosity decreases. The cooler the gas, the faster it flows.

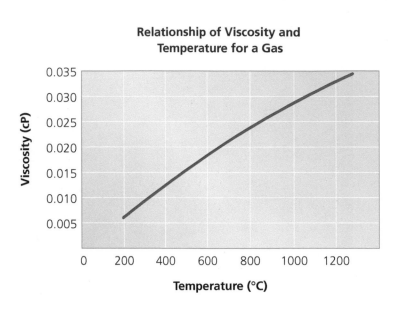

Relationship of Viscosity and Temperature for a Gas

Figure 8.5 As the temperature of a gas increases, its viscosity increases.

C16 *During Reading*

Thinking Literacy

Monitoring Comprehension with "Fix-up" Strategies

There are a number of things good readers do when they realize their understanding of a concept is breaking down. Many of these strategies happen naturally — you slow down the pace of your reading, reread, read ahead to see if it helps you make sense, or pause more often to think.

The reading comprehension strategies (making connections, visualizing, predicting, inferring, looking for patterns in the writing,

using the text features) you have been using in previous chapters can also help you "fix up" your comprehension.

As you read about friction and viscosity on this page and the next page, keep track of the "fix-up" strategies you use to help you make sense of the text. Share the strategies you used with a partner. Did you use the same strategies in the same places as your partner? Discuss the differences.

Viscosity and Flow Rate

Different substances have different viscosities because they are made of different particles with different forces of attraction between them. One way to compare the viscosity of different fluids is to compare their flow rates. The **flow rate** of a fluid is a measure of the speed at which a fluid flows from one point to another. Flow rate is determined by measuring the amount of fluid that flows past a given point in a given time. The greater the viscosity, the lower the flow rate.

Suggested Activity • · · · · · · · ·
C17 Design a Lab on page 214

Density

The amount of mass contained in a given volume is called **density**. Density describes how closely packed together the particles are in a substance. A substance is most dense when it is a solid and least dense when it is a gas. A solid is denser than a gas because the particles in a solid are much closer together (Figure 8.6).

Take It *Further*

Motor oil labels may contain viscosity ratings, such as 5W-30 or 10W-40. Investigate what these viscosity ratings mean. Start your research at ScienceSource.

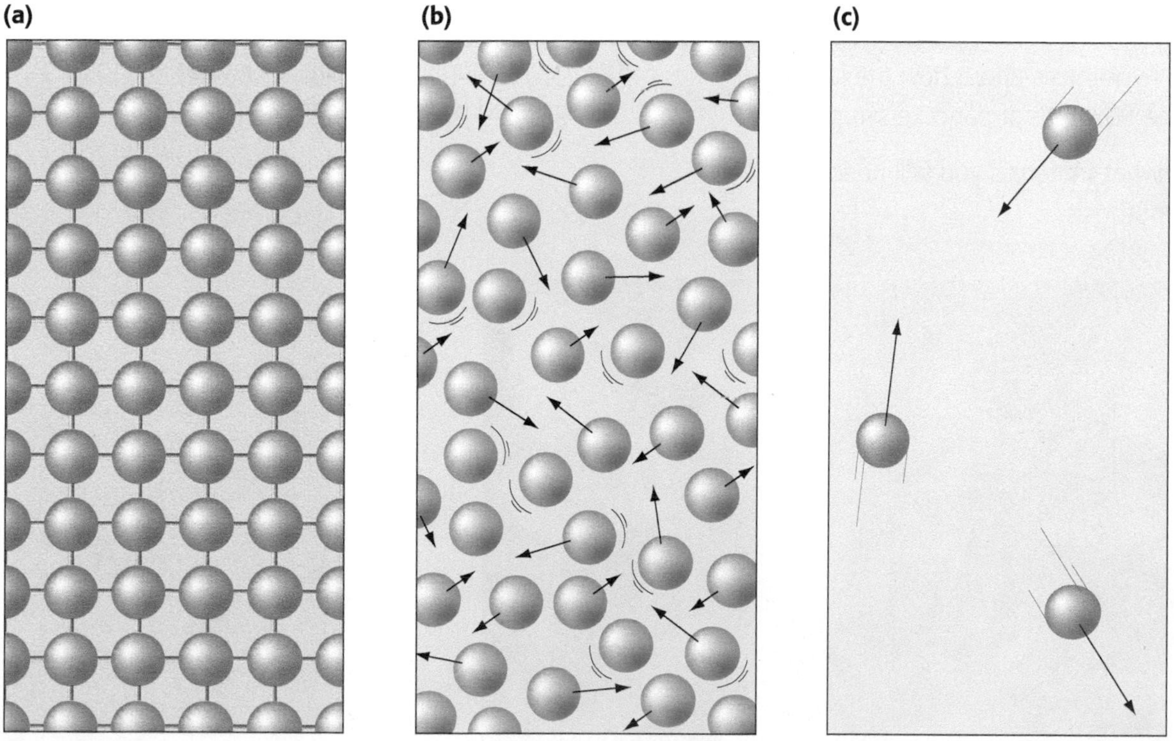

(a)   **(b)**   **(c)**

Figure 8.6 The particles in a solid (a) and a liquid (b) are packed closer together than the particles in a gas (c).

C17 *Design a Lab* | Toolkit 2

SKILLS YOU WILL USE
- Designing a fair test
- Using appropriate equipment and tools

Flow Rate of Fluids

Introduction

You can design an experiment to record the time it takes a fluid to travel a given distance. The distance divided by the time is the fluid's flow rate. Several factors can affect the flow rate of a liquid (Figure 8.7). These may include:

- changing the temperature of the liquid
- changing the angle, or tilt, of the slope the liquid flows down
- changing the diameter of the tube through which the liquid is poured

Question

How does the factor you identify affect the flow rate of pancake syrup?

Design and Conduct Your Investigation

1. With your group, decide which factor you are going to test.

2. Make a hypothesis about how the factor will affect the flow rate of pancake syrup.

3. Decide what materials you will need to test your hypothesis.

4. Plan your procedure. Think about these questions.
   (a) What evidence are you looking for to support your hypothesis?
   (b) What steps will you follow to collect the data you need?
   (c) How will you make sure the test you are planning is fair?
   (d) How will you make sure the test you are planning is safe?
   (e) How will you record your results?

5. Write up your procedure. Be sure to show it to your teacher before going any further.

6. Carry out your experiment.

7. Compare your results with your hypothesis.
   (a) Did your results support your hypothesis?
   (b) If not, what possible reasons might explain the difference?

8. Present your findings to the class or in a form suggested by your teacher.

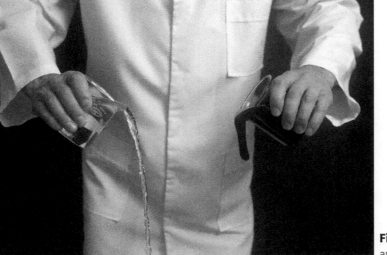

Figure 8.7 Molasses has a lower flow rate and higher viscosity than water.

Key Concept Review

1. Write a short paragraph to describe viscosity. Include at least two examples of fluids and the words "flow," "fluid," "particles," and "viscosity."

2. Draw a diagram to show what happens to the particles when a liquid is heated.

3. Draw a diagram to show what happens to the particles when a gas is heated.

Connect Your Understanding

4. You are making cookies that call for 3 tablespoons of molasses, but you are having trouble measuring out the thick, syrupy liquid. What could you do to make it easier to pour and measure this fluid?

5. Describe two substances that are useful because of their viscosity.

6. You are given three samples of the same shampoo at three different temperatures: 35°C, 50°C, and 75°C.

   (a) Which sample has the highest viscosity?

   (b) Which sample has the highest flow rate?

   (c) Which sample has the highest density?

Practise Your Skills

7. In a fair test, you should change only one variable so that you can see the effects of the variable you changed. Suppose you were investigating the flow rates of various liquids by measuring the time that each took to flow down a ramp.

   (a) What variable would you change during the tests?

   (b) What variables would you keep the same?

For more questions, go to ScienceSource.

C18 *Thinking about Science and Technology*

Measuring the Flow Rate of Gas

You can determine the flow rates of liquids by pouring them down an inclined plane. However, many technologies, such as a firefighter's air tank and helium used to blow up balloons, use gases rather than liquids as the fluid that flows through the system.

1. When might it be important to know the flow rate of a gas?

2. How is the flow rate of a gas controlled as it leaves a storage container?

3. How might understanding the flow rate of a gas be useful in preventing environmental disasters?

Here is a summary of what you will learn in this section:

- Density is the ratio of mass to volume.
- The solid state of a substance is usually denser than the liquid state. The liquid state is denser than the gas state.
- The upward force exerted by a fluid is called the buoyant force.
- Archimedes' principle states that the buoyant force on an object is equal to the weight of the fluid displaced by the object.

Figure 8.8 Some fluids are denser than others.

If you drop a grape into water, what happens? The grape sinks. However, if you drop the grape into corn syrup, it floats. Why does a substance float in some fluids, but sink in others?

- If the density of a substance is greater than the density of the fluid, the substance will sink.

- If the density of a substance is less than the density of the fluid, the substance will float.

- If the density of a substance is the very same as the density of a fluid, the substance will "hover" in place.

A grape floats on corn syrup, a plastic building block floats on water, and a cork floats on oil (Figure 8.8).

C19 *Starting Point*

Skills Ⓐ Ⓒ

Dense and Denser

You have six identical jars full of different materials in front of you.

Table 8.2 Different Densities

Contents of Jars	
1. water	4. aquarium stones
2. sand	5. shampoo
3. corn syrup	6. wood chips

1. Without opening the jars, rank them in order of highest density to lowest density.

2. What ranking did you choose? Be prepared to explain your reasons for the order of your ranking.

3. Keep your ranking handy. You may test these substances later in C21, Calculating Mass-to-Volume Ratio on page 222. You can then compare your ranking with the results of your investigation.

Sink or Float?

If all metals have a greater density than water, how is it possible for metal boats to float on water? The answer is that a boat consists of more than just metal. If you consider the density of the air inside the boat and the density of all the objects in the boat, you would find that the combined density of all parts of the boat is less than the density of the water (Figure 8.9).

The submarine described in the Unit Opener floats when its tanks are filled with air because the combined density of all parts of the vessel, including the air, is less than the density of water. When the tanks are filled with water, the combined density of the water in the tanks and all other parts of the vessel is greater than that of the surrounding water, so the submarine sinks.

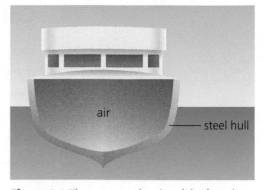

Figure 8.9 The average density of the boat is less than the average density of the water, so the boat floats.

Density and Temperature

A substance can have different densities, depending on its temperature. For example, imagine swimming in a lake on a hot summer day. The water on the surface of the lake is noticeably warmer than the water below it. The warm water floats on the cold water because it has a lower density than that of cold water.

You may have noticed that the air in a room is warmer toward the ceiling and cooler toward the floor. The warmer air has a lower density, so it rises above the cooler, higher density air along the floor.

According to the particle theory, particles in a substance move more quickly when energy is added. As a substance warms up, the particles move faster and farther apart. This causes the volume to increase even though the number of particles stays the same. With the same number of particles in a larger volume, the density decreases. A substance generally has a greater density in its solid state than in its liquid state and gas state. One exception to this is water (Figure 8.10).

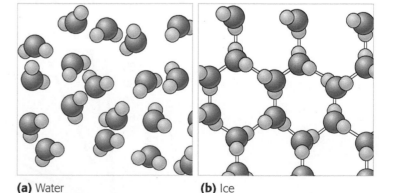

(a) Water   **(b)** Ice

Figure 8.10 The particles in water move slightly farther apart as the water freezes, so ice is less dense than liquid water.

Calculating Density

Density is the ratio of mass to volume. The unit for measuring the density of liquids is usually grams per millilitre (g/mL). For gases, the most commonly used unit is kilograms per litre (kg/L). The unit for measuring the density of solids is usually grams per cubic centimetre (g/cm^3). You can calculate the density of a substance by dividing its mass by its volume.

$$\text{Density } (D) = \frac{\text{mass } (m)}{\text{volume } (V)}$$

Sample problem: A 2.0 mL sample of oil has a mass of 1.76 g. What is its density?

$$D = \frac{m}{V}$$

$$= \frac{1.76 \text{ g}}{2.0 \text{ mL}}$$

Suggested Activity •········
C21 Inquiry Activity on page 222

The density of oil is 0.88 g/mL.

Comparing Densities

The graph in Figure 8.11 shows the densities of some common substances. A substance with a greater slope on the graph has a greater density than a substance with a shallower slope. Notice in the graph that gold, iron, and aluminum have greater densities than water. This means that these metals will sink in water. Which fluids are less dense than water? Vegetable oil, rubbing alcohol, and gasoline will all float on water. Some solids, such as pine wood, are less dense than some liquids. That is why wood floats on water or oil.

Suggested Activity •········
C22 Problem-Solving Activity
on page 224

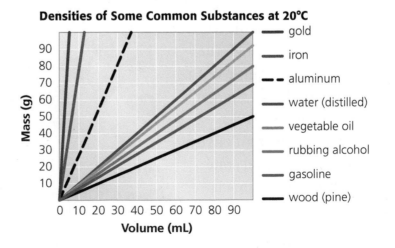

Figure 8.11 Notice which substances are less dense than water.

Calculate and Compare

1. A 15-mL sample of gasoline has a mass of 11 g. What is the density of the gasoline?

2. What is the density of a 2.5-cm³ glass marble that has a mass of 7.5 g?

3. The mass of 5.0 mL of rubbing alcohol is 4.0 g. The mass of an 8.0-cm³ block of wood is 5.6 g. Which of these materials has the greater density?

Use the graph in Figure 8.11 to answer the following questions.

4. Which substances have a lower density than rubbing alcohol?

5. If gasoline and vegetable oil were poured into the same container, which substance would be on top?

6. What is the mass of 30 mL of aluminum?

Forces in Fluids

A **force** is a push or pull that acts on an object. For example, weight is the amount of downward pull on an object due to the force of gravity. The measuring unit of force is the newton (N). One newton is approximately equal to the force you would exert to hold up a baseball.

Buoyancy

You have just learned that an object sinks when its density is greater than the density of the fluid it is in. **Buoyancy** is the tendency of an object in a fluid to rise or sink due to density differences with its surroundings. What is the connection between the object's density and the forces that act on it in a fluid?

Earth's gravitational force attracts matter downward toward Earth's centre. A fluid, however, exerts an opposite force that pushes matter upward. The upward force exerted by a fluid is called the **buoyant force** (Figure 8.12).

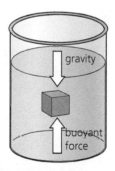

Figure 8.12 Gravity and the buoyant force act on an object in a fluid.

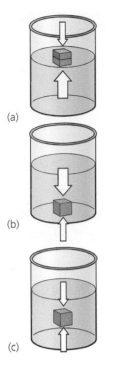

(a)

(b)

(c)

Figure 8.13 An object rises in a fluid (a). An object sinks in a fluid (b). An object floats in a fluid (c).

Buoyancy and Gravity

If you want to know whether an object will sink or float, you need to consider all the forces that are acting on the object (Figure 8.13).

- An object will *rise* in a fluid when:
- the density of the object is less than the density of the fluid
- the buoyant force on the object is greater than the force of gravity on the object

- An object will *sink* in a fluid when:
- the density of the object is greater than the density of the fluid
- the buoyant force on the object is less than the force of gravity on the object

- An object will *float* in a fluid when:
- the density of the object is equal to the density of the fluid
- the buoyant force on the object is equal to the force of gravity on the object

Archimedes' Principle

More than two thousand years ago, a Greek mathematician and inventor named Archimedes discovered an important principle about buoyancy (Figure 8.14). Archimedes' principle states that the buoyant force on an object is equal to the weight of the fluid displaced by the object.

Imagine two identical pieces of aluminum foil. If you take one piece of aluminum foil and crumple it up tightly, it will sink in water. But if you fold the second piece into the shape of a boat, it will float. It will even support a "cargo" of some pennies or paper clips. Even though both pieces of aluminum foil have the same mass, the piece shaped like a boat takes up a much greater volume and displaces more fluid. Therefore, the buoyant force acting on the boat and its cargo is greater, so it floats.

Figure 8.14 Archimedes (287–212 B.C.) discovered that the buoyant force depends on the weight of the displaced fluid, not on the weight of the object.

Applications of Buoyancy

Buoyancy is also an important factor in natural fluid systems. For example, a sperm whale has an oil-filled organ above its skull (Figure 8.15). When the whale is preparing to dive deep, it allows cold seawater into the organ, which solidifies the oil and increases its density. When the oil is allowed to warm, it becomes a liquid, and the whale's density is decreased so that it can rise to the surface.

Transportation technologies such as hot air balloons, airships, and research platforms use the concept of buoyancy in their design (Figure 8.16). Ships can travel around the world thanks to the buoyant force of water. But what happens when the density changes in the water through which they travel?

Figure 8.15 By changing the temperature of its oil, a sperm whale can dive deep or rise to the surface for air.

Plimsoll Line

Picture a fully loaded cargo ship sailing across the Atlantic Ocean. As it enters the fresh water of the St. Lawrence River, it sinks dangerously low. Why? The ship sinks lower in the water because fresh water is less dense than salt water. When a ship sails from cold northern waters into warm tropical waters, the same thing happens. Warm water is less dense than cold water, so the ship sinks lower into the water.

Because of density variations in the world's oceans and rivers, all cargo ships have a Plimsoll line painted on their hulls. The **Plimsoll line** shows how heavily a ship can be safely loaded in different water conditions as shown in Figure 8.17. The marks on the left indicate where the waterline should be in fresh water. The marks on the right indicate where the waterline should be in salt water.

Figure 8.16 FLIP is a research platform that floats out to sea. The platform becomes vertical when water is pumped into its tanks.

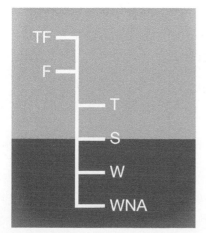

Legend

TF   tropical fresh water

F   fresh water

T   tropical salt water

S   summer salt water

W   winter salt water

WNA   winter North Atlantic

Figure 8.17 The Plimsoll line shows how heavily a ship can be loaded in different densities of water.

*Take It **Further***

Airships have the ability to change their density in order to ascend and descend. Find out how airships change their density. Begin your search at ScienceSource.

DI Anchor Activity

C21 *Inquiry Activity*

Toolkits 2, 7

SKILLS YOU WILL USE
- Measuring
- Recording and organizing data

Calculating Mass-to-Volume Ratio

Question

How can you calculate the densities of a variety of solids and liquids?

Materials & Equipment

- 250-mL beaker
- graduated cylinder
- triple beam or electronic balance
- water, sand, aquarium stones, shampoo, wood chips, corn syrup
- graph paper

Hypothesis

Write a hypothesis about how to calculate the densities of solids and liquids.

Figure 8.18 Steps 3 and 4. Carefully pour 50 mL of a substance into the beaker and record its volume and mass.

Procedure

Part 1 – Collecting Data

1. In your notebook, make a table using headings like the ones shown below to record your data. Give your table a title. Use a row in your table for each substance.

Table 8.3 Data Table

Substance	Volume of Substance (mL)	Mass of Beaker (g)	Mass of Beaker and Substance (g)	Mass of Substance Only (g)

2. Measure the mass of the beaker and record it in your table. (See Toolkit 7 for information on measuring mass.)

3. Pour 50 mL of one substance (other than corn syrup) into the beaker (Figure 8.18). Record the volume in the table. (See Toolkit 7 for information on measuring volume.) Clean up any spills immediately.

4. Place the beaker containing the substance on the balance and measure the mass. Record the mass in your table.

5. Repeat steps 3 and 4 for the substance with volumes of 100 mL, 150 mL, 200 mL, and 250 mL. Wash and dry the beaker. Return the substances as directed by your teacher.

6. Repeat this procedure for each of the other substances. The final substance you test should be the corn syrup.

7. Clean your equipment and return it to the proper location.

Part 2 — Graphing Your Data

8. When you have finished taking the measurements, enter your data into a spreadsheet program. Find the mass of each substance by subtracting the mass of the beaker from the total mass of the beaker and substance together as shown in Figure 8.19.

Mass of beaker + substance   Mass of empty beaker   Mass of substance

Figure 8.19 How to calculate the mass of the substance

9. Set up a line graph with mass on the vertical axis and volume on the horizontal axis like Figure 8.20. Plot your results for the first substance. Draw a straight line through or close to the points on the graph. Label the line.

10. Plot your results for the other substances on the same graph. Label each line.

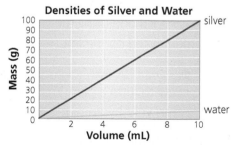

Densities of Silver and Water

Figure 8.20 An example of step 9 for silver

Analyzing and Interpreting

11. Compare the slopes of the lines in your graph.

  (a) Which slope is the steepest?

  (b) Which slope is the shallowest?

12. (a) Find the ratio of mass to volume for each substance by dividing the mass of the substance by the volume. This ratio is the density of each substance. For example:

- 200 mL of a substance has a mass of 400 g. The mass-to-volume ratio is

$$\frac{400 \text{ g (mass)}}{200 \text{ mL (volume)}}$$

$$\text{Density} = \frac{400 \text{ g}}{200 \text{ mL}} = \frac{2.00 \text{ g}}{1 \text{ mL}}$$

  (b) Record the mass-to-volume ratios in your data table.

  (c) What is the relationship between the average ratio for each substance and the slope of each line on your graph?

Skill Builder

13. Use your graph to determine the answers to the following questions.

  (a) What would be the mass in grams of 150 mL of corn syrup?

  (b) What would be the volume in millilitres of 225 g of sand?

  (c) What would be the mass in grams of 300 mL of shampoo?

Forming Conclusions

14. Write a summary paragraph that explains how you calculated the densities of the substances used in this investigation. Your summary should include the words "substance," "volume," "mass," "graph," "slope," "ratio," and "density." Include your graph with your summary.

Homemade Hydrometer

Recognize a Need

A hydrometer is a device that uses buoyancy to measure the density of a liquid (Figure 8.21). In this activity, you will work in groups to design and build your own hydrometer. By using solutions of known densities, you will be able to calibrate your hydrometer. Your group will then use the calibrated hydrometer to determine the densities of unknown liquids.

Problem

How can you build a hydrometer to compare the densities of different liquids?

Materials & Equipment

- 4 tall clear containers (canning jars or 1-L clear plastic bottles with the tops cut off)
- plastic straw
- modelling clay
- fresh water
- 3 different saltwater solutions prepared by your teacher labelled A, B, C
- fine-tipped permanent marker
- 2 unknown solutions

Criteria for Success

- Hydrometer is calibrated using four known densities.
- The constructed hydrometer can be used successfully to estimate the density of unknown liquids.

Brainstorm Ideas

1. Before you begin, read Toolkit 3 about the problem-solving process.

2. Consider the materials listed here or think of other materials you could use that are easy to get.

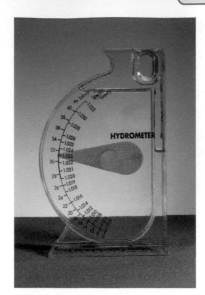

Figure 8.21 This commercial hydrometer can be used to measure the salt content in an aquarium.

3. Working by yourself or in a small group, generate ideas for designing and building a hydrometer.

4. Make a sketch of what your hydrometer will look like when you complete it. Show the sketch to your teacher for approval.

Build a Prototype

Part 1 — Fresh Water

5. Assemble the materials you need and build your hydrometer. Or you can follow steps 6 through 17 to build one using the materials and equipment listed on the left.

6. Press a small ball of modelling clay onto the end of the straw to form a plug. The straw and clay will become your hydrometer.

7. Fill your container full of fresh water.

8. With the clay end touching the water, carefully lower the hydrometer into the fresh water. Add or remove clay so that approximately 2 cm of the straw tip remains above the water.

9. Use a permanent marker to draw a line on the straw at the water level and label it "1." Your hydrometer is calibrated for the density of fresh water, which is 1.0 g/mL.

Part 2 — Salt Water

10. Remove the hydrometer from the fresh water and place it in the container that contains saltwater solution A.

11. Make a mark on the straw where the straw meets the water line and label this "2."

12. Remove the hydrometer from the solution A container and place it in the container that contains saltwater solution B.

13. Make a mark on the straw where the straw meets the waterline and label this "3."

14. Remove the hydrometer from the solution B container and place it in the container that contains saltwater solution C.

15. Make a mark on the straw where the straw meets the waterline and label this "4."

16. The densities corresponding to each of the marks on your hydrometer is given below.

Table 8.4 Density Values

Solution	Mark	Density (g/mL)
Fresh water	1	1.0
A	2	1.008
B	3	1.017
C	4	1.025

17. Make a sketch of your hydrometer showing the four marks. Label the density indicated at each mark.

Test and Evaluate

18. Your teacher will give you two unknown liquids. Use the hydrometer you built and calibrated to determine the densities of the unknown samples. You will need to estimate if the liquid comes between two of the lines on your hydrometer. Record your results.

19. Compare the densities you obtained with those of your classmates. How do your results compare with those of your classmates?

20. If your teacher has a commercial hydrometer, compare your results to the actual values.

Communicate

21. After you have determined the densities of the unknown samples, write a short report that describes:

(a) what you did

(b) your results

(c) one new thing you learned in this activity

Key Concept Review

1. In which state of matter is a substance the least dense?

2. What is the relationship of temperature to density?

3. What two opposing forces are acting on an object as it floats in a fluid?

Connect Your Understanding

4. The table below shows mass and volume data for mineral oil.

Table 8.5 Mineral Oil Data

Mass (g)	Volume (mL)
0.8	1.0
1.6	2.0
2.4	3.0
3.2	4.0

(a) What happens to the mass of the mineral oil as the volume changes?

(b) What is the density of mineral oil?

(c) What happens to the density as the mass and volume change?

Practise Your Skills

5. Suppose you were to graph the mineral oil data from question 4 on a graph with mass on the vertical axis and volume on the horizontal axis. Would the slope of the line for the mineral oil be shallower or steeper than the one for water? (The density of water is 1.0 g/mL.)

6. Draw a diagram to help you explain how a heavy ship can float on water.

7. What is the density of each of the following substances?

    (a) 2.0 mL of mercury with a mass of 27.1 g

    (b) 0.5 mL of silver with a mass of 5.25 g

    (c) 2.5 mL of lead with a mass of 28.5 g

8. If you had 100 mL of each substance in question 7, which one would have the greatest mass?

For more questions, go to ScienceSource.

C23 Thinking about Science and Technology

Worldwide Shipping

Improvements in technology have enabled larger and safer shipping around the world. Consider each of the following questions from the viewpoint of society and of the environment. Make a chart to record your ideas.

1. (a) What are some benefits that result from worldwide shipping of oil in oil tankers?

    (b) What are some problems that result from worldwide shipping of oil?

2. (a) What are some benefits that result from worldwide shipping of produce (vegetables and fruit)?

    (b) What are some problems that result from worldwide shipping of produce?

	Society	Environment
Benefits of shipping oil		
Problems from shipping oil		
Benefits of shipping produce		
Problems from shipping produce		

Here is a summary of what you will learn in this section:

- Pressure is the amount of force applied to a given area.
- Pressure increases with depth.
- Fluids will naturally move from an area of higher pressure to an area of lower pressure.
- Gases can be compressed easily. Liquids are very difficult to compress.

When you swim underwater, you might notice the pressure of the water around you, especially if you swim along the bottom of a deep pool. But did you know that there is also pressure around you when you are out of the water?

Pressure is the amount of force applied to a given area. Air is a fluid, and it exerts pressure around you all the time. Air pressure is the reason why your ears may "pop" when you change altitude quickly. When the air pressure outside changes, the air pressure inside your middle ear has to adjust, resulting in the popping sound (Figure 8.22).

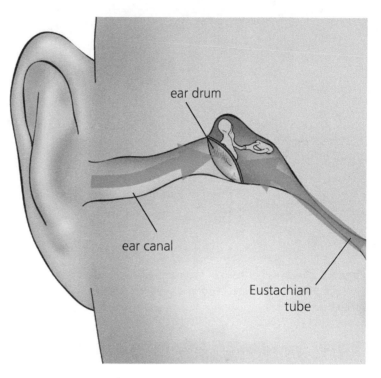

Figure 8.22 The air in the middle ear (Eustachian tube) is sometimes at a different pressure than the air in the outer ear (ear canal).

C24 Starting Point

Skills A C

Pressure Can — Teacher Demonstration

Observe as your teacher does the following.

1. Fill a large bowl with ice water.

2. Pour a spoonful of water into a clean, empty soft drink can. Place the can on a hotplate. Heat until the water boils and steam leaves the top of the can.

3. Using a pair of tongs, turn the can upside down and immediately plunge it into the ice water.

4. Observe what happens to the can. Give a possible explanation for your observation.

Changes in Pressure

Air pressure changes with altitude. How does the air pressure around you right now compare with the pressure at the top of a mountain?

The layers of air in Earth's atmosphere extend more than 160 km above Earth's surface. Close to the surface, we experience air pressure as a result of all those air particles above us being pulled toward Earth by the force of gravity. There is less air pressure if we travel to higher altitudes because there are fewer layers of air above us and the air there is less dense.

You can observe an effect of this change in air pressure on a weather balloon that is released from Earth's surface (Figure 8.23). As a weather balloon passes through upper layers, there is less air pressure acting on it from the outside, so it expands as it rises. Eventually, the balloon will expand so much that it will burst.

Figure 8.23 A weather balloon measures weather conditions at high altitudes. This weather balloon is being released in Antarctica.

*Take It **Further***

An ultrahigh-pressure water system forces water out of a hose with 275 000 kPa of pressure. This water jet can be used for cleaning, blasting, sanding, and processing materials. Find out more about applications of ultrahigh-pressure water systems. Begin your research at ScienceSource.

Pressure and Depth

Pressure in a fluid also changes with its depth. For example, the weight of water in the upper part of a swimming pool presses down on the water in the lower part of the pool. The greater the depth of water, the greater the pressure at that point. This is why you feel a greater pressure when swimming on the bottom of a pool than you do when swimming at the surface.

You can observe an effect of this change in pressure by making two holes in a container of water, one above the other (Figure 8.24). Water at the depth of the lower hole has a greater pressure on it than water at the higher hole. The greater pressure results in the water being released with more force from the lower hole.

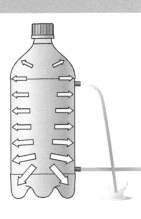

Figure 8.24 The greater the depth, the greater the pressure.

Pressure and Fluid Flow

If a fluid is allowed to move, it will always go from an area of higher pressure to an area of lower pressure. You make use of this property when you use a straw to drink from a juice box. Your mouth creates an area of lower pressure. The juice in the box is at a higher pressure, so it travels up the straw and into your mouth (Figure 8.25).

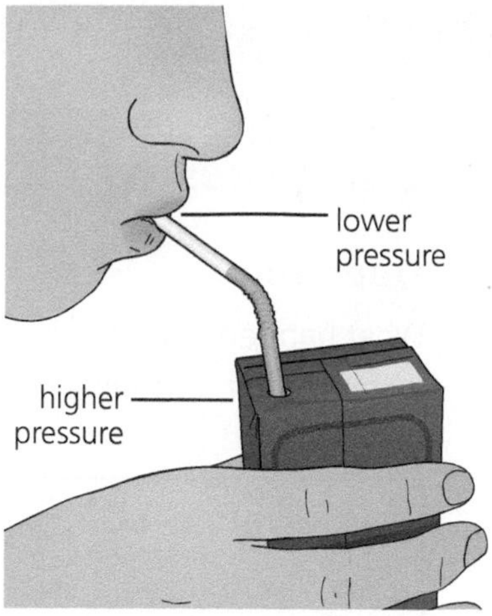

Pressure and Temperature

What happens to pressure inside a container when the temperature of a fluid is increased? The pressure exerted by a fluid is the sum of all the forces exerted by the individual particles in the fluid. When the temperature is increased, the particles move faster and strike the walls of the container more often and with more energy. At a constant volume, an increase in temperature results in an increase in pressure. If the volume of the container cannot increase, its pressure increases, possibly resulting in an explosion.

Figure 8.25 The fluid travels up the straw from an area of higher pressure in the box to an area of lower pressure in your mouth.

Compression

An important part of understanding how to use fluids in devices is knowing how they react under pressure. If you kick a soccer ball, you force the air particles inside into a smaller volume (Figure 8.26). The shape of the ball changes temporarily because the air particles inside it are compressed. **Compression** is a decrease in volume caused by a force.

There is a large amount of space between the particles in a gas like the air in the soccer ball. There is much less space between the particles in a liquid. This means that gases are much more compressible than liquids are. When a force is applied to the particles, much more compression takes place in the gas than in the liquid. In fact, very little compression occurs in liquids.

Compressibility is the property of being able to be compressed. Materials in a liquid state are said to be **incompressible**, which means they cannot be compressed easily. As you will see in Chapter 9, this property of liquids is very useful.

Suggested Activity •·········
C25 Inquiry Activity on page 230

Figure 8.26 Your foot compresses the air inside the soccer ball as you kick it.

Viscosity, density, and compressibility are all properties of fluids. **229**

Compressing Fluids

Question

What happens to air as it is compressed? Does water react in the same way?

Materials & Equipment

Part 1

- 50-mL syringe
- 5 cm of latex tubing
- bulldog clamp
- water
- sink or bowl

Part 2

- 2 burette clamps
- modified 50-mL syringe with platform
- 5 cm of latex tubing
- bulldog clamp
- four 1-kg masses
- water
- empty container

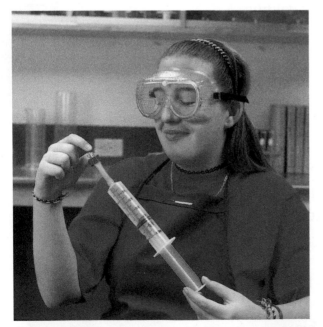

Figure 8.27 Step 1. The plunger should be three-quarters of the way up the tube.

Procedure

Part 1 — Compressing Air

1. Attach the latex tubing to the end of the syringe. Place the plunger of the syringe three-quarters of the way up the tube. Seal the tubing at the end of the syringe with the bulldog clamp (Figure 8.27).

2. Before you press the plunger down, predict how far the plunger will go. Record your prediction.

3. Press the plunger down and record the change in volume in the syringe.

4. Unclamp the tubing. Place the syringe in a sink or bowl of water. Pull up the plunger to draw in water until the syringe is filled to the same level as in step 1.

   If you get air in your syringe, turn the syringe upside down so the plunger points downward. Allow the air to rise to the top of the syringe. Then gently push the plunger up until all the air has escaped. Add more water if necessary. Clamp the end of the tubing shut.

5. Before you press the plunger down, predict how far you think the plunger will go. Record your prediction.

6. Record the volume in the syringe before you push down the plunger. Press down the plunger and record the change in volume in the syringe.

Part 2 — Compressing Water

7. Make a data table like the one below for recording your data. Give your table a title.

Table 8.6 Data Table

Force Acting on the Syringe (N)	Volume of Air (mL)	Volume of Water (mL)
0		
10		

8. Use the burette clamps to attach a modified syringe (with platform) to a support stand, as shown in Figure 8.28.

Figure 8.28 Step 8. Be sure to follow safe work procedures. Clamp the syringe tightly at right angles to the stand.

9. Attach the latex tubing to the end of the syringe. Pull the plunger to the 50-mL mark. Seal the tubing with the bulldog clamp.

10. Place a 1-kg mass on the centre of the platform that is attached to the syringe. (This mass applies a 10 N force.) Measure and record the volume of air in the syringe.

11. Repeat step 10 by adding another 1-kg mass so that you have 2-kg mass (20 N).

12. Repeat step 11 for 3 kg (30 N) and 4 kg (40 N). Place the masses in the centre of the platform.

13. Remove all of the masses.

14. Remove the syringe from the burette clamps and place it in a sink or bowl of water. Fill the syringe to the 50-mL mark by pulling on the plunger, not the platform. Remove any air bubbles as before. Re-attach the syringe with the burette clamps. Place an empty container under the syringe. Repeat steps 10, 11, and 12.

15. Clean your equipment and return it to the appropriate location. Wash your hands after you finish the activity.

Analyzing and Interpreting

16. How did your predictions compare with your results?

17. (a) Which fluid compressed more?
(b) Why do you think this happened?

18. How did the force affect the compression of the air and the water?

Skill Builder

19. Draw a line graph of the compression of the air and water from Part 2, using a different colour for each fluid. Put the volume on the vertical axis, and the force on the horizontal axis.

Forming Conclusions

20. Use the particle theory of matter to explain what happened when you compressed the air and the water. Focus your explanation on the differences in the amount of space between particles in air and water. Use your observations, and remember to refer to your graph to support your explanation.

Key Concept Review

1. What term describes the amount of force applied to a given area?

2. Why might your inner ears "pop" when you are driving through the mountains?

3. Explain why gases are easier to compress than liquids.

4. Use the terms "decreases" or "increases" to complete the following statements.

   (a) As you go deeper in a fluid, the pressure of the fluid _____.

   (b) A sealed container is cooled. The pressure of the fluid inside the container _____ .

Connect Your Understanding

5. Suppose a dam developed a hole from which the water started to leak out. Why would it be harder to stop the leak if the hole was near the bottom of the dam as compared to near the top?

6. On a cold winter day, you discover that the football you left outside is soft (has low pressure).

   (a) How could you increase the pressure inside the ball without adding more air?

   (b) Explain why you think your solution would work.

Practise Your Skills

7. Picture a device, such as a vacuum cleaner, that uses the motion of fluids in its design. Make a sketch of the device and show the direction that the fluid moves. Using your sketch, explain

   (a) where the areas of low pressure and high pressure exist

   (b) how the device creates areas with different pressure

For more questions, go to ScienceSource.

C26   *Thinking about Science and Technology*

Pipes and Plumbing

The pipes in your home's plumbing system bring fresh water to your taps and carry waste water away. The word "plumbing" comes from a Latin word meaning lead. At one time water pipes were made from lead. However, in the early 1900s, researchers discovered that lead is a poison. It builds up in the body and affects the nervous system.

1. What environmental factors would you have to consider in choosing material for building water pipelines?

2. What other factors would you have to consider in choosing material for building water pipelines?

Meteorologist

We live in a fluid world. A blanket of air extends above us for almost 160 km. Approximately three-quarters of Earth's surface is covered in water. These two fluids interact, causing changes in temperature and pressure and creating the variations in our weather. A meteorologist is a person who studies these interactions, and collects and analyzes data to forecast our weather.

Meteorologists use data collected from several locations to make a weather forecast. Weather forecasts can be for the same day, for short term, or for long term. Same-day forecasts usually are done by making simple observations. Data collected from radar and satellites are used when making short-term forecasts. Computer models are used for long-term forecasts. Some of the measurements that meteorologists use when making a forecast include temperature, wind, humidity, and air pressure.

Weather forecasting can save lives by giving advance warning of storms or sudden changes in temperature. Meteorologists provide weather forecasts that are essential for air and ocean travel. Agriculture and tourism also depend on the services of meteorologists.

On a global scale, meteorologists analyze the input of industrial projects and human activities on climate and air quality. Meteorologists also take part in studies involving the effect of air pollution on climate.

To become a meteorologist in Canada, you must first have a university degree in meteorology, mathematics, or physics. After your degree, you need to complete a nine-month training course provided by Environment Canada.

Figure 8.29 A meteorologist evaluates data on pressure systems for Hurricane Katrina on August 29, 2005.

Pressure Systems

Why is it important for meteorologists to measure air pressure? When the pressure in an area is higher than the pressure in surrounding air, a high-pressure system occurs. A high-pressure system usually provides us with sunny, dry weather. When the pressure in an area is lower than the surrounding air, a low-pressure system occurs. Clouds and precipitation usually accompany a low-pressure system.

Questions

1. List four types of data a meteorologist uses when forecasting the weather.

2. Describe the type of weather accompanied by
   (a) low-pressure system
   (b) high-pressure system

3. Suppose you had all the skills of a trained meteorologist. Explain how you would use these skills to improve the quality of life for people in your community.

Key Concept Review

1. (a) What is viscosity? *k*

   (b) Why is viscosity an important property of matter? *k*

2. How does temperature affect the viscosity of a fluid? *k*

3. What does density measure? *k*

4. Describe how you find the density of an object. *k*

5. How does the particle theory of matter help you explain why cold water is denser than hot water? *t*

6. What units are usually used for measuring the density of the following substances? *k*

   (a) solids

   (b) liquids

7. Use the particle theory to explain the differences in compressibility between liquids and gases. *k*

8. Use your answer for question 7 to identify which material in each pair below would compress more than the other. Provide a brief reason for each answer. *t*

   (a) a helium balloon or a water balloon

   (b) a solid rubber bicycle tire and an inflated mountain bike tire

   (c) plastic bubble pack or a baby's liquid-filled teething ring

   (d) a golf ball or a soccer ball

9. What does Archimedes' principle state? *k*

10. A full juice can has a hole at the top and another hole near the bottom. *k*

    (a) How will the juice flow out of the two holes?

    (b) Why is there a difference?

After Reading Thinking Literacy

Reflect and Evaluate

Revisit your KTW chart from the start of this chapter. Did you find answers to all the things you wanted to know?

Summarize your learning in the 3-2-1 organizer below:

3 important things I learned

2 fix-up strategies I used to monitor my comprehension

1 question I still have

ACHIEVEMENT CHART CATEGORIES
k Knowledge and understanding   *t* Thinking and investigation   *c* Communication   *a* Application

Connect Your Understanding

11. You have two fluids of unknown density. How could you find out which is denser without mixing the fluids? 🅣

12. Using the information you learned in this chapter, state whether air would flow into or out of a low-pressure system. Explain. 🅣

13. Explain why deep-sea fish are not crushed by the pressure of all of the water above them. 🅣

Practise Your Skills

14. (a) What is the density of a shampoo if 6 g of the shampoo fills a 5-mL container? 🅐

    (b) What is the density of vegetable oil if 50 g of the oil has a volume of 54 mL? 🅐

    (c) What is the density of gasoline if 90 mL of gasoline has a mass of 62 g? 🅐

    (d) If you had 50 mL of each of shampoo, vegetable oil, and gasoline, which of the three would have the least mass? 🅐

Unit Task Link

In your Unit Task, you will investigate the effect that a variable of your choice has on the movement of fluid in a pipeline. What properties of liquids will be part of your hypothesis? Be sure to include key ideas like viscosity, density, and pressure when you continue work on your task.

C27 Thinking about Science and Technology

Propane Tanks

Many people use propane tanks to fuel their barbecues. When a propane tank is filled, the propane gas is compressed into a liquid. When you open the valve on the tank, the propane is released as a gas.

1. Why should propane barbecues only be operated outdoors, in well-ventilated conditions?

2. There is a policy in some high-rise apartment buildings that propane barbecues are not allowed on balconies.

   (a) Why do you think that is?

   (b) Do you agree with the rule? Why or why not?

   (c) Do you think residents should be allowed to vote and decide if barbecues will be allowed? Explain.

Fluids are used to clean vehicles at an automatic car wash.

What You Will Learn

In this chapter, you will:

- explain how forces are transferred in all directions in fluids (Pascal's law)
- compare how fluids are controlled and used in living things and manufactured devices
- assess the social, economic, and environmental impacts of several fluid technologies
- assess the impact of fluid spills on society and the environment

Skills You Will Use

In this chapter, you will:

- investigate applications of the principles of fluid mechanics
- use technological problem-solving skills
- design, build, and test devices that use pneumatic or hydraulic systems

Why This Is Important

Our understanding of the properties of fluids allows us to design fluid systems that are safe and effective. We need to take care to prevent fluid spills.

Before Reading

Thinking Literacy

Compare and Contrast Writing
Often science is best understood when you look at related topics in terms of their similarities and differences. Scan this chapter to find related topics that could be written as a comparison and contrast.

Key Terms

- fluid system
- Pascal's law
- hydraulic system
- pneumatic system
- hoist
- piston
- pump
- valve

9.0 Getting Started

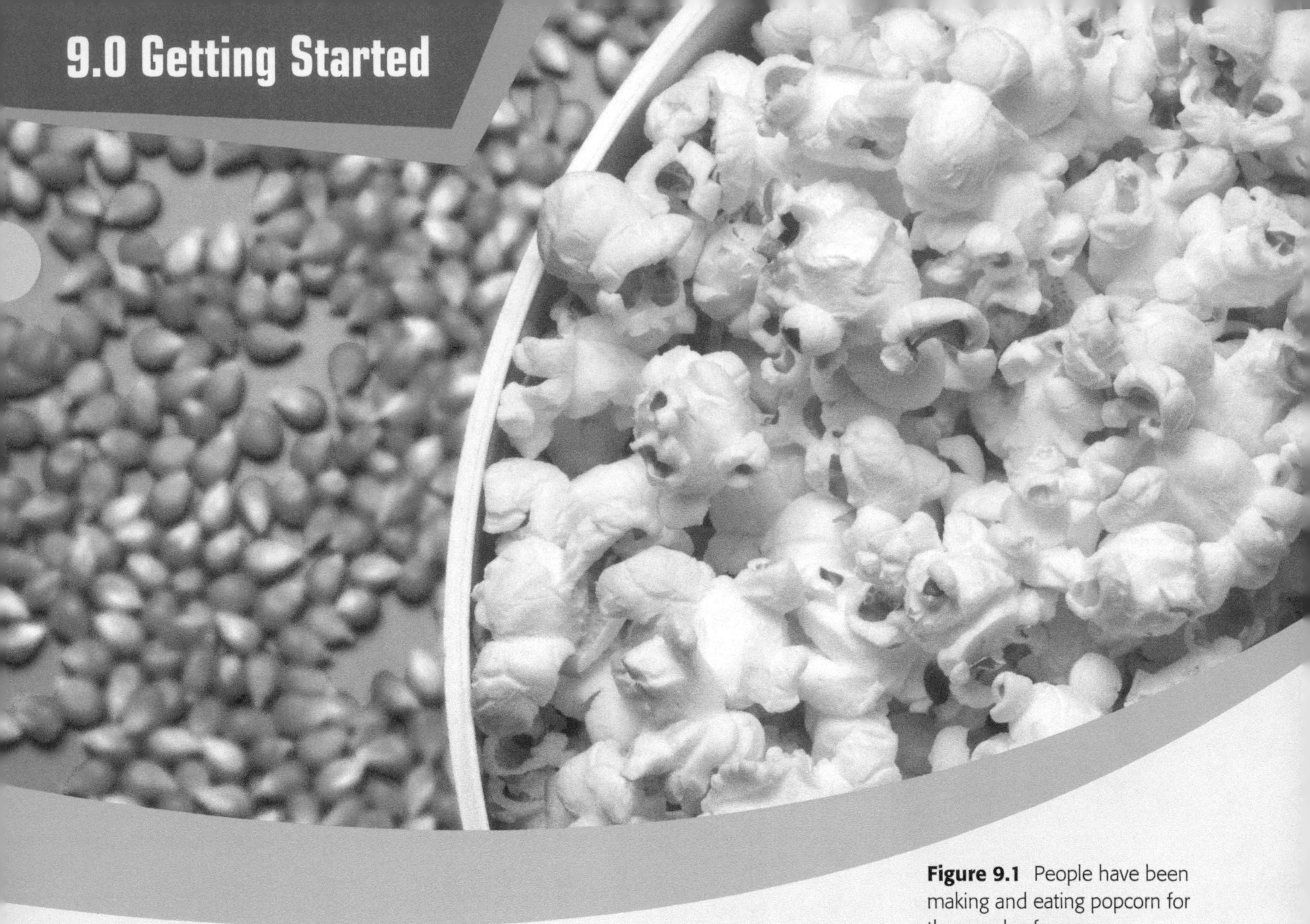

Figure 9.1 People have been making and eating popcorn for thousands of years.

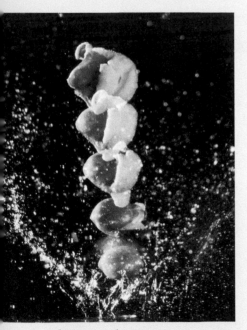

Figure 9.2 The steam escapes as the popcorn kernel pops.

Water, the most common liquid fluid on Earth, is the secret to making good popcorn. Each kernel of popcorn contains a small amount of water, stored in the soft, white starch. A hard casing surrounds the whole kernel. When the kernel of popcorn is heated, the water turns to steam. Since steam is a gas, it occupies more space than the liquid water. The result is that pressure is created inside the hard outer shell of the kernel of popcorn. Finally, when the pressure created inside by the steam is too great to contain, the kernel explodes. The steam escapes, and the kernel is turned inside out.

Have you noticed that some kernels do not pop? If the hard casing of the kernel has a small crack or hole, the steam is released while it is heated, so the pressure is not allowed to increase. Also, if the kernel is allowed to "dry out" before it is popped, there will not be enough water inside to make the steam to create the needed pressure. Popcorn kernels pop well only if their moisture content is between 11 and 14 percent. You should keep popcorn kernels in a sealed container so that they retain their water content.

C28 *Quick Lab*

Soap Foam

Foam is any substance that is produced when fluid, in the form of gas, becomes trapped in a liquid or a solid. Some materials can become foam when they are heated. This is often due to the expansion of water or air trapped in the material.

Figure 9.3 Examples of foam include whipped cream, shaving cream, and the suds created by a detergent (above).

Purpose

To observe what happens when a fluid expands within another material

Materials & Equipment

- bar of Ivory soap
- paper towel or microwave-safe dish
- microwave oven
- bar of another brand of soap

Procedure

1. Cut off a sample of the Ivory soap of approximately one-quarter of the whole bar. Place this sample on a paper towel or microwave-safe dish in a microwave oven.

2. With the power set to "high," turn on the microwave oven and observe the soap. Depending on the power of your microwave, the soap will reach its maximum volume within 30 to 60 s.

3. Allow the soap to cool for 1 min before touching it.

4. Repeat steps 1 to 3 for a different brand of bar soap.

Questions

5. Did both brands of soap behave the same way when heated in the microwave? Describe the differences in their behaviour.

6. Why did the Ivory soap become a foam when heated in the microwave? **Hint:** Refer to the information about popcorn, above.

7. What would you conclude is different between the two types of soap you tested?

Here is a summary of what you will learn in this section:

• Pascal's law states that when force is applied to an enclosed fluid, the increase in pressure is transmitted equally to all parts of the fluid.

• There are both natural fluid systems and manufactured fluid systems.

• Hydraulic systems are fluid systems that use liquid, such as water or oil, as the enclosed fluid.

• Pneumatic systems are fluid systems that use gas (usually air) as the enclosed fluid.

• Fluids can be transported within a fluid system by pumps and valves.

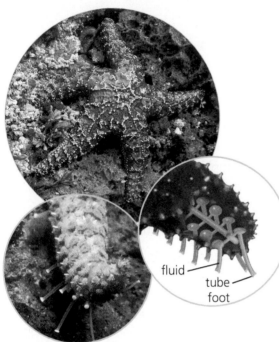

fluid
tube
foot

A **fluid system** is a group of parts, including at least one fluid, that interact with each other and function together as a whole. Natural fluid systems include our body's circulatory system and respiratory system, the movement of sap in trees, and the movement of sea stars (Figure 9.4). Sea stars have several rows of tube feet with suckers at the ends. Each tube foot contains fluid. The pressure in the fluid changes when a sea star contracts its muscles. These pressure changes allow the sea star to move and gather food by pushing down and pulling up its suckers.

Figure 9.4 A sea star moves by changing the pressure of the fluid in its feet.

C29 Starting Point

Skills P C

Pressure Push

You can observe how pressure is transferred through a liquid.

1. Fill an empty 2-L plastic bottle to the top with water so that no air is allowed in. Screw the cap on tightly.

2. Lay the bottle on its side on a table in front of you. Hold each end of the bottle.

3. Push in with your left thumb at one end of the bottle. Hold your thumb in, and push in with your right thumb at the other end. What do you notice?

4. Repeat step 3 using two different positions on the bottle.

5. Each time you push in with your right thumb, what happens to the water pressure? How do you know?

Pascal's Law

An important breakthrough in our understanding of fluids occurred in the mid-1600s. The French mathematician, philosopher, and physicist Blaise Pascal (Figure 9.5) investigated what happens when a force is applied to a fluid in a closed system. After many experiments, a law was developed to describe his and others' observations. **Pascal's law** states that when force is applied to an enclosed fluid, the increase in pressure is transmitted equally to all parts of the fluid (Figure 9.6).

Figure 9.5 Blaise Pascal, 1623–1662

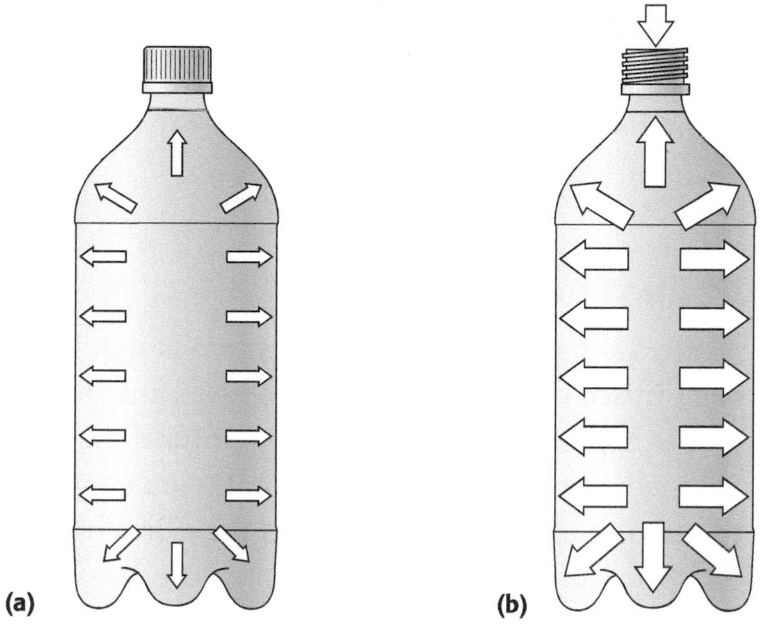

(a)

(b)

Figure 9.6 The fluid in the bottle exerts pressure in all directions (a). When the stopper is pushed farther into the bottle, the pressure increases everywhere in the fluid (b).

You have observed Pascal's law in effect if you have squeezed the end of a toothpaste tube and watched the fluid pushed out of the opening. If you have pressed on one end of an air mattress to push the air out of the opening at the other end, you have again seen the effect that Pascal's law describes.

Keeping in the Pressure

What would happen if a hole was cut into the side of the bottle in Figure 9.6(b), above? When you pushed down on the cork, the increased pressure would force the water out through the hole. For a fluid system to function properly, the entire system must be completely sealed. Even the smallest hole or leak can cause the system to fail.

Hydraulic Systems

Hydraulic systems are systems that use a liquid under pressure to transmit a force and do work. Some examples of hydraulic systems are shown in Figure 9.7.

Figure 9.7(a) Hydraulic systems are used to move materials, such as rock, soil, and scrap metal.

Figure 9.7(b) Rescue workers use hydraulic systems in the Jaws of Life® to free people trapped in vehicles.

Liquids Cannot Be Compressed

One of the useful properties of hydraulic systems is that liquids cannot be compressed by ordinary means. This means that when pressure is applied to a liquid in a pipe or tube, the force can be transmitted over a distance. For example, you could have a long hose connected to a water tap at the side of the building. When you turn on the water, the pressure is transmitted along the hose and forces water out at the other end of the hose. This property is useful for moving fluids over long distances, such as transporting water or oil in pipelines.

Multiplying the Force

Another benefit of hydraulic systems is that they can multiply the force exerted by a liquid. Figure 9.8, on the next page, shows a fluid system called a hoist. A **hoist** uses two pistons of different sizes to create pressure to lift a vehicle. A **piston** is a disk that moves inside a cylinder. The small piston is the input piston, which pushes down on the liquid to create pressure. This pressure is then transmitted through the liquid, where it pushes up on the large piston. The large piston is the output piston.

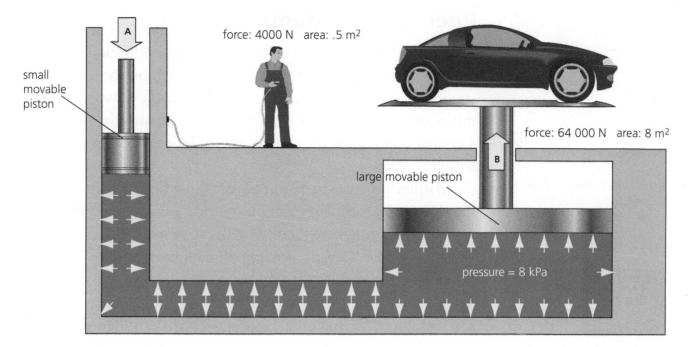

force: 4000 N   area: .5 m²

small movable piston

force: 64 000 N   area: 8 m²

large movable piston

pressure = 8 kPa

Figure 9.8 Hoists are used in repair garages so that mechanics can work under cars more easily.

The arrows in the liquid in Figure 9.8, indicate the pressure transmitted throughout the system. The pressure is the same everywhere in the system.

You can see in Figure 9.8 that the output piston has a much larger area than the input piston does. The area of the output piston in this example is 16 times larger than the area of the input piston. The result is an output force 16 times greater than the input force — a force large enough to lift a car. In order to move the large piston, the small piston must move much farther than the large piston does.

C30 *During Writing*

Thinking Literacy

Using a Venn Diagram to Compare and Contrast

As writers research their topics, they often record information in a graphic organizer. You have just been reading about hydraulic systems and will read next about pneumatic systems. Use a Venn diagram to show the similarities and differences between these two systems. You will use this research later to write a compare and contrast paragraph.

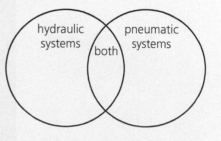

hydraulic systems | both | pneumatic systems

Figure 9.9 Compressed air drives the mechanism that makes the dentist's drill spin.

Pneumatic Systems

Imagine a visit to your dentist's office. You sink back into the chair, and your dentist presses a pedal to turn on the drill. Do you picture that the drill is electric? Actually, it uses something much safer as its fuel: air (Figure 9.9). A **pneumatic system** is a system that uses a gas, usually air, under pressure to transmit a force.

In order for a gas to be put to work in a fluid system, it must first be compressed. For example, natural gas is compressed and transported through a system of pipes to reach the furnace or stove in a home. Two advantages of pneumatic systems are safety and reasonable cost. Compressed air is safe to use, as the devices do not create sparks within the system. You can see some examples of pneumatic systems at work in Figure 9.10.

Another advantage of pneumatic systems is that they are more reliable over a larger temperature range than are hydraulic systems. This is an important consideration in designing bus doors and ramps for use in Canadian winters.

Figure 9.10(a) A pneumatic nail gun uses compressed air to drive nails into wood.

Figure 9.10(b) A mechanic uses a pneumatic wrench to change a tire.

Figure 9.10(c) Bus ramps and bus doors operate using changes of pressure in pneumatic systems.

Air under Pressure

People are able to dive deep below the surface of oceans and lakes because of the invention of a familiar pneumatic system — scuba. Scuba gear includes an air tank filled with compressed air and a regulator to maintain the flow of air.

Another fluid-based technology helps a scuba diver deal with the stress of making a deep dive. At greater water pressures, nitrogen gas dissolves in the blood and tissues at a much higher concentration than normal. When a scuba diver ascends slowly to the surface, the extra gas leaves the body gradually as the water pressure decreases.

However, a problem arises when a diver ascends too quickly. The sudden change in pressure causes the nitrogen gas to bubble out of the blood and tissues, a condition known as "the bends" or decompression sickness. These bubbles can collect in other body parts and cause considerable pain or even death.

One treatment for decompression sickness is to place the affected diver in a hyperbaric chamber (Figure 9.11). This chamber increases the pressure surrounding the diver's body. The greater pressure forces the gas bubbles to redissolve into the blood and tissues. When the pressure in the chamber is slowly decreased back to normal, the gas slowly leaves the body.

WORDS MATTER

Scuba stands for self-contained underwater breathing apparatus.

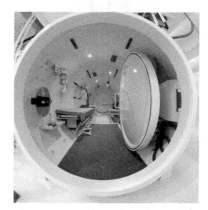

Figure 9.11 A hyperbaric chamber.

Suggested Activities

C32 Decision-Making Analysis on page 248
C33 Problem-Solving Activity on page 249

Pumps

Suppose you want to add air to a basketball or filter the water in your aquarium (Figure 9.12). What would you use to move the fluid in each case? For both examples, you may have thought that a pump would be the solution.

Most fluid systems include the movement of fluids from one location to another. A **pump** is a device that moves a fluid through or into something. For example, your heart pumps blood to your lungs for oxygen and then pumps the blood through your body.

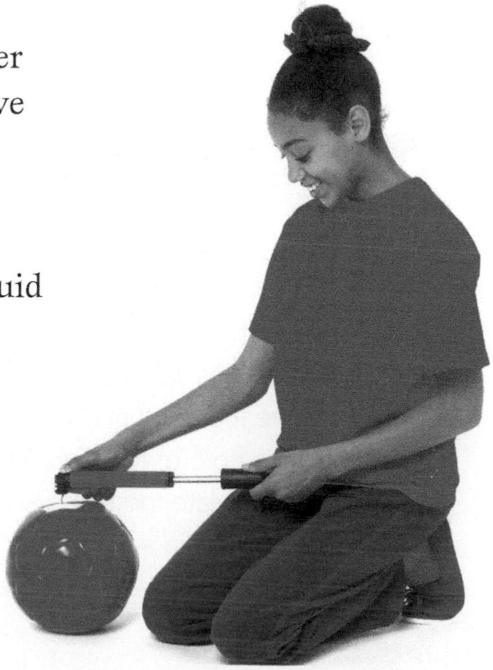

Figure 9.12 A pump moves air into the ball.

Figure 9.13 When force is applied to the air in the cylinder, the pressure increases.

The Bicycle Pump

A bicycle pump has a piston that moves up and down in a cylinder (Figure 9.13). When you pull up the piston, air fills the cylinder. By pushing down on the piston, you apply a force to the air in the cylinder. This compresses the air. The pressure of the air in the pump therefore increases. If the opening at the bottom of the cylinder is connected to an area of lower pressure, the air will move to that area. For example, the area of lower pressure could be a flat bicycle tire or an uninflated soccer ball.

The Archimedes Screw Pump

Some pumps can raise water from a lower elevation to a higher elevation (Figure 9.14). Other pumps can force air into a bicycle tire or oil through a car's engine. Although there are many different types of pumps, they work in a similar way, by creating areas of high and low pressure.

Figure 9.14 One of the earliest uses for the Archimedes screw pump was to remove water from the hold of a ship.

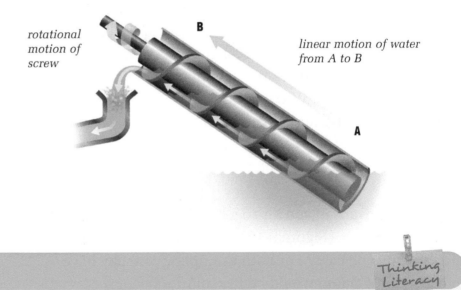

rotational motion of screw

B

linear motion of water from A to B

A

C31 *During Writing*

Thinking Literacy

Talk Time — A Rehearsal for Writing

Share your Venn diagram on hydraulic and pneumatic systems with a partner. Take turns explaining one feature that is common to both systems. Make note of the "linking" words your partner uses to relate the two systems to each other. Record these in a T-chart as "Comparison Signal Words." Now explain a difference between both systems. What "linking" words did you use? Record these in your chart as "Contrast Signal Words."

You can now use the information in your Venn diagram and the T-chart above to help you write a paragraph comparing and contrasting hydraulic systems and pneumatic systems.

Valves

Valves are devices that control the flow of fluids. For example, valves also control the amount of water flowing through a faucet. Turning a tap one way allows water to flow out. Turning a tap the other way closes off the flow of water. There are also valves in your body, such as in your heart and blood vessels. Many veins in your body contain one-way valves that ensure that your blood flows in the correct direction (Figure 9.15).

Valves can also be used to control the water level in the toilet tank (Figure 9.16). The float in the toilet tank is connected to a valve that closes off the flow of water when the water reaches the right level. That is why your toilet tank does not overflow when you flush the toilet. Two other valves are shown in Figures 9.17 and 9.18.

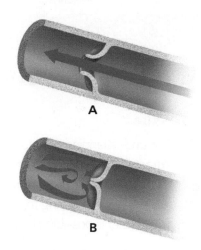

Figure 9.15 The flaps of the valve stay open when the blood flows in the correct direction (A). The flaps close if the blood flows backward (B).

Figure 9.16 When a toilet tank refills with water, the float eventually rises high enough to turn the valve off.

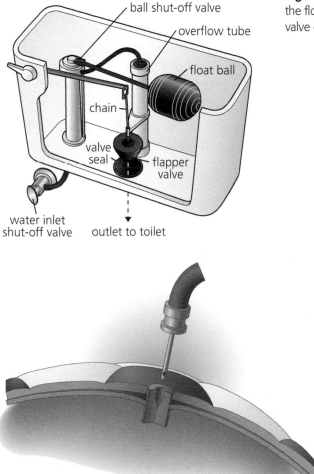

ball shut-off valve
overflow tube
float ball
chain
valve seal
flapper valve
water inlet shut-off valve
outlet to toilet

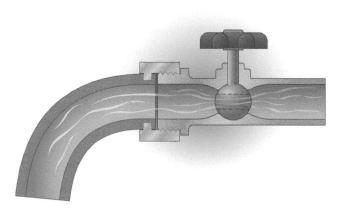

Figure 9.17 A ball valve works by turning. Turned on, it allows water to flow through. Turned off, it stops the flow. This ball valve is in the faucet.

Figure 9.18 This type of valve allows you to inflate a ball, but it also keeps air from leaking out. To open the valve, you insert a hollow pin. You inflate the ball by pumping air through the pin. You deflate the ball by allowing air to escape through the pin.

Take It Further

Doctors and engineers have been working for many years to develop artificial hearts that will help save lives. Find out how valves and pumps are being used in this technology. Visit ScienceSource.

The "Cost" of Extracting Oil

Issue

Our understanding of fluid technology allows us to extract oil from Earth's crust. We use this oil to heat our homes, run our factories, and fuel our cars. However, burning this oil has caused air pollution and possible climate change.

Background Information

Most of the crude oil that is extracted from Earth is located more than 1.5 km below the surface. Our scientific understanding of the properties of fluids combined with the technology of building pumps allows us to bring this oil to the surface (Figure 9.19). Without the use of science and technology, this oil would not be accessible to human needs.

Currently, Canada uses approximately 2 million barrels of oil each day. The world consumption is 76 million barrels per day. The oil industry provides employment to millions of people world wide. In 2007, Canada's largest growth in employment was in the oil industry.

The consumption of fossil fuels also has a negative impact on our planet. Burning fossil fuels produces huge carbon emissions. These carbon emissions have been linked to the greenhouse effect and global warming. Even when the fuel is not burned, the impact of an oil spill can be devastating.

When you consider the social, economic, and environmental effects of burning oil for a fuel, is it a good choice or a poor choice to pump oil from deep inside Earth's crust?

Your task is to choose the "pro" or "con" side of the following resolution:
Be it resolved that Canada should drastically reduce crude oil exploration, mining, transportation, use, and export.

Figure 9.19 Oil pump

Research the issue, considering the social, economic, and environmental effects of burning oil for fuel. You will present your findings as a debate or in a class presentation. Your teacher will provide more details about how to present your information.

Analyze and Evaluate

1. Go to ScienceSource to begin your search for information.

2. Look in print materials such as magazines, newspapers, and books for information.

3. Summarize the information you find in a short report for presentation to your class or for use in a debate. Be sure to include only information that supports your viewpoint or refutes the opposite view.

C33 *Problem-Solving Activity*   Toolkit **3**

SKILLS YOU WILL USE
- Designing, building, and testing
- Making technical drawings

Golf Ball Loader

Recognize a Need

A hydraulic device or a pneumatic device is often used to lift heavy objects. Some systems involve the use of more than one hydraulic system or pneumatic system. For example, when an excavator moves dirt into a dump truck, one set of hydraulics lifts the soil into the bucket and another set of hydraulics is used to dump the soil.

Problem

Design and build a hydraulic arm or pneumatic arm that will lift a golf ball vertically a minimum of 15 cm and dump the ball into an empty coffee can.

Materials & Equipment
- syringes
- rubber tubing
- water
- golf ball
- empty coffee can
- wood, nails, glue, etc., as needed

Criteria for Success

- Motion should be produced by hydraulic pressure or pneumatic pressure created by the syringes.
- The golf ball should be lifted a minimum of 15 cm.
- The golf ball should be released into the empty coffee can.

Brainstorm Ideas

1. Working by yourself or in a small group, generate ideas on how you could design your device.

Build a Prototype

2. Create a plan for how you will build your device. Your plan must include a detailed sketch of your device and a list of the equipment you will need.

3. Show your plan to your teacher for approval.

Test and Evaluate

4. Build and test your device.

5. If you make changes to your original plan, make a note of these changes. Explain why you made these changes.

6. Continue to refine your device until it successfully meets the criteria.

Communicate

7. Make a technological drawing of your final design. Be sure to label the parts. Your drawing may be done using media such as poster paper or computer drawing.

8. Present your device to the class. Your presentation should include:
   - an explanation of the function of each part of your device (use your technological drawing to aid in your presentation)
   - any modification you made to your original design (as recorded in your journal)
   - a demonstration of your device accomplishing the task

Key Concept Review

1. What does Pascal's law state?

2. How is a hydraulic system different from a pneumatic system?

3. Explain why liquids are more difficult to compress than gases.

4. How is a force multiplied in a hydraulic system?

5. If the output piston in a car hoist was replaced by a piston of twice the area, what would happen to the output force of this system?

6. What is the purpose of a valve?

Connect Your Understanding

7. Suppose you used a needle to poke two holes in a sealed tube of toothpaste. One hole is near the cap and one hole is near the middle of the tube. You then squeeze the tube at the base. Compare how the toothpaste will leave each needle hole. Explain.

8. Why might a pump be needed in a hydraulic system?

9. Suppose that the oil in a hydraulic hoist is replaced by air. Would the hoist still operate as well? Explain.

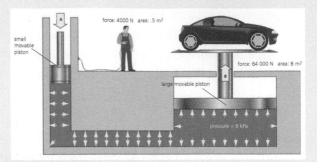

force: 4000 N area: .5 m²
small movable piston
force: 64 000 N area: 8 m²
large movable piston
pressure = 8 kPa

Hoists are used in repair garages so that mechanics can work under cars more easily.

Practise Your Skills

10. Look at the hand bicycle pump shown in Figure 9.13 on page 246 and the valve shown in Figure 9.15 on page 247. How does the particle theory help to explain how a hand bicycle pump and tire valve operate? Draw a labelled diagram to help explain your answer.

For more questions, go to ScienceSource.

C34 *Thinking about Science and Technology*

ST
SE

Transporting Fluid

Our knowledge of fluids has allowed us to transport fluids in a variety of ways. A common way to transport fluid is through a pipeline.

1. With a partner, identify three types of fluids that might travel through pipelines near a larger town or city.

2. Suppose a pipeline did not exist for each of these fluids. Suggest an alternative way in which each of these fluids could be transported.

3. Compare the environmental impact of transporting fluids by pipeline with environmental impact of your alternative methods.

The Impact of Fluid Spills

Here is a summary of what you will learn in this section:

- Fluid spills on water are generally more environmentally damaging than fluid spills on land.
- The majority of fluid spills occur on land and these spills are carried to rivers and oceans by run-off.
- Methods of cleaning up oil spills include booms, skimmers, sorbents, dispersants, burning, and bioremediation.
- Everyone can help to prevent fluid spills.

On March 24, 1989, a tanker called the *Exxon Valdez* struck a reef 20 km off the coast of Alaska and dumped more than 50 million litres of crude oil into the ocean (Figure 9.20). This oil spill is considered to be one of the worst ecological disasters of all time, affecting 1700 km of Alaska's shoreline. Estimates of damage include the deaths of more than 250 000 sea birds, 3000 sea otters, hundreds of seals and bald eagles, and several whales.

The cost of cleaning up the oil spill was more than $2.5 billion. Now, 20 years after the spill, it is estimated that 100 000 L of oil still remains embedded in the sandy shoreline.

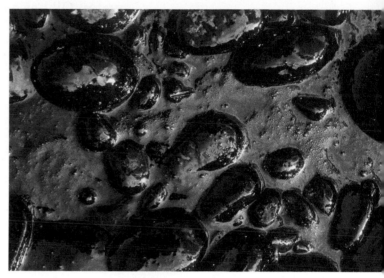

Figure 9.20 Oil from the tanker *Exxon Valdez* coated rocks, plants, birds, and mammals.

C35 *Starting Point*

Skills **I** **C**

Not Every Oil Spill Is the Same

Four months before the *Exxon Valdez* disaster, an oil tanker split in half and caught fire before sinking in the Atlantic Ocean, 1400 km off the coast of Newfoundland. Even though the *Odyssey* spilled more than three times as much oil as the *Exxon Valdez*, the environmental impact of the *Odyssey* spill was much less.

1. Brainstorm factors that might determine the severity of an oil spill.

2. Compare your list with that of another student.

3. Choose what you believe are the three most significant factors.

4. Share the factors in a class discussion.

Oil Spills on Water

Oil is the most common pollutant of water. More than three million tonnes of oil pollute Earth's water systems each year. Oil spills, such as from tankers, account for less than 10% of the total oil pollution. Much of the oil that pollutes water comes from the run-off and wastes from large cities and industries (Figure 9.21).

When oil is added to water, it floats on top, as shown in Figures 9.22 and 9.23. Oil floats because it is less dense than water. Oil has a density of 0.88 g/cm³, whereas fresh water has a density of 1.0 g/cm³. Salt water has a density of 1.02 g/cm³.

The fact that oil floats on water makes the clean-up easier. Could you imagine trying to clean the oil from the bottom of an ocean or lake? Even though the oil floats, if the surface of the water is moving quickly, the oil can "mix" with the water. This is similar to how you need to shake salad dressing in order for the oil and vinegar to mix. On a large body of water, such as an ocean or lake, waves can cause the oil to mix temporarily with the water.

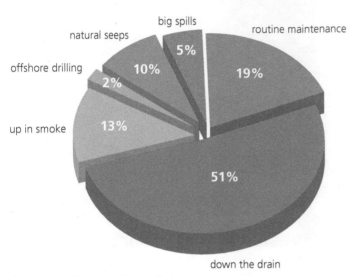

natural seeps
big spills
5%
10%
offshore drilling
2%
routine maintenance
19%
up in smoke
13%
51%
down the drain

Figure 9.21 Sources of oil pollution

Figure 9.22 Oil is less dense than water so it floats.

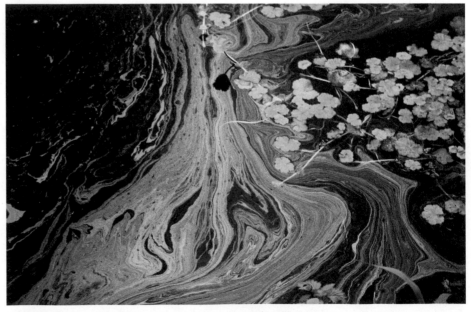

Figure 9.23 You may have seen evidence of an oil spill in water.

The Impact on the Environment

The extent of damage caused by an oil spill depends on many factors, such as the type of oil, the location of the spill, and the size of the spill (Figures 9.24 and 9.25). Waves and wind also have an effect on the amount of environmental damage. Oil spills affect the marine environment as shown in Table 9.1.

Table 9.1 Results of Oil Spills

Cause	Effect
Oil coats the plants living on nearby shorelines.	• The oil blocks the sunlight and prevents gas exchange, causing the plants to die.
Oil breaks into smaller particles and is ingested by zooplankton and small fish.	• The ingested oil becomes part of the marine food chain.
Oil coats the feathers and fur of birds and mammals.	• The oil reduces the insulating ability of the feathers or fur. The animals die of hypothermia. • The animal is much less buoyant in the water. • Oiled feathers make it difficult for birds to fly, find food, or avoid predators. • When the animals try to clean themselves they ingest the oil, which causes kidney damage and digestion problems.

Figure 9.24 A sea bird covered in oil after the *Sea Empress* ran aground near Wales, in February, 1996. This oil spill was one of the largest and most environmentally damaging in European history.

Figure 9.25 Soldiers remove crude oil spilled from the oil tanker *Hebei Spirit* on a beach near Seoul, in South Korea, December 15, 2007.

Clean-up Methods

Suggested Activity • · · · · · · ·
C38 Inquiry Activity on page 258

There are different methods that can be used to clean up oil spills on water (Table 9.2). The choice of which methods to use on a spill depends on factors such as cost, time, and environmental impacts.

Table 9.2 Common Clean-up Methods for Oil Spills on Water

Method	Description	Example
Booms	Oil is easier to clean up if it is contained in one area. Booms are large, floating barriers that act like a fence to contain the oil.	
Skimmers	Skimmers are machines like vacuum cleaners that pull up the oil from the surface of the water. The water must be calm in order for skimmers to be effective.	
Sorbents	Sorbents are large, sponge-like materials that absorb the oil. A problem arises when the oil-soaked sorbents become denser than the water and sink.	
Dispersants	Dispersants are chemicals that act like detergents and break the layer of oil into smaller pieces. The oil remains in the water, where it may continue to be harmful to marine life.	
Burning	Burning the oil can remove over 90 percent of the spill. The spill must be more than 3 mm thick and have happened recently in order for this method to work. Burning is not successful if the winds are strong.	
Bioremediation	Bioremediation involves using bacteria and fungi to break down oil. Nitrates or fertilizers are added to the spill to provide nutrients for quicker growth of the bacteria and fungi.	

Classifying Clean-up Methods

You can classify the methods used to clean up oil spills into three categories: mechanical, chemical, and biological. A mechanical method means that the oil is being physically moved. A chemical method means that the oil is changed into a new substance. In a biological method living organisms are used. Identify the category that each of the six methods belongs to.

Oil Spills on Land

Much of marine oil pollution comes from oil spills that originally occurred on land. In Canada, an average of 12 spills of more than 4000 L are reported every day. An average of 11 of these spills occur on the land (Figure 9.26). Run-off brings this oil into the water system.

The environmental impact of a spill on land is much more localized than that of a spill in water since the spill does not spread as quickly. The methods used to clean up an oil spill on land are similar to those used for an oil spill on water. Barriers are placed around the spill to contain the oil. Sorbents are used to soak up as much oil as possible. As well, the top layer of contaminated soil may be excavated and removed.

Figure 9.26 A major spill of crude oil occurred in Burnaby, British Columbia, on July 24, 2007. An excavator accidentally broke a crude oil pipeline, causing 240 000 L of oil to be released. The spilled oil coated the ground, vehicles, and homes.

Oil Is Not the Only Problem

An oil slick floating on the surface is an obvious clue that the water is contaminated. Many other fluids do not provide such visible clues when they are spilled into the water. In August of 1985, 11 000 L of dry-cleaning fluid (perchloroethylene) spilled into the St. Clair River near Sarnia, Ontario. This chemical has a density greater than water and sank to the bottom of the riverbed. Materials that sink in water are more difficult to clean up than those that float and also pose a greater threat to the marine environment.

Since most of the pollution in our waters is the result of run-off, we must be aware of what we dump on our land. Antifreeze or brake fluid dripping from a car or liquid fertilizer seeping into the farmer's ditch could end up in our water system (Figure 9.27).

Fluid spills have both an economic and an environmental impact. The average cost of cleaning up a fluid spill is between $20 and $200 for every litre spilled. Accidental spills and natural sources account for approximately 30 percent of the pollution entering our water. More than half of the pollution is a result of our day-to-day use of fluids. If we improve our behaviour as citizens, we can improve the health of our environment (Figure 9.28).

Figure 9.27 Even small fluid spills can damage the environment.

Suggested Activity •·········
C37 Decision-Making Analysis on page 257

*Take It **Further***

On June 9, 2005, the Ontario government passed Bill 133, "the spills bill." Find out how Bill 133 helps reduce the amount of spills in Ontario. Begin your search at ScienceSource.

Figure 9.28 Leftover household fluids can be taken to special disposal sites instead of being poured down the drain.

Disposing of Household Fluids

Issue

Every day, households across Ontario pour consumer products down the drain and into the ground. These products have the potential to cause serious damage to the environment. However, these products can be disposed of safely, and some can be recycled. In this activity, you will find out what facilities are available in your community to ensure these products are disposed of or recycled in a manner that does not harm the environment.

Background Information

If you put batteries into the garbage, they eventually end up in a landfill. Over time, the chemicals inside the battery slowly leak out into the environment. This may not seem like a big problem for your three or four batteries, but consider the potential problem. In 2007, Canadians bought 550 million non-rechargeable batteries. Up to 90 percent of these batteries ended up in a landfill.

The improper disposal of various household products such as paints and stains, paint thinners, fertilizers, pesticides, oil filters, antifreeze, non-rechargeable batteries, engine coolant, and propane tanks pose a serious problem for our environment.

Recently, governments have addressed this problem by creating plans to make recycling depots for a variety of consumer products that have a negative impact on the environment. It is expected that with these new depots over 23 000 tonnes of waste material will be recycled rather than placed into the landfill.

An interesting part of this program is that most of the cost for these programs is coming from companies that produce consumer products. You may recall from previous science classes the idea of "cradle to grave" for a product. The recycling of these consumer products is another example of the cradle-to-grave lifespan of a product.

Your task is to find out what your community is doing to recycle consumer wastes that otherwise could potentially harm the environment. After finishing your research, decide on how you will tell people about your findings. This may be a poster, computer-generated presentation or video. Once you have completed the task, be prepared to present your findings to your class and then out to your community.

Analyze and Evaluate

1. Go to ScienceSource to begin your search for information.

2. Look in print materials such as magazines, newspapers, and books for information.

3. Summarize the information you find and create a poster or use another form of media that will educate your classmates and people in your community about what materials can be recycled. Be sure to include only information that can be supported by your research.

Figure 9.29 All of these fluids can be disposed of safely instead of being poured down the drain.

DI Anchor Activity

C38 *Inquiry Activity*

Toolkit 2

SKILLS YOU WILL USE
- Recording and organizing data
- Evaluating procedures

Oil Spill Clean-up

There are various methods for cleaning up oil spills. Some methods allow oil to be recovered, whereas others do not. Some methods are more expensive than others, some are more efficient than others, and some have more of an environmental impact than others (Figure 9.30). Regardless of the method used, cleaning up oil spilled on water is a very time-consuming and difficult task.

In this activity, you will model various methods used for cleaning up an oil spill on water.

Question

Which method is most efficient in cleaning up an oil spill on water?

Materials & Equipment

- 3 containers for the oil-and-water mixture (such as soup bowls)
- graduated cylinder or measuring cup
- water
- vegetable oil
- medicine dropper
- plastic cup
- shredded paper towel
- spoon
- powdered and/or liquid detergent

Hypothesis

Write a hypothesis about which method is the most efficient and why it is the most efficient.

Figure 9.30 The toxins in the detergents used to clean up an oil spill can be more harmful to the environment than the oil.

Procedure

1. Copy the following table into your notebook. Give the table a title.

Table 9.3

Method	Equipment	Observations	Rank
Skimmer	Medicine dropper		
Sorbents	Shredded paper and spoon		
Dispersant	Detergent and spoon		

2. Using the graduated cylinder, add 150 mL of water to each of the three containers.

3. Using the graduated cylinder, measure 20 mL of vegetable oil. Slowly pour the oil into the first container so that the surface of the water is covered. Repeat this process for the other two containers. Clean up any oil or water that you spill.

4. Your task is to clean up the "oil spill" using a skimmer, sorbents, and a dispersant. Try to remove as much oil from the surface of the water as possible. Try to not allow the oil to mix with the water. Observe which method works most quickly and recovers the most oil.

(a) Skimmer – Using the medicine dropper as a vacuum skimmer, collect the oil from the surface of one of your containers. Place the oil you collect in the cup. Continue until you have removed as much oil as possible. Record your observations in the table.

(b) Sorbents – Tear your paper towel into small pieces. Scatter the shredded paper towel onto the surface of the water in your second container. Once the pieces of paper towel have absorbed the oil, use the spoon to remove the paper towel. Place the oil-soaked paper towel in the cup. Continue adding and removing shredded paper towel until you have removed as much oil as possible. Record your observations in the table.

(c) Dispersants – Add a spoonful of detergent to the third container. Then use the spoon to collect the oil. Continue adding detergent and collecting the oil until you have removed as much oil as possible. Record your observations in the table.

5. In your table, rank each method to show which method you think was the most efficient.

Analyzing and Interpreting

6. When you slowly poured the oil onto the water, did it float or sink? Explain your observation in terms of density.

7. Which of the three methods do you think would have the least impact on the environment? Explain.

8. If a strong wind was blowing and the surface of the water was rough, which method do you think would work the best? Explain.

9. Was cleaning up your oil spill more difficult or easier than you thought it would be? Explain.

Skill Builder

10. In science, it is often useful to use numbers or measurements when comparing different methods. Suppose you wanted to take a measurement so that you could compare the three methods. Explain what measurement you would take and how you would change the procedure to collect the measurement.

Forming Conclusions

11. Two factors that determine the efficiency of the clean-up method are how quickly the oil was cleaned up and the amount of oil that was cleaned up. Using these two factors, explain which method you believed was the most efficient.

Key Concept Review

1. Most of the oil that enters our water comes from what source?

2. What scientific concept explains why oil floats on water?

3. Match each of the following clean-up methods to the correct description.

   1. ___ boom
   2. ___ skimmer
   3. ___ sorbents
   4. ___ dispersants
   5. ___ burning
   6. ___ bioremediation

   (a) sponge-like materials that absorb the oil
   (b) using fire to remove the oil
   (c) floating barriers that act like a fence
   (d) chemicals such as detergents
   (e) living organisms that break down the oil
   (f) device that pulls the oil from the surface

4. Choose the method in question 3 that has the least impact on the environment. Explain your answer.

Connect Your Understanding

5. Give three reasons why fluid spills in water are more damaging than fluid spills on land.

6. Explain why a spill of a fluid with a density greater than water might cause more damage than the spill of a fluid that is less dense than water.

Practise Your Skills

7. Oil poured down drains and leaked during routine maintenance accounts for a large proportion of the total oil pollution. Use the graph below to estimate the total volume of oil added to our environment by these two sources.

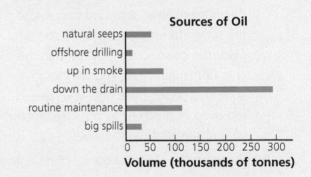

For more questions, go to ScienceSource.

C39 *Thinking about Science and Technology*

S T S E

Searching for the Source of Spills

When an oil tanker spills crude oil, the source of the spill is obvious. However, some spills are more difficult to trace. For example, fluids that leak from cars on highways can eventually wash down sewers and appear in streams and ponds many kilometres from where the spills occurred.

What steps would you recommend that a community take if it was affected by fluid spills that were difficult to trace?

Making Connections

DAILY PLANET

Jay Ingram

Jay Ingram is an experienced science journalist and is the host of *Daily Planet* on Discovery Channel Canada.

Quicksand

Of all the horrible ways to die, surely falling into quicksand and being pulled under would be one of the worst. Well, cheer up! It cannot happen.

Quicksand is sand all right, but it is mixed with water, clay, and salt. Sand makes up about 40 percent of the total. That means it is hazardous stuff. Think of a stack of oranges in a supermarket: the oranges make up about two-thirds of the space of the stack. Imagine trying to remove nearly half of the oranges and still maintain the stack.

It is the clay in quicksand that holds it all together by forming a jelly-like framework — about the consistency of yogurt — around the sand grains. If you were to put just your foot lightly on the quicksand you might be fine, but as soon as you move, the clay liquefies (like stirring the yogurt) and the whole thing collapses. You start to sink because nothing is really holding you up.

The change is pretty dramatic because the viscosity — how much the quicksand resists flowing — practically disappears, and rather than sinking a few millimetres per hour, you drop by a metre per second!

Worse still, you cannot just step back out. The salt ensures that the mix of sand, clay, and salt that holds you in is so finely packed that it would take the same amount of force to pull you out as it would to pull a car out.

So you are really stuck. But the good news is you will not drown, because this mix is twice as buoyant as water. You might sink a little, but you will not sink forever. You will just float there, half in, half out. If you move your legs very, very slowly in circles, water will flow in around your legs and you will gradually rise to the top — and be able to escape.

Figure 9.31 It is much easier to step into quicksand than it is to get back out.

Key Concept Review

1. According to Pascal's law, what happens to the pressure at the top of a container if the pressure at the bottom is increased? *k*

2. State the type of fluid used in:

   (a) a hydraulic system *k*

   (b) a pneumatic system *k*

3. A hydraulic system has a greater output force than input force. How does the area of the output piston compare to the area of the input piston? *k*

4. Give two examples of hydraulic systems that occur in nature. *k*

5. Give two examples of pneumatic systems. *k*

6. State two reasons why a person might choose a pneumatic system rather than a hydraulic system. *a*

7. (a) What are three different pumps you have used?

   (b) What fluid was moved in each case?

8. Valves are used to control both the direction of the flow of fluid and the amount of flow. *k*

   (a) Give an example where a valve controls the direction of flow. *k*

   (b) Give an example of where a valve controls the amount of flow. Use a different example from the one you used in (a). *k*

9. Which fluid pollutes our water the most often? *k*

10. List six methods used to clean up an oil spill on water. *k*

11. What is the average cost of cleaning up an oil spill? *k*

After Writing *Thinking Literacy*

Reflect and Evaluate
Reflect with a partner on the process involved when writing with the Compare and Contrast organizational pattern. What elements are necessary when a writer uses this pattern? Did both you and your partner organize the information in the same way? How does the ability to recognize Compare and Contrast writing help you as a reader? Share your observations with the class.

ACHIEVEMENT CHART CATEGORIES
k Knowledge and understanding *t* Thinking and investigation *c* Communication *a* Application

Connect Your Understanding

12. When you are vacuuming under your bed, a piece of paper gets stuck on the end of the hose. Explain why it takes a large amount of force to remove this piece of paper if the vacuum cleaner is still turned on. ⓐ

13. Suppose an oil spill has occured 50 km off the shore of Lake Ontario. Suggest several reasons why it is important to clean up the oil spill as quickly as possible. ⓣ

14. Suppose you wanted to increase the force that a hoist produces, but you were not able to increase the force that you applied to the small piston. What else could you do? Explain.

15. Identify pumps and fluid control valves and their function in all of the following locations: ⓐ

    (a) your body

    (b) your home or school

    (c) an automobile

Practise Your Skills

16. Draw a diagram of a hydraulic system that could be used to lift a person sitting in a hairdresser's chair. ⓐ

17. Make a sketch of a bicycle pump. Indicate the areas of high and low pressure. Use an arrow to show the direction in which the air flows. ⓐ

Unit Task Link

Pascal's Law states that the pressure applied to any point in a confined fluid is transmitted equally to all parts of the fluid. How does Pascal's Law apply to the pipeline you are testing? Be sure to consider the environmental effect caused by a leak in a "real" pipeline.

C40 Thinking about Science and Technology

Taking Care of Fluids

The photograph at the beginning of this chapter showed a vehicle being cleaned in an automatic car wash. What fluids do you know that are used in cleaning? Create a chart like the one shown below.

Table 9.4 Fluids for Cleaning

Type of Fluid	Function of Fluid	How Can We Prevent Spills?

1. Make a list of all of the types of fluids used in cleaning.

2. Identify the function each fluid performs.

3. Suggest ways to prevent spills so these fluids do not have a negative impact on the environment.

UNIT C Summary

7.0   Fluids are used in technological devices and everyday materials.

KEY CONCEPTS

- Fluids are an important part of many systems.
- The particle theory of matter explains the differences between solids, liquids, and gases.

CHAPTER SUMMARY

- Fluids are substances that can flow. Fluids include liquids and gases.
- Fluids can transport solids, hold other materials, and become solids if they are cooled.
- Matter is made of tiny particles that are always moving, may be attracted to each other, and have spaces between them.

8.0   Viscosity, density, and compressibility are all properties of fluids.

KEY CONCEPTS

- Different fluids have different viscosities.
- Density = $\frac{mass}{volume}$
- Gases are much more compressible than liquids.

CHAPTER SUMMARY

- Viscosity is the resistance of a fluid to flow. Viscosity can change with temperature changes.
- Density is the amount of mass contained in a given volume. In most substances, density decreases when heat is added.
- Archimedes' principle states that the buoyant force on an object is equal to the weight of the fluid displaced by the object.
- Pressure increases with depth in a fluid.

9.0   Many technologies are based on the properties of fluids.

KEY CONCEPTS

- There are both natural fluid systems and manufactured fluid systems.
- Fluid spills have negative impacts on the environment and the animals that live there.

CHAPTER SUMMARY

- Hydraulic systems use a liquid as the enclosed fluid.
- Pneumatic systems use a gas as the enclosed fluid.
- Pumps and valves are used to control the flow of fluid through a system.
- It can be difficult and expensive to clean up fluid spills. Ontario is developing prevention programs to help avoid the damage caused by spills.

Planning a Pipeline

Getting Started

Modern pipelines move enormous volumes of hydrocarbon fluids, such as oil and natural gas, over vast distances. Much of the land that pipelines pass through is remote, ecologically sensitive, and subjected to severe weather conditions. Pipelines are also built close to homes, schools, and businesses. Designers must plan pipelines carefully to avoid the possibility of fluid spills.

Your Goal

To answer the question: how does the variable you identify affect the movement of fluids in a pipeline?

What You Need

- plastic tubing
- 1 or more syringes
- water and/or other liquids as approved by your teacher
- optional: stopwatch, thermometer, hot plate, ice water, etc.

CAUTION: Be careful handling hot liquids.

Steps to Success

1. As a group, decide which variable you will test: distance, temperature of fluid, resistance (number of bends in pipeline), or type (density) of fluid.

2. Make a hypothesis about how your variable will affect the flow of a fluid through your pipeline.

3. Brainstorm design possibilities for building your pipeline, which will be a closed hydraulic system made of plastic tubing and a syringe or syringes.

4. Decide what materials you will need to test your hypothesis.

5. Plan and record your procedure. Think about these questions.

    (a) What evidence are you looking for to support your hypothesis?

    (b) What steps will you follow to collect the data you need?

    (c) How will you make sure the test you are planning is fair?

    (d) How will you record your results?

    (e) How many trials will you make?

    (f) What safety precautions will you need to follow?

    (g) How will you ensure that there are no leaks in your system?

6. Have your teacher approve your plan.

7. Carry out your experiment.

How Did It Go?

8. Compare your results with your hypothesis. Did your results support your hypothesis? If not, what reasons might explain the difference?

9. Share and compare your experimental plan and findings with your classmates' plans and findings. Did anyone plan an experiment exactly like yours? Similar to yours? Completely different from yours? How do your results compare with theirs?

10. Present your findings to the class or in another form suggested by your teacher.

Key Terms Review

1. Create a mind map that illustrates your understanding of the following terms. Ⓚ

   - buoyancy
   - compression
   - density
   - flow rate
   - fluid
   - fluid system
   - friction
   - hoist
   - hydraulic system
   - mass
   - matter
   - particle theory
   - Pascal's law
   - piston
   - pneumatic system
   - pressure
   - pump
   - thermal expansion of matter
   - valve
   - viscosity
   - volume

Key Concept Review

7.0

2. What are three important properties of fluids? Ⓚ

3. Give an example of a technology that uses each property in question 2. Ⓚ

4. Use the particle theory to explain the difference between a liquid and a gas. Ⓚ

5. Use the particle theory to explain an example of thermal expansion. Ⓚ

8.0

6. What is the relationship between viscosity and flow rate? Ⓚ

7. Use the particle theory of matter to describe what happens to the density of a substance when it cools. Ⓚ

8. Draw and label a diagram to explain why a liquid compresses much less than a gas does. Ⓚ

9. In order for water to travel up in a vertical pipe, how does the pressure at the bottom of the pipe compare to the pressure at the top of the pipe? Ⓚ

10. Liquid A floats on top of liquid B. How does the density of liquid A compare to the density of liquid B? Ⓚ

9.0

11. (a) Describe Pascal's law. Ⓚ

    (b) Give one example of its application. Ⓚ

12. When a cut flower is placed in water, the water travels up the stem to the flower. Is this an example of a hydraulic or pneumatic system? Explain. Ⓣ

13. Describe, using the concepts of high pressure and low pressure, how a pump is able to inflate a soccer ball. Ⓚ

14. Explain what is meant by the statement "most water pollution originates on land." Ⓚ

15. Describe three techniques used for cleaning up an oil spill on water. Ⓚ

ACHIEVEMENT CHART CATEGORIES
Ⓚ Knowledge and understanding   Ⓣ Thinking and investigation   Ⓒ Communication   Ⓐ Application

16. What is the average cost to clean up an oil spill, in dollars per litre? ⓚ

Connect Your Understanding

17. Aerosol cans contain a warning not to put them in a fire because they will explode. Describe why the can will explode when heated. Use the following words in your description: gas, particle, expansion, and pressure. ⓣ

18. An inflated balloon is taken from the pool deck to the bottom of the deep end of the pool. What happens to the volume of the balloon? Explain your answer. ⓣ

19. On the coast of British Columbia, a fishing boat loaded with fish sank when it left the ocean and entered the Fraser River. Why do you think this happened? ⓣ

20. How is it possible to lift a heavy car with a small force? ⓚ

21. Suggest reasons why some oil spills on water are more difficult and more costly to clean up than others. ⓣ

22. A woman with a mass of 50 kg who is wearing high-heeled shoes can exert about three times more pressure on a floor than an elephant of 5000 kg. Explain how this could be so. ⓣ

23. A penny will sink in water but float in mercury. Use your understanding of density to explain why this happens. ⓣ

24. Suppose the door of an airplane flying at a high altitude suddenly opened. Would air move into or out of the airplane? Explain. ⓔ

25. List three effects of an oil spill on a marine environment. ⓚ

26. Suggest two ways to help reduce fluid spills. ⓔ

27. Burning can remove over 90 percent of an oil spill. Suggest reasons why burning is not always used as the method to clean up an oil spill. ⓣ

28. What is the relationship between the buoyant force of a liquid and its density? ⓚ

29. Two blocks of wood have the same volume, but Block A is denser than Block B. Explain how this could be so. ⓣ

30. Suppose you filled three of the same-sized balloons with the same amount of water. You used the same amount of force to press on Balloon A with the bottom of a can, on Balloon B with your finger, and on Balloon C with a needle. ⓣ

(a) Which item produced the greatest amount of pressure on a balloon?

(b) If only one of the balloons popped under the pressure, which balloon do you predict it was?

31. (a) Which has a greater flow rate, a milkshake with a temperature of 2°C or a milkshake with a temperature of 6°C? Explain using the particle theory. (k)

    (b) Which milkshake has a greater density? Explain using the particle theory. (k)

32. What fluid technologies can you see being used in these photographs? Describe them in detail. (a)

33. A new pipeline is being built across northern Ontario to bring water to remote communities. Your job is to design a machine that can work year round to lift the heavy pipes and put them in place. Would you design a machine that used a hydraulic system or one that used a pneumatic system? Explain the reasons for your choice. (a)

34. What is one technology described in this unit that you would like to learn more about? Explain. (c)

Practise Your Skills

35. What is the density of olive oil if 20 mL of olive oil has a mass of 18 g? (a)

36. What is the density of the corn syrup if 10 cm³ of corn syrup has a mass of 13 g? (a)

37. Plan an experiment that would test the compressibility of three different fluids. (a)

    (a) What materials do you need?

    (b) What procedure would you use?

    (c) What variables would you need to control?

ACHIEVEMENT CHART CATEGORIES
(k) Knowledge and understanding   (t) Thinking and investigation   (c) Communication   (a) Application

Revisit the Big Ideas

38. Many mechanical systems make use of hydraulics and pneumatics. Analyze two different mechanical systems, stating the purpose(s) of the hydraulic and pneumatic components to the system. *a*

39. (a) State two technological innovations that are based on the properties of fluids.

(b) Suggest a job or industry that uses each technology.

(c) Discuss the environmental impact of using each technology. *a*

40. Suppose you are asked to design a new piece of equipment that uses a fluid to transfer forces. The requirements are that the fluid should travel quickly through a hose but not compress when pressure is applied. Describe the fluid you would choose, using as many of the following terms as possible: "liquid versus gas," "viscosity," "flow rate," and "density." *c*

41. (a) Make of list of natural fluid systems that use water.

(b) Make a list of human-designed technologies that use water.

(c) Suppose that the density of all water on Earth doubled. What effect would the new density have on your list of natural fluid systems?

(d) What effect would the new density have on your list of human-designed technologies? *t*

C41 *Thinking about Science, Technology, Society, and the Environment*   **ST SE**

Pipeline Problems

Pipelines cross our country bringing water and fuel to homes and communities. Usually, the fluids are transported without problems, but sometimes spills can occur.

1. Go to ScienceSource to find out the fluids that travel across Canada in pipelines.

2. For each fluid, identify what environmental problems could be caused by leaks.

3. For each fluid, identify any danger to people if a leak should occur.

4. Who should be responsible for cleaning up a pipeline fluid spill that occurs in a community? Who should have to pay the costs?

D Water Systems

Unit Overview

Fundamental Concepts

In Science and Technology for grades 7 and 8, six fundamental concepts occur throughout. This unit addresses the following three:

- Sustainability and Stewardship
- Systems and Interactions
- Change and Continuity

Big Ideas

As you work through this unit, you will develop a deeper understanding of the following big ideas:

- Water is crucial to life on Earth.
- Water systems influence climate and weather patterns.
- Water is an important resource that needs to be managed sustainably.

Overall Expectations

By the end of this unit, you will be expected to:

1. assess the impact of human activities and technologies on the sustainability of water resources

2. investigate factors that affect local water quality

3. demonstrate an understanding of the characteristics of Earth's water systems and the influence of water systems on a specific region

Water is so valuable that some people have called it "blue gold." This image, taken at Rushing River Provincial Park, near Kenora, Ontario, seems to reflect that idea.

Exploring

Many children in the world must spend so much time getting water for their families that they often have little or no time left to go to school.

Without water, there would be no life. All living things need water to survive. Humans, for example, cannot live for more than a few days without water. We cannot breathe, digest food, or grow without water. Almost two-thirds of our body is composed of water, and we need to drink about 1–2 L of water daily to keep our organs working properly.

Water is also essential to the survival of other animals and plants. Even animals and plants that live in the desert require water to stay alive.

Imagine how your life would change if you had to walk several kilometres a day to fetch water for drinking, cooking, and washing.

Canada's Water Wealth

People cannot drink ocean water because it is too salty. We can drink only fresh water. In Canada, there is no shortage of fresh water. We never have to go far to see or stand beside a river, lake, pond, or wetland. Most of us have clean, potable water piped right into our homes. Potable water is fresh water that is safe and suitable for drinking. It is water that is free of harmful microorganisms and does not have an unpleasant taste, smell, or appearance. In many countries, the supply of potable water is limited.

Limited Supplies of Clean Water in the World

Access to clean drinking water is very limited in many places on Earth. This is especially a concern where the world's largest populations live. China and India, for example, have more than one billion people each. That equals about 35 percent of the world's total population. Those two countries, however, have only about 10 percent of the world's entire freshwater supply.

By comparison, the Great Lakes hold 20 percent of the world's freshwater supply. Yet, less than 1 percent of the world's population uses the lakes as a source of drinking water.

Not having easy access to water affects the way a person lives. Millions of people, most of them in Africa and Asia, must spend several hours each day collecting water for their daily needs. In many cultures, this task is the responsibility of the women and children in a household. They may have to travel as far as 6 km every day to collect one or two heavy containers of water.

As Earth's population continues to grow, so will demand for potable water.

The Great Lakes provide almost 10 million Canadians and more than 30 million Americans with fresh drinking water.

...MORE TO EXPLORE

Taking a Closer Look at Earth's Population

Our world population is expected to reach nine billion by the year 2050. All of these billions of people, along with every other living thing on our planet, are expected to share the same amount of water that we have on Earth right now.

Purpose

To investigate how Earth's population has grown and to compare that with the growth of bacteria

Materials & Equipment

- population data for Earth
- population data for one kind of bacterium
- graph paper
- pencil
- ruler

Procedure

1. Using the population data for Earth that your teacher gives you, draw a graph of Earth's population growth. Plot time on the x-axis and population size on the y-axis.

2. Using the bacteria population data that your teacher gives you, draw a graph of the bacteria population's growth. Plot time on the x-axis and population size on the y-axis.

3. Give both graphs a title.

Questions

4. (a) Describe the shape of the curve for Earth's population.

   (b) Describe the shape of the curve for the bacteria population.

   (c) How are the shapes similar?

5. During what years did most of Earth's population growth happen?

6. The bacteria population data that you were given was for bacteria that were allowed to grow in a test tube. Eventually, the population will die off because they will use up all of the nutrients in the test tube. Suppose that Earth is our "test tube." As a class, discuss how a limited supply of water would affect the growth of Earth's human population.

D2 *Thinking about Science, Technology, Society, and the Environment*

S T S E

Caring for Our Global Water Supply

Not everyone understands how essential potable water is to the survival of living things. You are part of a group that wants to start an awareness campaign about the importance of caring for and respecting our water supply.

Your group is designing a poster that would communicate three key messages to the general public about this issue. What three things do you think your group should say on the poster?

UNIT D

Contents

Unit Task

Clean drinking water may be a human right, but it is not easily available for an estimated 1.1 billion people worldwide. In the Unit Task, you will use a simulation to experience in a small way the effort of having to collect water daily from a community well for your family's needs. You will then analyze the idea that water is more valuable in places where it is less available.

Essential Question

Can the value of clean, safe water be determined in terms of the time and effort needed to gather and store the resource?

Getting Ready to Read

Thinking Literacy

Activating Prior Knowledge

Read the contents list above for this unit. Without looking through the unit, record several facts that you already know about each of the topics. In a separate paragraph, indicate which topics are new to you.

Water on Earth exists in different states and is always moving and changing.

These icebergs, floating in the Atlantic Ocean just offshore from a Newfoundland community, will gradually melt away completely.

What You Will Learn

In this chapter, you will:

- identify the three states of water on Earth
- describe how Earth's water is distributed and how it circulates
- explain what a watershed is
- explain how large water bodies influence weather and climate

Skills You Will Use

In this chapter, you will:

- follow established safety procedures when using apparatus in labs
- use scientific inquiry and research to investigate water on Earth
- use appropriate science and technology vocabulary in oral and written communication

Why This Is Important

Understanding how and where water exists on Earth helps us to understand how water systems affect our lives and how our activities affect water systems.

Before Reading

Thinking Literacy

Determining Importance

Read each statement in the summary box at the start of section 10.1. Write down the key words in your notebook. Next, look for these words in section 10.1. What pattern do you notice about where these key words appear? How does this help you determine what the important concepts are as you read?

Key Terms

- salinity
- water table
- polar icecap
- groundwater zone
- aquifer
- watershed
- heat capacity

Water on Earth exists in different states and is always moving and changing.   **277**

Figure 10.1 Vast amounts of goods are shipped up and down the St. Lawrence River by freighters.

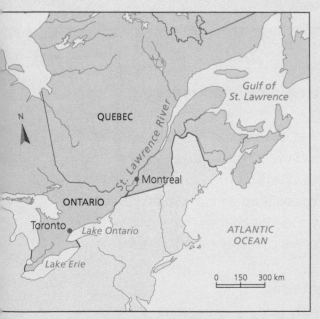

Figure 10.2 Location of the St. Lawrence River

The St. Lawrence River has long been like a highway from the interior of North America to the world (Figure 10.1). It starts in the Great Lakes and flows more than 3000 km to the Atlantic Ocean, passing through Ontario and Quebec (Figure 10.2).

The St. Lawrence has supported human life for thousands of years. First Nations and, much later, European explorers and settlers travelled, hunted, fished, and farmed along the river. Today, millions of people live near the St. Lawrence. Large cities, factories, and industrial areas are located along its edges. Many people still depend on the river and its tributaries for drinking water.

In the 1950s, a series of canals and locks were built along parts of the river so that even large freighters could safely pass between the river and the Great Lakes. Before that, many rapids and shallow areas made the journey treacherous.

All of this human activity has caused high levels of pollution in the river over the past century. Oil spills and the dumping of chemical waste by industries are two major sources of this contamination.

One victim of the river's pollution is the beluga whale (Figure 10.3). Studies have found high levels of toxins in the bodies of these whales. Mercury, lead, and other chemicals are common. Scientists believe that the food the whales are eating, such as eels, is what is being contaminated first. Industrial waste along the Great Lakes and upper part of the river has polluted the eels' habitat, and they are absorbing that waste.

Efforts have been under way for nearly two decades to help the St. Lawrence River's beluga population recover. Solving the pollution problem is a necessary first step.

Figure 10.3 The beluga whales of the St. Lawrence River are suffering the effects of the river's pollution.

D3 *Quick Lab*

Would You Drink It?

It is not just the beluga whale that concerns scientists. A growing number of animal species are at risk from pollutants in our water systems. We know that diluting pollutants in large bodies of water does not solve the pollution problem. In this activity, you will test this for yourself.

Materials & Equipment

- 6 test tubes, each containing 10 mL water
- test tube rack
- 6 rubber stoppers or plastic wrap
- 1 mL cornstarch
- 1-mL dropper pipette
- iodine solution

Procedure

1. Add the cornstarch to the first test tube. Cover the tube with a rubber stopper or plastic wrap and shake well.

2. Before the mixture settles, use the pipette to remove one pipette volume from this test tube and put it into the second test tube. Cover and shake well. Rinse the pipette with clean water.

3. Repeat steps 2 and 3 until all test tubes contain about 1 mL from the tube before it.

4. Add one drop of the iodine solution to each test tube. Record what happens.

Questions

5. Iodine turns purple in the presence of a starch.

   (a) Describe the colour variations in the six tubes.

   (b) Did any test tube show an absence of cornstarch?

6. If you had used a toxic substance instead of cornstarch in your mix, would you drink the water from any of the diluted samples? Explain your answer.

Here is a summary of what you will learn in this section:

- Water exists on Earth in three states – liquid, solid, and gas – and is constantly changing from one state to another in a never-ending cycle.
- About 70 percent of the planet is covered with water, most of which is salt water contained in oceans.
- Fresh water exists on Earth's surface, under its surface, and in its atmosphere.
- A watershed is an area of land in which all water present (lakes, rivers, wetlands, and underground sources) eventually drains into one large main water body.

Earth is a very watery planet. About 70 percent of its surface is covered by water.

As you may recall from previous studies, there are two kinds of water: **salt water** and **fresh water**. If you have ever visited an ocean, you know that the water tastes salty. The reason for this is that the concentration of dissolved salts in ocean water averages 3.5 percent. **Salinity** refers to how much salt is dissolved in water. Fresh water also contains dissolved salts, but in amounts of less than 1 percent.

D4 *Starting Point*

Skills Ⓟ Ⓒ

Water Systems Alphabet

Working with a partner, write the letters of the alphabet in a list in your notebook. Think of a word starting with each letter, that describes a place that water is stored or found naturally. Use the pictures in Figure 10.4 (a) to (c) to get you started. As you work through this chapter, you will be able to add to the list.

(a)   (b)   (c)

Figure 10.4 Start your list by adding the names of these three water objects to it.

It is salt water that fills the world's oceans and makes up 97 percent of the water on the planet (Figure 10.5). Fresh water, the only water we can drink, represents only 3 percent of Earth's total water supply, but even that is not in a state we can easily use. Most of the planet's fresh water occurs as ice and snow or moves through the ground below the surface. Therefore, although water is abundant on Earth, the water that is readily available to use is in much smaller supply.

Figure 10.5 Most of Earth's water lies in its oceans.

Three States of Water

Water exists on Earth in three states: liquid, solid, and gas. You will remember the processes that change water from one state to another. Add enough heat to liquid water and it evaporates, changing into a gas (water vapour). Take enough heat away from liquid water and it freezes into its solid state.

Figure 10.6 shows the distribution of water on Earth.

Liquid Water

Liquid water is found both above and below the ground.

Surface Water

The oceans are massive bodies of surface salt water, with an average depth of 3.2 km. They are often called the planet's water reservoirs.

Surface fresh water is a common sight everywhere in Canada. It is the water in rivers, streams, lakes, ponds, and wetlands (such as marshes and swamps). In many communities, fresh water is also collected in human-made reservoirs such as artificial lakes and water towers. Precipitation (such as rain and snow) helps keep these water bodies filled.

WORDS MATTER

A reservoir is a place for collecting and storing something. The word comes from the French *réserver*, meaning to reserve.

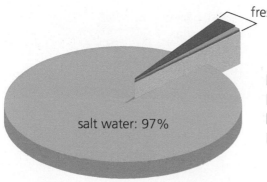

fresh water: 3%

salt water: 97%

Breakdown of fresh water:
- ice: 76%
- ground water: 23%
- lakes, rivers, wetlands: 0.34%
- gaseous water, soil moisture, and other water: 0.66%

Figure 10.6 The distribution of water on Earth

Underground Water

It might be hard to believe, but more of Canada's fresh water exists underground than on the surface. This underground water is called ground water. In fact, scientists estimate that one-third of the world's fresh water lies underground.

As rainwater falls, it soaks into the soil and flows down between the soil particles. Slowly it continues draining downward through more soil and rocks until it reaches a layer that is difficult to permeate (meaning pass through). This may be a layer of rock or a very compact layer of clay. The area where water fills all the air spaces in the soil and in the tiny cracks in the rock is called the **groundwater zone**. This freshwater storage zone exists in all soils, but the depth differs from region to region. The upper surface of the groundwater zone is called the **water table** (Figure 10.7).

Some rock and soil layers in the ground exist in such a way that allows large amounts of water to collect within them naturally. This underground freshwater reservoir is called an **aquifer**. Most rural homes and small farms drill **wells** (long, hollow shafts) down into aquifers to obtain fresh water.

Ground water is always moving slowly out of our sight. Eventually, it reaches a wetland, river, lake, or ocean, or flows to the surface in what is called a natural spring. Where ground water reaches the surface in a desert, an oasis forms.

Suggested Activity •·········
D8 Inquiry Activity on page 288

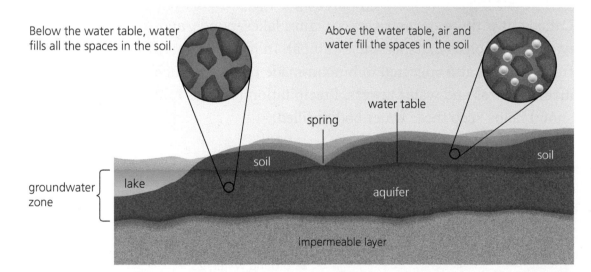

Below the water table, water fills all the spaces in the soil.

Above the water table, air and water fill the spaces in the soil

water table

spring

soil

soil

groundwater zone

lake

aquifer

impermeable layer

Figure 10.7 Fresh water below ground

D5 Learning Checkpoint

Liquid Water

1. What distinguishes salt water from fresh water?

2. How much more salt water is there on Earth than fresh water?

3. What is the upper surface of the groundwater zone called?

Solid Water

All of the solid (frozen) water on Earth is fresh water. Ocean water can freeze, but salt water requires a lower temperature than fresh water does to become ice (Figure 10.8). How much colder depends on the salinity of the water, but an average freezing temperature for ocean water is $-1.8\,°C$. As well, because the salt in salt water does not freeze with the water, all ocean ice becomes frozen fresh water.

In Earth's polar regions and on the tops of its high mountains, most fresh water exists in a solid state as ice and snow. It is estimated that glaciers and ice sheets contain more than 40 million km^3 of frozen fresh water.

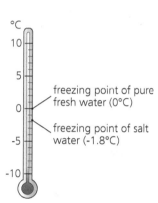

Figure 10.8 Salt water needs a colder temperature than fresh water to freeze.

Mountain Glaciers

In many mountain regions, temperatures are below freezing much of the year and the snow that falls never gets a chance to melt. The snow accumulates over centuries, producing a mass that becomes heavier and thicker. Over time, as the snow in the lower layers becomes more compacted, most of the air spaces are squeezed out. As this happens, the compacted snow begins to change into a solid mass of ice. A **glacier** is a mass of ice and overlying snow that moves slowly down a mountain slope under the influence of gravity (Figure 10.9).

Figure 10.9 The Salmon Glacier in northwestern British Columbia

Ice Sheets

An **ice sheet** is a particularly large glacier that covers the land. Only two of these huge glaciers exist on Earth, one in Greenland and one in Antarctica (Figure 10.10). The term **polar icecap** is sometimes used to refer to these big ice masses at the poles. An ice sheet forms in the same way as a mountain glacier does, but on a much larger scale. The Antarctic ice sheet, for example, has an average thickness of more than 2 km.

Because ice floats, when an ice sheet reaches the ocean, the ice may float on the water. The floating ice is called an ice shelf. Large sections of an ice shelf that break off are called icebergs. As they float, icebergs melt, change shape, roll over, and eventually become part of the ocean water.

Gaseous Water

Water also exists in a gaseous state in the atmosphere. When liquid water evaporates from oceans, lakes, and rivers, it forms water vapour. You cannot see water vapour, but you can feel it as humidity in the air. Warm air can hold more water vapour than cold air, which is why summer can bring such muggy, humid days. As water vapour is carried upwards into the atmosphere, it becomes colder and condenses into droplets of water that form clouds (Figure 10.11).

Plants and animals also put water vapour into the atmosphere (Figure 10.12). Transpiration is the process of water evaporation from plant leaves, and animals exhale water vapour during respiration.

Figure 10.10 View of a portion of the Antarctic ice sheet

Figure 10.11 Clouds are made up of condensed droplets of water vapour.

Figure 10.12 When we exhale in cold air, like these horses, the water vapour in our breath condenses and we can see it.

The Cycling Nature of Water

The water on Earth is always changing state. In the time it will take you to read this paragraph, at least 5 L of every 100 000 L of Earth's total water will have cycled into another state. Somewhere in the world right now, water vapour is freezing into snowflakes, icebergs are melting, and puddles of rainwater are evaporating under the midday sun.

Figure 10.13 shows the processes by which water changes state as it moves from Earth's surface into the atmosphere and back to Earth again. This non-stop circulation is called the water cycle. The Sun provides the thermal energy that drives the whole cycle. Although the water in glaciers may stay frozen for thousands of years, even it will eventually change state and move through the cycle.

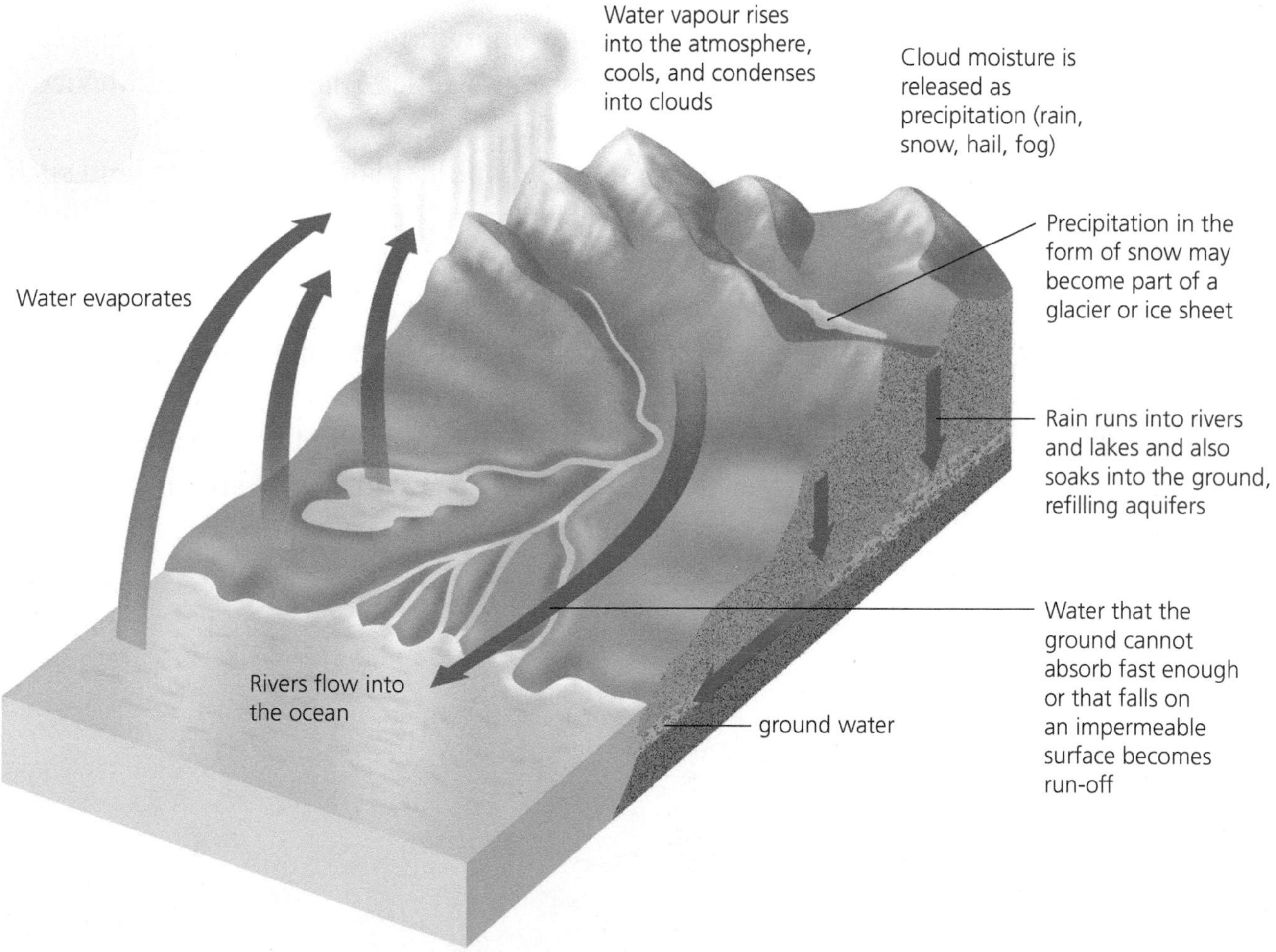

Water vapour rises into the atmosphere, cools, and condenses into clouds

Cloud moisture is released as precipitation (rain, snow, hail, fog)

Precipitation in the form of snow may become part of a glacier or ice sheet

Water evaporates

Rain runs into rivers and lakes and also soaks into the ground, refilling aquifers

Rivers flow into the ocean

ground water

Water that the ground cannot absorb fast enough or that falls on an impermeable surface becomes run-off

Figure 10.13 The water cycle. There is no beginning or ending to the cycle. Any place could be a starting point.

Watersheds

We all live in an area that is part of a water drainage basin known as a watershed. A good way to visualize a watershed is to think about making a small model boat that is unsinkable and could move downstream with a river's current all the way to an ocean. If you put your boat in a river in Jasper, Alberta, it would end up in the Arctic Ocean. If you lived near the Great Lakes, your small vessel would end up in the Atlantic Ocean. If you lived in the southwestern corner of Saskatchewan, your boat would flow south to the Gulf of Mexico.

A **watershed** is an area of land where all the water eventually drains into one main water body, such as a stream, river, wetland, lake, or ocean. Activities that affect water in one part of the watershed therefore have an effect downstream in the watershed.

Many smaller watersheds connect to other larger watersheds and finally empty into an ocean. North America has five ocean watersheds: Arctic, Atlantic, Gulf of Mexico, Hudson Bay, and Pacific (Figure 10.14).

As water cannot flow uphill, high points in the land such as mountain ridges create natural "divides." These are boundaries that direct where water flows. Mountain chains or especially long areas of high land mark the boundaries of major watersheds on the continents. For example, the Rocky Mountains act as a divide and are often referred to as the Great or Continental Divide. If you are west of the Rockies, much of the water flows to the Pacific Ocean. If you are on the east side, it flows to the other main watersheds.

Take It **Further**

Find out about your own watershed and how it connects to others. Begin your research at ScienceSource.

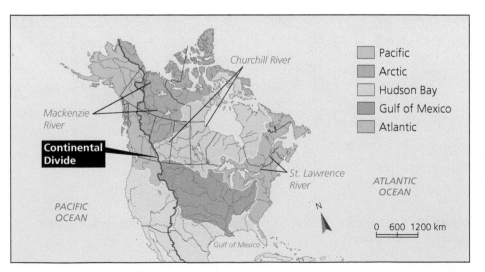

Churchill River

Pacific
Arctic
Hudson Bay
Gulf of Mexico
Atlantic

Mackenzie River

Continental Divide

St. Lawrence River

ATLANTIC OCEAN

PACIFIC OCEAN

N

0   600 1200 km

Gulf of Mexico

Figure 10.14 The five ocean watersheds of Canada. Approximately 60 percent of Canada's fresh water flows north in the Arctic and Hudson Bay watersheds.

The Watershed Connection

Think about the following statement: "Only communities located downstream in a watershed need to be concerned about how the water resources are managed in the watershed." In a paragraph, explain whether you agree or disagree with this statement and give at least two reasons for your opinion.

D7 **Quick Lab**

How Much Fresh Water Is Available for Use?

You have learned that a great deal of Earth's fresh water is stored in its frozen state and is therefore unavailable to use.

Purpose

To find out how much fresh water is available for all living things to use

> ### Materials & Equipment
> - 100-square grid paper
> - pencil crayons or markers
> - ruler

Procedure

1. Draw a border around 100 squares.

2. Using different colours of crayons, colour the squares inside this border as follows.

   (a) Colour 97 squares (97 percent) to represent the salt water on Earth. The remaining three squares (3 percent) represent fresh water on Earth.

   (b) Divide the three freshwater squares into 10 equal sections.

   (c) Colour seven of these sections to represent frozen fresh water.

   (d) Colour two of the sections to represent ground water.

   (e) Colour the last section to represent fresh water available for human consumption.

Questions

3. Describe how the available freshwater portion of your grid compares to the remainder of the coloured areas.

4. Why might Earth's supply of frozen fresh water be considered as a source of drinking water in the future?

5. Why is it important to keep our usable supply of fresh water clean?

Make a Model Aquifer

You have learned that water collects underground naturally in aquifers. In this activity, you will make a model of an aquifer.

Question

How can water become stored underground naturally?

Materials & Equipment

- 1 shallow, rectangular, transparent plastic container
- gravel
- coarse sand
- about 10–12 small rocks
- plastic drinking straw
- measuring cup or graduated cylinder
- tap water

Hypothesis

Examine the materials available to use. Write a hypothesis for your investigation.

Procedure

Part 1 – Making the Aquifer

1. Working in a small group, fill the container about one-quarter full of gravel.

2. Pour sand over the gravel layer until the container is three-quarters full. Smooth it down. Then, at one end of the container, add more sand to build up a hill.

3. At the shallow end of the sand, dig a small hole to the bottom of the container. Pile the rocks in this hole. Stand the straw in the middle of the rocks.

4. Wash your hands after handling the gravel and sand.

Part 2 – Filling the Aquifer

5. Over the next seven days, you will add small amounts of water to the container. Your teacher will give you a table on which to record your actions and observations.

6. On day 1, slowly begin pouring a measured amount of water onto the hilly end of your model. Continue adding water until all the sand on the top layer is uniformly moist. Record how much water you used to do that.

7. Continue adding water until the gravel layer becomes saturated. Record how much water you used and what you observe in the straw.

8. Observe your aquifer daily for the next six days. Add water each day to keep the sand wet, recording the amount on your table.

Analyzing and Interpreting

9. (a) What does the plastic container represent?

   (b) What does the layer of gravel represent?

   (c) What do the pile of rocks and the straw represent?

   (d) Draw a side view of your model. Label your diagram using the following words: water table, ground water, aquifer, well.

Skill Builder

10. Why is it important in this activity to observe your aquifer over several days?

Forming Conclusions

11. (a) Why did you need to add water to your aquifer each day?

   (b) In a paragraph, describe how what happened in your model is like what happens in the real world.

Key Concept Review

1. Give two examples for each state of fresh water: (a) solid, (b) liquid, (c) vapour.

2. Copy the following table into your notebook. Then fill in the blanks for each column, Fresh Water and Salt Water.

Comparing and Contrasting Fresh Water and Salt Water

	Fresh Water	Salt Water
salt concentration		
freezing point		
distribution on Earth		
locations on Earth		

3. (a) What is a watershed?

   (b) What geographical features create natural boundaries for water to flow toward one ocean or another?

Connect Your Understanding

4. Think about the role that trees play in the water cycle. What are two of the ways in which they are part of the cycle?

5. Explain how spraying pesticides on your lawn could affect communities downstream in your watershed.

Practise Your Skills

Below is a map of the main watershed for Sault Ste. Marie, Ontario. Use it and Figure 10.14 on page 286 to answer the following questions.

6. To what main ocean watershed does Sault Ste. Marie, Ontario, belong?

7. Explain what this means for the rivers in the Sault Ste. Marie area.

Sault Ste. Marie Watershed

For more questions, go to ScienceSource.

D9 *Thinking about Science and the Environment*

Canada's Groundwater Mapping Program

The Canadian government is gathering and mapping detailed information about Canada's main aquifers. The maps show where the aquifers are located, how much water each one holds, how they are being used, and other groundwater information.

As a class, think about who would find these maps useful. Discuss ways you think the information on the maps could be put to use.

Here is a summary of what you will learn in this section:

- Water has a higher heat capacity than land or air. As a result, it heats up more slowly than land or air does, but stays warm longer.
- Oceans and large lakes have a moderating effect on the air temperature of coastal areas, keeping these areas warmer in the winter and cooler in the summer than inland areas.
- The interaction of large water surfaces and the atmosphere above can produce severe storms.

If you look at Canada on a globe or world map and move your finger along the 48th line of latitude, two places you touch are Victoria, British Columbia, and Timmins, Ontario. Both are located the same distance from the equator, yet their climates are very different from each other. The average temperature of Timmins ranges from 17°C in July to –18°C in January. That of Victoria ranges from 16°C in July to 5°C in January. Timmins receives an average of 313 cm of snow a year, while Victoria receives only 26 cm of snow.

The main reason for this difference in climate is that Victoria sits next to an enormous body of water, the Pacific Ocean. Timmins is far from any ocean or big lake.

D10 *Starting Point* Skills **P C**

The Water Cycle and Weather

Look at the photographs in Figure 10.15. Discuss with a partner the role the water cycle is playing in creating the weather shown in these scenes.

(a)   (b)

Figure 10.15 What part does the water cycle play in creating the weather shown in photographs (a) and (b)?

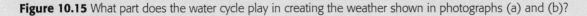

Main Idea or Supporting Detail?

Good readers have several strategies to help them decide what is important in the text they are reading and what is an interesting or supporting detail. Read the statements in the summary box at the start of section 10.2. Which summary statement is talked about in the information on page 290? Use the key words in this summary statement to help you as you reread this information. Record "Important Information" and "Supporting Details" in a T-chart.

Also watch for "signal words" that tell you an important point is about to be made. Record these signal words and phrases in your notes on your T-chart. Then read further to add more of these words and phrases to your list.

Large bodies of water have a moderating effect on atmospheric temperatures and therefore on the climate of the nearby region. This means that the large surface area of the water keeps the region from experiencing very high temperatures in the summer or very low temperatures in the winter compared to areas farther inland.

How Water Moderates Air Temperature

As you may recall from previous studies, Earth is surrounded by an atmosphere made up of a mixture of gases, including water vapour. This atmospheric layer extends for many kilometres above the planet. Heat from the Sun passes through the atmosphere, reaching Earth's surface (Figure 10.16). The amount of energy absorbed at any location depends on what is at the surface.

Figure 10.16 Sun's energy reaching Earth's surface

Heat Capacity

If you have ever swum or dipped your toe into a lake or unheated pool after dark on a summer night, you know how warm the water feels compared to the surrounding air. The reason for this difference is that water has a higher heat capacity than either the air or the land. **Heat capacity** refers to the ability of a material to absorb heat. When testing a material's heat capacity, scientists measure how long the material takes to heat up (absorb heat) and cool down (release heat).

Moderation in Action

Water takes longer than air or land to absorb heat, but it can hold the heat it absorbs longer. In a large water body such as an ocean or lake, this results in an enormous amount of heat being constantly absorbed and released into the atmosphere above it. This moderates the nearby area in two ways.

During the day and in the summer, the land gets hotter than the nearby water does. When the warm air rises, the cooler air from the ocean or a large lake blows in to replace the rising air. The coast area thus maintains a lower temperature than areas farther inland do (Figure 10.17, top).

The opposite happens at night and in the winter. The air over the land cools faster than the air over the water. The warmth from the ocean or lake provides heat to the cooler land (Figure 10.17, bottom).

The land absorbs heat from the Sun more quickly than the water does. The air over the land becomes warmer as some of this absorbed heat is radiated back into the air. The warmer air begins to rise, and the cooler air over the water moves in to take its place.

As the Sun goes down, the land cools off quickly, but the water does not. The water radiates some of its stored heat into the air, and this warmed air begins to rise. The cooled air over the land moves in to take the place of the rising warm air over the water.

Figure 10.17 How a large body of water moderates air temperature on land

Water's Heat Capacity

1. (a) How does a large body of water such as Lake Superior affect the climate of the surrounding land during the nighttime?

   (b) How does it affect the climate during the daytime?

2. Why does water heat up more slowly than soil does?

Water Bodies and Regional Climate

In every part of the world, the presence of large water bodies is a major contributor to climate differences experienced from region to region.

The Great Lakes are also notable for the strong moderating effect they have on the climate of the areas that border them. Their extensive water masses keep both summer and winter temperatures moderate. They also provide large amounts of moisture to the air. In the winter, this moisture eventually falls as snow. The heaviest snowfalls anywhere in Ontario occur in the stretch of land that extends east from Lake Huron and up to Georgian Bay.

Microclimates

Farmers living close to the Great Lakes typically enjoy a much longer frost-free period than farmers living elsewhere in Ontario. The warmer air from the lakes keeps nighttime temperatures on the shore above freezing longer into the fall than in areas further inland.

The Great Lakes are responsible for contributing to small pockets of microclimates in the surrounding regions. A **microclimate** is an area with a small, localized climate variation that differs from the larger climate area around it. These differences in climate can occur over a very small scale. Inside a greenhouse, for example, can be a microclimate that is much warmer and moister than the climate outside (Figure 10.18).

Figure 10.18 Even in the winter, a warm microclimate can be created inside a greenhouse.

Water Bodies and Global Climate

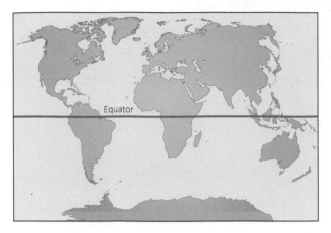

Figure 10.19 The southern hemisphere has more water area than the northern hemisphere does, and this affects climates on a global scale.

In the same way that water bodies affect climate at a regional scale, so their influence is felt at the much larger global scale.

You may have noticed when looking at a globe or map of the world that Earth's continents are not evenly distributed on both hemispheres (Figure 10.19). The northern hemisphere is 39 percent land and 61 percent ocean. The southern hemisphere is 19 percent land and 81 percent ocean.

Because of the greater proportion of water surface south of the equator, the moderating effect on that hemisphere's climate is notably greater than on the northern hemisphere's climate. In the southern hemisphere, annual average temperatures vary by only about 7.3°C from summer to winter. In the northern hemisphere, they differ by about 14.3°C.

Coastal Storms

In August 2005, Hurricane Katrina devastated much of the north-central coast of the Gulf of Mexico (Figure 10.20). Dramatic weather events such as this occur when air moves across large water bodies and picks up moisture and heat.

Hurricanes are a severe type of storm that starts out as a thunderstorm over warm ocean waters. Its air mass begins to swirl rapidly. For such a storm to be categorized as a hurricane, its winds must reach speeds of at least 119 km/h. If the path of a hurricane takes it over land, the result can be extensive destruction and flooding.

Hurricanes and somewhat less severe storms are fairly common in the Maritime provinces. Their after-effects can sometimes be felt inland as far as Ontario. Rarely are they still classified as hurricanes by the time they reach Ontario. Hurricane Hazel was an exception. It hit the Toronto area in October 1954, releasing 214 mm of rain over three days. Extensive flash flooding resulted. More than 20 bridges in the city were destroyed and 81 people were killed.

Figure 10.20 New Orleans, in the U.S. state of Louisiana, suffered the worst damage of any city affected by Hurricane Katrina in 2005.

The Great Lakes are well known for the winter storms they help create. Usually in the late fall each year, cold weather systems sweeping down from Alberta reach the Great Lakes region at about the same time as storm systems moving up from the U.S. Midwest. As both of these systems pass over the lakes, the water and air interactions create high winds and large amounts of precipitation.

Take It Further

Since the mid-1800s, at least 25 Great Lakes storms have been severe enough to capsize boats and freighters and cause much loss of life. Learn more about the long history of storms on the Great Lakes. Begin your research at ScienceSource.

D13 *Quick Lab*

Investigating Climate Data

As you read at the start of this section, the climate in Victoria, British Columbia, is moderated by the Pacific Ocean. Timmins, Ontario, is located inland, away from any large water body.

Purpose

To interpret what annual monthly temperatures indicate about climate

Procedure

1. Use the data in the following table for Timmins and Victoria to answer the questions below.

Table 10.1 Average Monthly Temperatures (°C) for Timmins and Victoria

Month	Timmins	Victoria
January	−18	5
February	−14	6
March	−8	8
April	1	10
May	10	12
June	15	14
July	17	16
August	16	16
September	10	15
October	4	11
November	−4	7
December	−13	5

Questions

2. For each city, calculate the temperature difference between the coldest month and the warmest month.

   (a) Which city has fewer average temperature extremes in a year?

   (b) Explain your answer for (a).

3. How do the average monthly temperatures in Victoria influence the kinds of plants that can live there?

4. In which season is there the greatest difference in temperatures between the two cities?

5. How would your daily life be different if you were living in Victoria in the season you identified in question 4?

Can It Take the Heat?

It is the high heat capacity of water that enables it to affect our climate. In this activity, you will take a closer look at this property of water.

Question

How do equal volumes of water and sand heat up over a 6-h period?

> **CAUTION:** Light sources can get hot. Keep them away from combustible material and your skin.

> ### Materials & Equipment
> - 2 L of water at room temperature
> - 2 L of coarse sand at room temperature
> - 2 identical light sources
> - 2 identical metal or glass pans
> - thermometer

Hypothesis

Write a hypothesis for this inquiry. Begin it with "I think ..."

Procedure

Part 1 — Preparing the Samples

1. Make a table to record your temperature data and give your table a title.

2. Working with a partner or in a small group, prepare the samples *the day before* as described below.

   (a) Measure 2 L each of the water and the sand.

   (b) Spread the sand out in one pan, ensuring that the surface is even.

   (c) Pour the water into the second pan.

   (d) Set up the light sources so that they are placed at the same height above the samples. Do *not* turn them on yet.

Part 2 — Adding Heat

3. First thing in the morning the next day, use the thermometer to take an initial temperature reading of both samples. Record the readings in your table.

4. Turn on the lights over the pans.

5. Take temperature measurements every 30 min for 6 h.

Analyzing and Interpreting

6. Draw a line graph of your temperature measurements. Record both samples on the same graph. Give your graph a title. Label the *x*- and *y*-axes.

7. Compare the graphs for the two samples.

   (a) How are they the same or different?

   (b) How do your results compare with your hypothesis?

8. Why was it necessary to begin this activity with dry sand?

Skill Builder

9. It is important to hold a thermometer at eye level when taking temperature readings. Explain why.

Forming Conclusions

10. (a) Write a statement that summarizes what you have observed in this activity.

    (b) Connect this statement to the real world. How do your results explain microclimates near large bodies of water?

Key Concept Review

1. What is a microclimate?

2. Describe how a large water body can affect the amount of snowfall a region receives in the winter.

Connect Your Understanding

3. The average annual snowfall in Owen Sound, located on Georgian Bay, is about 345 cm. Belleville, located in eastern Ontario, averages 151 cm of snow annually. Explain why these two cities receive such different snowfall amounts.

4. Explain how a microclimate can affect crop production.

Practise Your Skills

5. The following temperature graph shows the annual average monthly temperatures for City A and City B.

Both cities are located at the same latitude. Look at the graph and answer the question below.

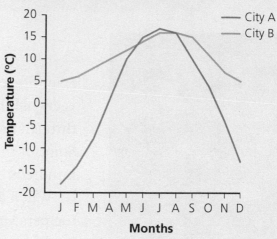

Average Monthly Temperatures for Cities A and B

Which city is more likely situated closer to a large water body than the other city? Give two pieces of evidence from the graph to support your answer.

For more questions, go to ScienceSource.

D15 Thinking about Science and the Environment

Weather in the Media

Weather is a popular topic of conversation. It is so popular that there are media channels dedicated to reporting the weather exclusively.

What to Do

1. List all the ways you receive information about the weather.

2. Working with a partner, discuss the method you rely on most for learning information about the weather.

Consider This

3. Why do you think weather is such an important topic of conversation?

4. What types of media do you think are the most accurate at predicting the weather?

5. Why do you think people are so fascinated by severe weather events?

Here is a summary of what you will learn in this section:

- The global climate has undergone natural periods of cooling and warming since Earth formed.
- When temperatures and precipitation amounts change significantly over time, glaciers and ice sheets are affected, increasing or decreasing in size.
- Changes in the size of glaciers and ice sheets influence local and global water systems.

Figure 10.21 Scraped rock such as this is evidence of glaciation.

Scientific evidence suggests that Earth is more than 4.5 billion years old. During that time, the planet's climate has gone through natural cycles of cooling and warming many times. Some of these periods of cooling or warming have lasted for hundreds of thousands of years.

When a period of global cooling occurs, Earth's temperatures decline, and ice begins to accumulate. This results in glaciers and ice sheets expanding in size. Scientists call these times glacial periods. The last great expansion of ice sheets ended about 10 000 years ago. It affected North America, Europe, and northern Asia. Ice sheets covered almost all of Canada. As the global climate gradually began to warm again, the ice retreated (Figure 10.21).

D16 *Starting Point*   Skills Ⓐ Ⓒ

Predicting the Effects of Water System Changes

Look at the river scene in Figure 10.22. Predict how the scene would change if the river's normal water level became:

(a) 1 m higher 50 years from now

(b) 1 m lower 50 years from now

Figure 10.22 How might this scene change?

When a period of warming occurs, Earth's glaciers and ice sheets begin to disappear. These times are called interglacial periods. Earth is now in an interglacial period that started more than 11 000 years ago.

Factors Affecting Mountain Glaciers and Ice Sheets

You read in Section 10.1 about how glaciers form. Where temperatures on Earth are below freezing, precipitation falls as snow. When snow builds up over time, it creates glaciers. If the cold conditions continue, the glaciers continue to grow larger and spread.

Suggested Activity •·········
D17 Inquiry Activity on page 301

On the other hand, if temperatures begin to rise and annual precipitation patterns change, glaciers start to shrink in size. Warmer temperatures mean that precipitation, even on mountaintops, is likely to fall as rain instead of snow. At the same time, the warmer temperatures cause the existing glaciers to melt. When they begin getting smaller in size, they are said to be receding or retreating (Figure 10.23).

Figure 10.23 A receding glacier

Weather's Effects on Ice

Glaciers frequently go through short periods of shrinking or growing. Such changes are caused by normal seasonal variations in weather. Think of a ski trip or outdoor hockey game that got cancelled in the middle of January because warm, rainy weather melted the snow and ice. Think of a cold snap in May that suddenly brought snow flurries just when you had put away your winter clothes. When unusual weather lasts over several months or years in high mountain areas, it will affect the size of the glaciers there.

Climate's Effects on Ice

In recent decades, glaciers in many parts of the world have been receding at a steady rate. The Arctic ice is also melting in a way that humans have not seen before. Most scientists agree that these changes reflect the warming trend occurring in some parts of the world. One overall trend, for example, is an increase in average nighttime temperatures.

Human activities that put more carbon dioxide and other gases into the atmosphere are thought to be part of the reason for this rise in temperatures. When the concentration of these gases builds up, heat that would normally be reflected back into space from Earth is blocked from doing so. That heat gets trapped right above Earth's surface. This is called the greenhouse effect.

What is not clear to scientists is whether the warming trend is simply a usual variation or the beginning of a longer period of changing climate conditions. The Antarctic ice sheet is not shrinking, but has been growing in recent years. Observations such as this make it difficult to come up with one explanation for any new climate trend.

*Take It **Further***

Find out where the term "greenhouse effect" came from and how it applies to Earth's atmosphere. Begin your research at ScienceSource.

How Ice Changes Affect Water Systems

When mountain glaciers and ice sheets increase in size, it means that even less water is available to be part of the world's oceans, atmosphere, and other water systems. Extreme examples of this occur during ice sheet expansion. Scientists estimate that with nearly a third of the planet covered in thick ice during the last expansion, sea levels on Earth were more than 100 m lower than they are now. Figure 10.24 shows the extent of what was known as the Laurentide ice sheet that once covered Canada.

The opposite happens when glaciers and ice sheets shrink. Their frozen water is released in liquid and gaseous states. The melting glaciers slowly add more fresh water into the streams, rivers, and lakes they empty into. In turn, these bodies of water empty into oceans, adding to the volumes there. The increased amount of fresh water dilutes the seawater, reducing the salinity of the surrounding ocean water.

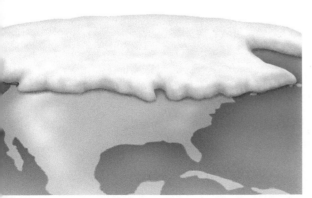

Figure 10.24 About 10 000 years ago, the Laurentide ice sheet covered all of Canada.

Researching a Changing Glacier

Throughout Earth's history, glaciers have gone through a normal cycle of advancing and retreating. Scientists are concerned that the pattern of retreating that has been noticed over the past 100 years may not be part of this normal cyle. In this activity, you will investigate how some of Canada's glaciers have changed.

Question

How have some of Canada's glaciers changed in the past century?

Materials & Equipment

- science section of newspapers
- magazines (for example, *Canadian Geographic*)
- ScienceSource

Procedure

1. Choose a glacier to research from the following list:

   (a) Helm Glacier, Garibaldi Provincial Park, British Columbia

   (b) Illecillewaet Glacier, Glacier National Park, British Columbia

   (c) North Moraine Hill Glacier, Nahanni National Park Reserve, Northwest Territories

   (d) Peyto Glacier, Rocky Mountains, near Calgary, Alberta

2. Find information from two sources on the glacier that you have decided to research. Go to ScienceSource for Internet research.

3. Summarize the information that you have collected in a report.

4. Present your findings to the class.

Analyzing and Interpreting

5. By how much has the front edge of the glacier that you researched changed (advanced or retreated) in the past century?

6. (a) As a glacier retreats, what will happen to the volume of melting water that a mountainous region normally receives?

   (b) How will this affect the mountain streams and rivers downstream?

7. Think back to how a glacier is formed. What factor could contribute to a glacier advancing instead of retreating?

8. The graph below shows the change in the front edge (the "terminus") of two glaciers in 100 years. For each glacier, calculate how much its terminus has changed in that time.

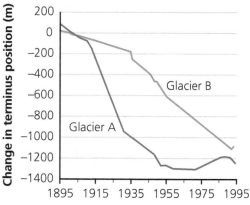

Terminus Position vs. Time

Figure 10.25 Change in the terminus of two glaciers between 1895 and 1995

Skill Builder

9. Why is it important to use more than one source when doing this kind of research?

Forming Conclusions

10. Make a concluding statement about the glacier you have researched.

Key Concept Review

1. Explain what is meant by the term "glacial period."

2. What conditions cause glaciers:
   (a) to grow larger and advance?
   (b) to shrink and recede?

3. What have scientists noticed is happening to Arctic ice in recent decades?

Connect Your Understanding

4. Melting ice sheets increase the volume of water in the oceans and reduce the salinity of the water. How would this affect:
   (a) sea animals in polar regions?
   (b) coastal areas already at sea level?

Practise Your Skills

5. The glacier in the photograph below once covered much of the rock shown in the foreground.

   (a) Describe what has happened to the glacier over time.
   (b) List two events that could have caused this result.

For more questions, go to ScienceSource.

D18 *Thinking about Science and the Environment*

The Unfreezing of the Northwest Passage

The world's shipping traffic travelling west from Europe to Asia goes through the Panama Canal in Central America. For centuries, however, explorers and others have tried to find a much shorter route through the northern Arctic — a route named the Northwest Passage.

Because the area was frozen for much of the year, few countries have challenged Canada's claim to owning the northern waterways. Now, with the recent melting of ice in the Arctic, this is changing. As passageways become free of ice in the summer, some countries are suggesting that the Northwest Passage is an international route that anyone can use. Canada is moving to defend its right to control this territory. What do you think about the issue?

Consider This

1. In what ways would northern communities be affected if the world's shipping companies felt they could travel through the Northwest Passage as though it were an international waterway?

2. How might the environment be affected by increased shipping traffic?

3. If Canada can maintain its sovereignty (right to rule) over the waterways of the north, what are the pros and cons of this position?

Point Pelee: A Great Lakes Microclimate

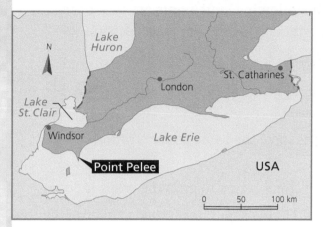

Figure 10.26 Point Pelee National Park is located on Lake Erie.

Where in Canada can you go if you want to see migrating monarch butterflies and dozens of species of birds? The answer is Point Pelee National Park, a 15-km² peninsula that sticks out into Lake Erie. A greater variety of animals and plants lives here than anywhere else in Canada. Some plants, such as the hop tree, native to Mexico, are not found elsewhere in the country.

Point Pelee, sitting almost exactly on the 42nd parallel, is the southern-most point of the Canadian mainland. It is at the same latitude as Rome, Italy. Just as Rome's climate is modified by the presence of the Mediterranean Sea, so Point Pelee's climate is influenced by the presence of the Great Lakes. With an average daily temperature of 8°C, Point Pelee has a warmer climate than other places in North America along the same latitude. The winds blowing from Lake Erie warm the surrounding land in the winter, creating this microclimate.

For many animals and plants, Point Pelee is the northern limit of where they can live.

Questions

1. Explain why Point Pelee is a suitable home to animal and plant species at the northern range of their habitat.

2. What role do the Great Lakes play in influencing the climate of Point Pelee?

3. In a short paragraph, describe what makes Point Pelee unique in Canada. Use the term "microclimate" in your answer.

Figure 10.27 Most of Point Pelee National Park is wetland. A boardwalk protects this fragile marsh and allows visitors to observe the wildlife.

Figure 10.28 Point Pelee is a migration stop for the monarch butterfly.

Key Concept Review

1. Decide whether the following statements are true or false. Give one piece of evidence to support your decision. ⓚ

(a) Most of Canada's fresh water lies below the ground.

(b) Salinity is the term given to the humidity that you feel on a hot, summer day.

(c) Lakes and oceans have the same concentration of salt in them.

(d) The greenhouse effect refers to growing crops indoors.

(e) The Continental Divide separates Canada from the United States.

2. Draw the water cycle for the area that you live in. ⓐ

3. What three things do you do in a typical day that are part of the water cycle? ⓣ

4. Reproduce the following diagram in your notebook. Write a fact about salt water on each spoke that comes out of the centre circle. You may add more spokes to your diagram if necessary. ⓣ

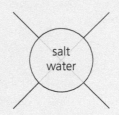

salt water

Connect Your Understanding

5. What human activities can affect a watershed? ⓚ

6. List five ways that ground water could become polluted. ⓣ

7. The Columbia Icefield is located between Banff and Jasper in Alberta. It covers an area of more than 300 km² and has ice that is up to 365 m thick in some places. How can studying this icefield give scientists information on climate patterns? ⓣ

After Reading   Thinking Literacy

Reflect and Evaluate

Work with a partner to list all the strategies you know and have learned that help you determine importance when you are reading informational text. Create a short writing piece in a format of your choice that communicates these strategies to a student new to the intermediate division. Share your writing with the class.

Practise Your Skills

8. The graph below compares the lengths of Canada's longest rivers. Answer the following questions by using the information provided in the graph. ⓐ

    (a) What is the name and length of Canada's longest river?

    (b) The Yukon River is actually 3185 km long. The graph shows its Canadian length. How much of the Yukon River flows in the United States?

    (c) How much longer is the St. Lawrence River than the Ottawa River?

Unit Task Link

You have learned that very little fresh water on Earth is in a usable state. How does this knowledge help you understand the struggles of countries that do not have an adequate supply of fresh water?

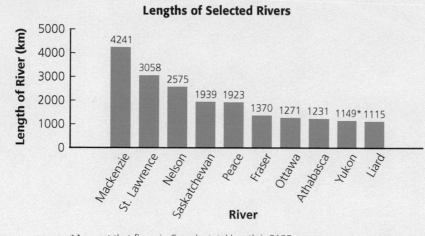

Lengths of Selected Rivers

*Amount that flows in Canada; total length is 3185.

D19 Thinking about Science and the Environment

Predicting Major Storms

Many weather bureaus around the world use a technology called Doppler radar to predict when and where thunderstorms, hurricanes, and other major weather events will occur. An antenna from the radar system sends radio waves out into the atmosphere. The moisture in the air, such as raindrops, snowflakes, hail, and sleet, reflects the radio waves back to the antenna. The strength and frequency of those waves are then converted by a computer into maps. People trained in interpreting these maps are able to see where severe storms are building and in what direction they are moving. This information is passed on to the public in weather forecasts and warnings in the media.

What to Do

With a partner or in a group, discuss and record your ideas in response to the following questions.

1. How has technology such as Doppler weather radar improved the lives of residents located in areas where major storms are common?

2. Is predicting weather all that is needed to ensure people are prepared for coping with severe rain, snow, and wind storms? Explain your answer.

Monitoring water systems is critical for maintaining water supply and quality.

The sedimentation tanks are part of the the wastewater treatment plant in Canadian cities and towns.

What You Will Learn

In this chapter, you will:

- explain how natural events and human activities can change the water table and affect our water supply
- explain the stages involved in processing drinking water and treating waste water
- design and build a water filter and test its efficiency
- analyze a local water issue and develop a plan of action

Skills You Will Use

In this chapter, you will:

- follow established safety procedures when using apparatus
- design, build, and test a water filtration device
- test water samples for a variety of chemical characteristics

Why This Is Important

Regularly monitoring our water systems enables us to ensure that our water is clean and safe to drink now and in the future.

Before Reading

Asking Questions

Science inspires readers to be curious. Think about the title for Chapter 11. Then, use the 5Ws and "How" to turn parts of the title into questions. For each question, indicate whether the answer would require the reader to (1) have a fact or knowledge or (2) form an opinion or make an evaluation.

Key Terms

- chlorine
- recharge
- discharge
- contaminants
- septic tank

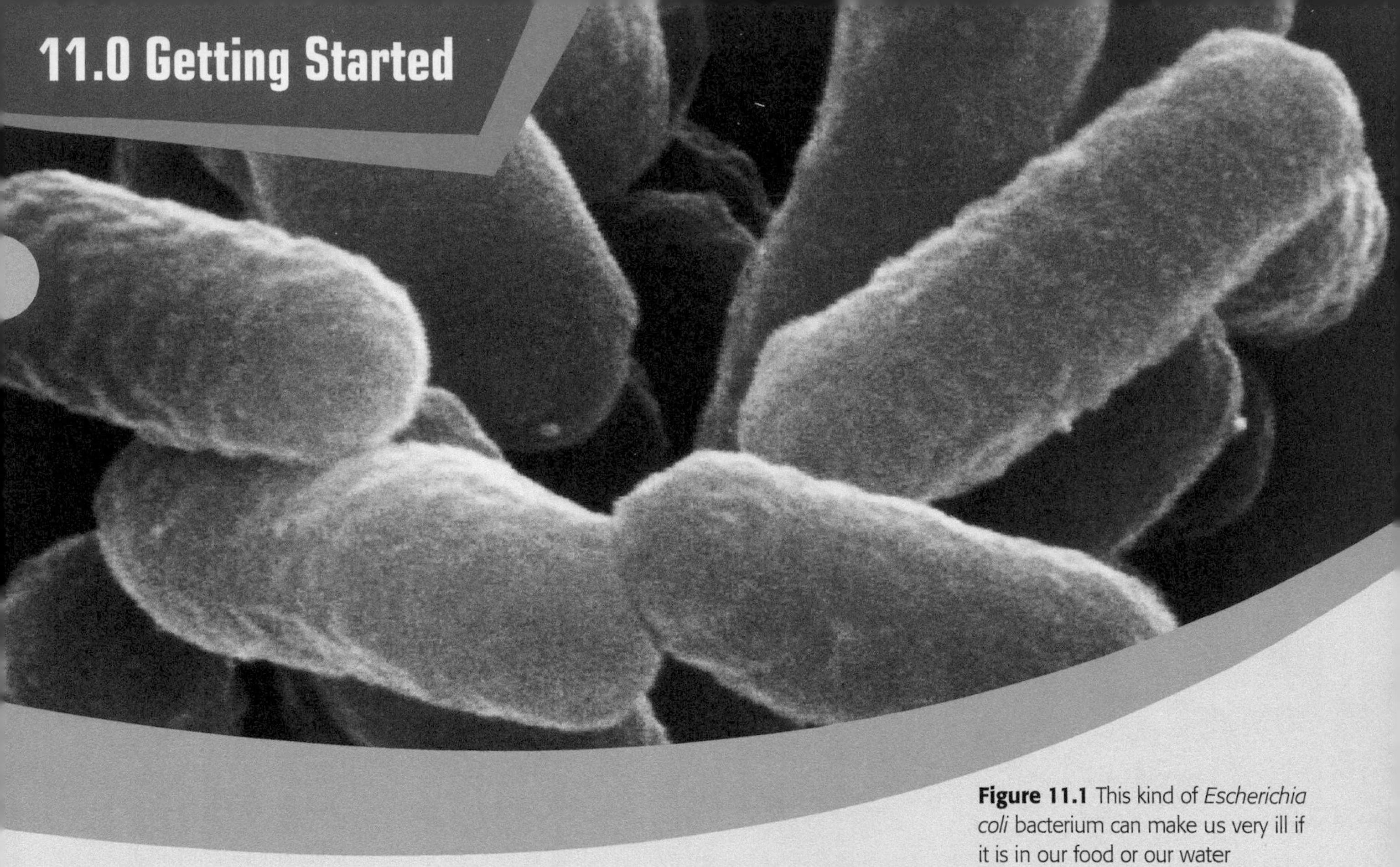

Figure 11.1 This kind of *Escherichia coli* bacterium can make us very ill if it is in our food or our water (magnification of 50 000×).

Figure 11.2 The tragedy in Walkerton, Ontario, reminded everyone about the serious consequences of unsafe drinking water.

You read in Chapter 10 that whatever happens in one part of a watershed can influence its other parts, affecting the health of forests, wildlife, and people. In May 2000, the people of Walkerton, Ontario, learned this first-hand (Figure 11.2).

Walkerton is a rural community of about 5000 people near the city of Owen Sound. Three large wells supply drinking water to the people living there. In the spring of 2000, the drinking water in one of the wells became contaminated because three things happened at the same time.

- A normal farming activity (spreading cow manure on a field as fertilizer) resulted in bacteria seeping into the ground and washing into the well water.

- The amount of chlorine usually added to treat the water in the well was not being monitored. **Chlorine** is a chemical used to disinfect (meaning kill organisms in) water. If enough chlorine had been added to the well water, the bacteria would have been killed.

- Testing and reporting of the well's water quality was not being done properly.

As a result of these three things, the residents of the area who drank this contaminated, improperly chlorinated water became ill. Seven people died and more than 2000 others became ill.

As you may recall from previous studies, bacteria exist all around us. Some can harm humans. The bacterium that contaminated the Walkerton well water is called *Escherichia coli* O157:H7 (Figure 11.1). This is the same bacterium that can be found in uncooked ground beef. There are many, many other kinds of *Escherichia coli* (*E. coli* for short), but not all are harmful. *E. coli* bacteria are found in the intestines of mammals. A lot of them are present in your intestines right now, helping to keep them functioning normally. The O157:H7 kind, however, can make us very ill or even kill us. Cows, on the other hand, are not affected by it. *E. coli* O157:H7 can live in a cow's intestines and a farmer would not know it.

The sad story of Walkerton's contaminated water supply reminds us of the importance of checking to see that our drinking water is safe. Even water that looks clear and clean may contain harmful bacteria and other microorganisms that are invisible except under a microscope. For this reason and many others, it is critical that our water systems be monitored.

D20 *Quick Lab*

Dissecting a Water Filtering Device — Teacher Demonstration

Many people use small purchased water filtering devices in their homes. These are designed to filter out some heavy metals that might get into tap water from old pipes. Your teacher will cut a filter apart so that you can see what is inside.

Materials & Equipment

- 1 water filter
- hacksaw

CAUTION: The hacksaw blade is very sharp. Use the saw with care.

Procedure

1. Watch as your teacher opens up the side of the water filter.

Questions

2. Draw a diagram of the cross-section of the opened water filter.

3. What is the filter capable of removing from the water?

Here is a summary of what you will learn in this section:

- Natural occurrences such as flooding, droughts, and earthquakes can cause changes in the height of the water table.
- Overuse of wells has the potential to alter groundwater supplies permanently.
- How much water we take from our environment and how we alter it before disposing of it can affect both the supply and the quality of water.

Imagine that you have a large rain barrel filled with water. Every time you need to use water outside, it must come from the barrel. That includes watering plants and washing the car. The barrel can only recharge after a rainfall. **Recharge** means refill. Therefore, if you were to use water faster than the supply in the barrel could recharge, you would soon run out.

Like the rain barrel, a watershed receives only a certain amount of water each year. That water recharges above-ground reservoirs, such as rivers and lakes, and underground reservoirs, such as aquifers. Because most of the fresh water in Canada lies below the surface, we need to pay attention to natural and human factors that can affect our groundwater supply.

D21 *Starting Point*   Skills **P** **C**

Nature and the Water Table

Draw a three-column K-W-L chart.

- In the first column, write down three statements that you know about nature's water table. At the top of the column, put K ("What I know").

- In the second column, write down three questions that you would like to have answered about the water table. At the top of the column, put W ("What I want to learn").

- As you are studying this section, fill in the third column with statements describing what you learned about the water table. At the top of the column, put L ("What I learned").

The Rising and Falling Water Table

The rain barrel described earlier is a lot like a watershed. If more water leaves a watershed than enters it, a shortage will result. The usual water levels in lakes and rivers will start to drop. Below ground, the level of the water table will drop as the amount of ground water decreases (Figure 11.3).

On the other hand, if more water fills a watershed than can leave it, a different problem occurs. When it rains, water soaks into the ground, filling up the layers of soil and aquifers. If the rain continues, the top of the water table will rise closer to the ground's surface. In low-lying areas, this means that the water table might reach the surface and lead to flooding (Figure 11.4). Flooding may not only damage property but also cause drinking water to become contaminated. For example, when flooding occurs in saltwater areas, the water table may become contaminated with salt, making it unsuitable for drinking.

Both natural factors and human activities can affect our water supply by changing the water table. The result can be a scarcity of water for consumption or too much water, which can lead to flooding and possibly contamination.

Figure 11.3 The results of a falling water table

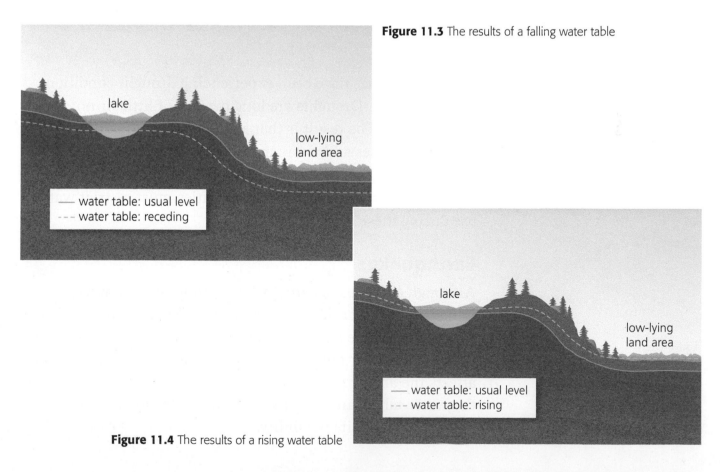

Figure 11.4 The results of a rising water table

Figure 11.5 Many streets and basements filled with water during the 2004 flood in Peterborough, Ontario

Natural Water Table Changes

On July 15, 2004, Peterborough, Ontario, received 200 mm of rain (Figure 11.5). Basements flooded and waste water backed up in pipes. People with drilled wells were told to boil their drinking water. Floods are natural occurrences within a watershed.

As water cycles from water bodies to the atmosphere and back again, water levels naturally rise and fall. Droughts and earthquakes are other natural occurrences that affect water supply.

Flooding

Flooding can be brought on by heavy rainfall, ice-jams, sudden spring thaws, and storms. Flash floods are floods that come without much warning. They are caused by heavy, concentrated rainfall such as the kind you would see during a thunderstorm. The rain flows rapidly across bare ground and paved surfaces, causing the water level in storm drains to rise, overflow, and back up. Surface flooding then occurs.

Drought

Canada's Prairies have been experiencing drought conditions in recent years. Droughts are long periods of little or no precipitation. The result is that a watershed gradually starts to lose water. Lakes and rivers may experience falling water levels. As less ground water collects, the upper surface of the water table gradually drops. Communities must restrict water use during these drought periods.

Earthquakes

Although earthquakes are not that common in central Canada, they can affect the water table directly. In earthquake-prone areas of the world, scientists have noticed a drop in the water table by as much as 1 m after a quake. This affects the ability of wells to draw water. Such a disruption in the water table can also cause ground water to become cloudy, affecting its potability.

Suggested Activity • • • • • • • •
D23 Problem-Solving Activity
on page 315

Your Water Table K-W-L Chart

Referring to the reading that you have just completed on natural water table changes, add two sentences about what you learned to the third column (column L) in your K-W-L chart.

Human Causes of Water Table Changes

Human activities can also affect the water supply. For example, flooding may occur if a dam or other human-made water reservoir collapses. Most often, however, it is our overuse or misuse of water that hurts the supply.

Overuse of Wells

More than 25 percent of Canadians rely on ground water for their water needs. Most of these users live in rural areas. As you read in Chapter 10, wells are drilled into aquifers to obtain the water (Figure 11.6).

The water cycle naturally recharges our groundwater supply. An unusually dry summer or a winter with little snow results in less water sinking into the ground and collecting in aquifers. Because we cannot do anything about a dry cycle in nature, it is important that users of wells be aware of the reduced precipitation and draw less water from the ground. Overuse of wells can deplete underground aquifers, often for long periods.

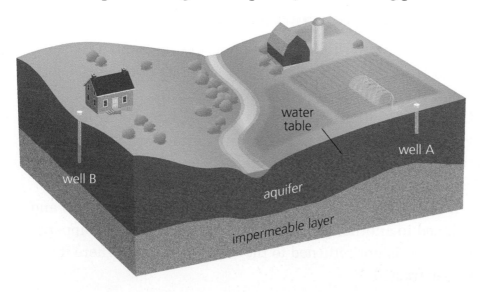

Figure 11.6 This cross-section of ground shows two wells. Well A has run dry because the depth of the water table has fallen below it. Well B is continuing to produce water because the well still reaches the aquifer.

Farming and Industry Practices

Many large-scale farms and industries need immense quantities of water in their operations. That is one reason why many industrial plants are located beside a river or lake. After the water is used, it is discharged back into the environment. **Discharge** means to release or pour out. The used water may be discharged directly into a water body, the atmosphere, a wastewater drainage system, or a ground filtration system. Often, the water that is put back is not as clean as it was when it was taken out of the environment. Also, sometimes less water is put back into the natural system than was removed.

Figure 11.7 Producing electricity in nuclear power plants, such as this one at Pickering, Ontario, uses a great deal of water.

Examples of large-scale water use include crop irrigation, power generation other than hydroelectric (Figure 11.7), and industries such as pulp and paper production and mining. The oil sands development in northern Alberta's Athabasca River basin is of particular concern because of the enormous effect it is having on the supply and quality of fresh water in the region (Figure 11.8).

Figure 11.8 The mining and petroleum industries use large volumes of water. In Alberta's Athabasca River basin, hot water is used to separate the oil from the oil sands deposits.

Water Diversion and Export

The bottled water industry also removes large quantities of water from our water supply. The majority of Canada's bottled water industries are in Ontario, Quebec, and British Columbia. Millions of litres of water are removed from a variety of sources, including springs, municipal water treatment systems, aquifers, and glaciers. If more water is removed than replaced, the height of the water table will be affected. Also, water may be pumped out of one location and shipped to another province or country. When this happens, the water is not returned to the watershed from where it was extracted.

D23 *Problem-Solving Activity*

Toolkit 3

SKILLS YOU WILL USE
- Identifying possible solutions
- Designing, building, and testing

Clearing Muddy Waters

Recognize a Need

Events such as flooding can cause soil to dirty well water. The first step in bringing this water back to a usable condition is to filter out the soil. In this activity, you will design, build, and test a device for filtering soil sediment out of water.

Problem

What is the best way to filter muddy water?

Materials & Equipment

- one 2-L plastic pop bottle
- scissors
- 1 L muddied water (from your teacher)
- coarse, dry sand
- cotton balls
- 2 sheets of paper towel
- approximately 250 mL of pebble-sized gravel

Criteria for Success

Your water filter must:

- allow at least 250 mL of the muddy water to pass through it without clogging up.
- remove enough of the soil particles so that the water that has passed through the filter is noticeably clearer.

Brainstorm Ideas

With a partner, discuss how you might use the materials provided to create a filter. In a design brief, write down all your ideas.

Make a Drawing and Build a Prototype

1. Decide on the best idea for your filter. Make a drawing first of the outside of your filter structure and then of the inside of the filter, showing the layers.

2. Build your water filter.

Test and Evaluate

3. Obtain the sample of muddy water from your teacher. Test your filter by *slowly* pouring the muddy water into the filter.

4. Observe what happens to the water as it passes through the filter layers. Record your observations on your design brief.

5. Suggest one improvement that you could make to the water filter you designed.

Communicate

6. Present your results to the class, including how they met the two design criteria set out.

7. How did the construction of your filter compare with that of other groups in your class? Which group's filter removed more of the soil particles than other filters did? Why?

8. As water moves through the ground layers on Earth, it is naturally filtered. How does your water filter compare with Earth's natural water filter in cleaning our ground water?

9. Think back to what you learned about the Walkerton tragedy at the start of this chapter. Even though you have removed soil from the muddy water, is it safe to drink? Explain your answer.

Figure 11.9 The design materials

Key Concept Review

1. Why does heavy rainfall sometimes result in flooding?

2. (a) Name two large user groups of our freshwater supplies.

   (b) Explain how each group's actions can affect our water supply.

3. Describe two ways in which humans have negatively affected ground water.

Connect Your Understanding

4. A bottled water company wants to set up a plant in your community. What are two concerns that your community might have?

5. Flood water can be contaminated with chemicals, salt, and unsafe levels of microorganisms. Explain why this should be a concern to the people in the community.

Practise Your Skills

The table below contains data on some historical floods in Canada. Use the information to answer question 6.

Date	Location	Cause	Estimated Property Damage (year 2000 dollars)
Sept. 1999	Maritime provinces	Heavy rainfall (Tropical Storm Harvey and Hurricane Gert)	$12.0 million
April 1999	Melita, MB	Flooding of Souris River	$103.0 million
May 1997	Manitoba	Flooding of Red River and Assiniboine River valleys	$815.0 million
July 1996	Québec	Flooding of Saguenay River valley	$1.5 billion
May & June 1974	Québec	Excessive snow melt and higher-than-normal rainfall	$359.0 million
Oct. 1954	Toronto area, ON	Heavy rainfall (Hurricane Hazel)	$1.0 billion

6. Create a graph to display the property damage figures for the flood events shown in the table.

For more questions, go to ScienceSource.

D24 Thinking about Science, Society, and the Environment

Competing for Water Use

Most golf courses require large amounts of water to keep their fairways green. In communities where the supply of fresh water is already at low levels, some groups have argued that using a limited natural resource for a recreational activity should not be allowed. What do you think about this? Should recreational businesses have the same access to water resources as industries, farm operations, and public facilities such as hospitals do?

What to Do

1. Discuss the issue as a class. Make a list of the social, economic, and environmental consequences of both sides of the argument.

2. Think of what actions could be taken to help resolve the concerns on both sides.

Here is a summary of what you will learn in this section:

- Water quality can be affected by physical, biological, or chemical contaminants.
- We obtain the water we need from underground and aboveground sources.
- Water that is removed from our water systems must be treated and tested before it is safe to drink.

You have learned how important having a steady supply of water is to us and to our environment. Just as important is the quality of our water systems, because they provide us with drinking water. Our drinking water must be clean and free from harmful organisms and chemical substances (Figure 11.10). To ensure that it is, we treat it.

We have a responsibility not to take our treated water for granted. More than one billion people in the world do not have access to clean drinking water. Many developing countries cannot afford to build facilities to treat or test drinking water. People wash and drink directly from the same river water where human and animal wastes have been discharged. Illnesses caused by contaminated water kill thousands of people in these countries every year.

Figure 11.10 The water we drink and even the water we play in needs to be clean and free from harmful chemicals and from organisms that can cause disease.

D25 *Starting Point*

Skills A C

How Much Do You Know about Your Drinking Water?

Answer the following questions orally with a partner to determine how much you know about the water you drink.

1. What is the source of the drinking water (for example, the name of a lake or river) in your home?

2. Is your drinking water chlorinated?

3. What water storage facilities (for example, water tower) exist in your community, and where are they located?

(a) *Cryptosporidium parvum* (greatly magnified)

(b) Chemical pesticides

(c) Visible sediment (on the left)

Figure 11.11 Examples of water contaminants: (a) biological, (b) chemical, and (c) physical

Factors Affecting Water Quality

The water that flows into your sink or bathtub has flowed through your local watershed. Therefore, whatever human activities or natural events affect the water systems in your watershed will affect the water that reaches your home.

You might think that a factory 50 km away that discharges harmful chemicals into a nearby river has nothing to do with you or with your community's health. Yet, the factory's actions do affect you because that river is likely part of your watershed. The same is true if home gardeners and golf course operators near you are using harmful chemicals that can seep into the water system. All of these actions are connected to you because they all have the potential to contaminate your community's water supply. **Contaminants** are contents that are harmful to humans, other animals, and the environment.

The contents of water are typically categorized into three types:

- biological: both visible (such as zebra mussels) and microscopic organisms (such as bacteria and viruses)

- chemical: dissolved substances that come from natural processes (such as dissolving limestone) or human activity (such as dissolved road salt)

- physical: all materials that do not dissolve in water (such as animal waste and plant debris)

Not everything that water contains is harmful. Figure 11.11, however, shows examples of contents that are. When water is removed from the environment for drinking, it must be treated and then tested to ensure that contaminants do not harm our health.

Treating Groundwater Sources

For the many Canadians who get their water from a well, the water is usually filtered before drinking to remove contaminants. The water must also be tested regularly to ensure that it is safe to drink. Samples of the water can be sent to laboratories for testing.

Canada has some very large aquifers that supply ground water to industry and municipalities. One such aquifer in the Kitchener-Waterloo area of Ontario provides much of that region's water.

Treating Aboveground Water Sources

We generally cannot drink the water as it exists in our freshwater systems. As you have learned, water in our streams, rivers, and lakes can contain harmful organisms and substances that can be hazardous to our health. The water from aboveground water sources needs to be treated before it becomes drinking water. Boiling water before drinking it will kill harmful organisms, but it will not remove chemical or physical contaminants.

Most Canadians obtain their drinking water from a lake, river, or reservoir. The water is treated and distributed by the town or city where they live so that it is safe to drink. The type and amount of treatment the water receives depends on the condition of the water at its source. Polluted sources require more treatment than cleaner sources. Water treatment is very expensive, however. This is another reason to keep our water supply clean.

The Water Treatment Plant

Imagine standing on a steel floor grid with water churning and bubbling beneath your feet. Behind you is the lake where the water came from. In that lake, at least 0.5 km from shore, is the opening of the intake pipe that brings the water to this building, a water treatment plant (Figure 11.12).

A first stage in the treatment process is to pass the raw water through extremely fine membrane filters to remove contaminants. The filters are so fine that they can remove an organism called *Giardia*, which causes an illness called "beaver fever." *Giardia* is a microscopic parasite often found in the feces of beavers and other animals. If it gets into drinking water, it can make people very ill.

Figure 11.12 Inside a water treatment plant, you would see a complicated system of pipes and controls such as the ones shown here.

Most of us in Canada rely on a water treatment facility such as this to purify our water so that it is safe to drink. Not all cities use the same treatment method. Figure 11.13 shows the basic treatment stages that are typically followed.

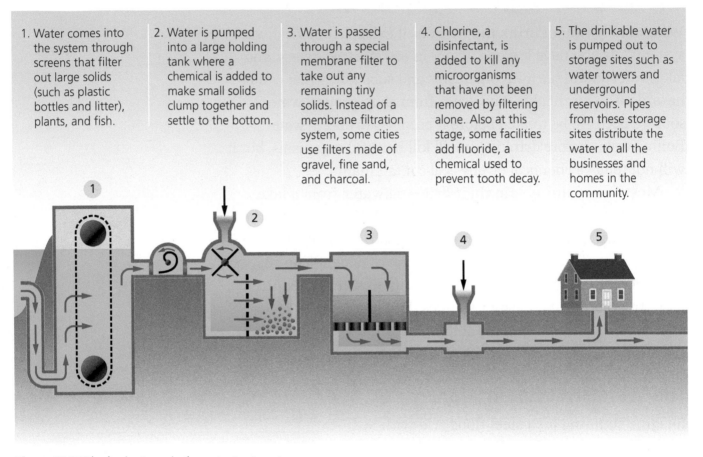

1. Water comes into the system through screens that filter out large solids (such as plastic bottles and litter), plants, and fish.

2. Water is pumped into a large holding tank where a chemical is added to make small solids clump together and settle to the bottom.

3. Water is passed through a special membrane filter to take out any remaining tiny solids. Instead of a membrane filtration system, some cities use filters made of gravel, fine sand, and charcoal.

4. Chlorine, a disinfectant, is added to kill any microorganisms that have not been removed by filtering alone. Also at this stage, some facilities add fluoride, a chemical used to prevent tooth decay.

5. The drinkable water is pumped out to storage sites such as water towers and underground reservoirs. Pipes from these storage sites distribute the water to all the businesses and homes in the community.

Figure 11.13 The basic stages in the water treatment process

Water treatment plants are very sophisticated and expensive facilities. They use a computerized system of checks, rechecks, monitors, and alarms to ensure that no step in the treatment process fails. Samples are tested often to show that everything is working properly and that the finished water does not have harmful concentrations of such things as bacteria and a broad range of chemicals. The people who monitor the system are highly trained to recognize problems immediately.

The Water You Drink

1. Give one reason why it is important to keep our supply of drinking water clean.

2. What causes "beaver fever," and how is water treated to prevent this illness?

3. Why is chlorine sometimes added in the water treatment process?

Testing Water Quality

In past centuries, before technology such as the microscope was invented, no one knew why people could sometimes become ill or die from drinking water. Today, we have the knowledge and the equipment to detect microscopic contaminants even after the water is treated so that we can be sure it is truly safe to use.

Water samples from treatment plants are sent to scientists in laboratories to test. In larger communities, the tests might be done inside the water treatment plant itself. Biological, chemical, and physical tests are performed (Figure 11.14).

Drinking water samples are also taken from sites that receive the processed water, such as hospitals and schools. If an abnormal test result is obtained, the cause is investigated. Sometimes the pipes that transport the water may have caused the problem. Action is always taken immediately to repair any problems found.

In addition to biological testing for the presence of harmful bacteria, our drinking water is tested for harmful chemical substances (such as lead and nitrates) and radioactive matter. Test results are compared with government standards for safe limits. Contamination that is above the acceptable standards means that the water must not be consumed.

Suggested Activity • • • • • • • • •
D27 Inquiry Activity on page 322

Figure 11.14 This microbiologist is analyzing a drinking water sample.

DI Anchor Activity

D27 *Inquiry Activity*

Toolkit 2

SKILLS YOU WILL USE
- Measuring
- Drawing conclusions

Be a Water Quality Inspector

In this activity, you will measure the pH and salt and chlorine content of four sources of water.

Question

Which water sample will have the highest and which will have the lowest values for each test?

Materials & Equipment

- a chart for recording test results
- water-soluble marking pen
- 4 water samples to test, collected in clean 250-mL containers: tap water, rain water, bottled water, and water from a river, stream, or pond
- pH test strips
- clock or watch that reads seconds
- 4 microscope slides
- four 1-mL dropper pipettes
- light source
- 4 test tubes
- silver nitrate (1 percent weight per volume solution) in a dropper bottle ☠

CAUTION: Do not taste any of the water samples. Follow your teacher's instructions for handling and disposing of chemicals.

Hypothesis

Write a separate hypothesis for each of the three tests you will peform. Refer to all four water samples.

Procedure

Part 1 — Measuring pH

1. Put a separate pH test strip into each sample of water for about 10 s. Remove the test strip and wait 1 min.

2. Note the colour change (the pH value) and compare it with the values shown on the test kit. Write the pH value in your chart.

Part 2 — Measuring Salt Content

3. Put a clean pipette into each water sample and leave it there for the remainder of the tests.

4. With the marking pen, label each microscope slide with one of the four water sources. With the pipette, drop 1 mL of each water sample onto its labelled slide. Place the slides under the light until they dry.

5. Examine each slide for salt residue and record your observations.

Part 3 — Measuring Chlorine Content

6. Label each test tube with one of the four water sources. With the pipette, drop 5 mL of each water sample into its labelled test tube.

7. Add four drops of silver nitrate solution to each tube.

8. Examine each tube for a change and record your observations.

Analyzing and Interpreting

9. Compare your test results with your hypotheses. Did any result surprise you? If so, which one?

10. For each water sample, explain the results that you observed for pH, salt, and chlorine.

Skill Builder

11. Why must you add the same amount of silver nitrate to the same amount of each water sample tested?

Forming Conclusions

12. (a) Would you ever expect to find salt in rainwater? Explain your answer.

    (b) What could be a source of salt in a pond water sample?

Key Concept Review

1. Name four sources of drinking water for Canadians.

2. Explain what is meant by the term "water treatment."

3. (a) How are the contents of water categorized?

   (b) When are those contents of concern to scientists who test our drinking water?

Connect Your Understanding

4. You have learned from previous studies of water that it is an excellent solvent. Explain how this property of water contributes to drinking-water contamination.

Practise Your Skills

5. For each item in the list below, indicate whether it should be classified as a biological, chemical, or physical contaminant of a freshwater system. Explain your decision.

   (a) dissolved fertilizer from a riverfront golf course

   (b) spill of gasoline while refuelling a motorboat

   (c) lawn clippings from storm drain run-off

   (d) dog waste washed into the lake from a nearby campsite

   (e) smoke from a smokestack in an industrial plant

   (f) chlorine bleach used in household laundry

For more questions, go to ScienceSource.

D28 *Thinking about Science, Society, and the Environment*

Down the Drain

Many people are unaware of what gets poured down the drains in their home or school. When cleaning products, laundry detergents, medicines, hair dye, and many other products are disposed of in this way, it is easy to think they have just disappeared. This is not the case, of course. The products flow into septic tanks or wastewater pipes. Regardless of treatment, the risk of our water supply becoming contaminated is always a concern.

What to Do

1. For the next week, keep a small notebook in the kitchen of your home. Every day, record all the things that you and other family members wash down the drains in your house. (You do not need to record food items or human waste.)

2. At the end of the week, analyze your results. If you have questions about the contents of certain products, do some research to find answers. Begin at ScienceSource.

3. Propose a plan of action that would enable your family to improve the quality of the water disposed of down the drains in your home.

Here is a summary of what you will learn in this section:

- How we dispose of our waste water affects the quality of our water systems.
- Protecting our water systems is important to maintaining safe drinking water sources.

Figure 11.15 All of the waste water in your home goes into an underground collection system of pipes.

When we turn on a tap to get water, we usually give little thought to where the water is coming from. The same holds true when we flush a toilet. We are fortunate to be able to do this. Most of us in Canada obtain water from a municipal water supply like the one you just read about in section 11.2.

Municipalities also manage the removal of waste water. The sink drains and toilets in urban homes and businesses are connected to a pipe. The pipe joins a large system of underground pipes (Figure 11.15). Pumping stations send all that waste water to a treatment plant, where chemical contaminants and harmful microorganisms are removed. After that, the water is discharged to a nearby stream, river, lake, or ocean.

Treating our waste water is part of an overall plan to manage our water systems and keep them healthy.

D29 *Starting Point*   Skills Ⓐ Ⓒ

How Much Do You Know about Waste Water?

Answer the following questions orally with a partner to determine how much you know about the waste water that leaves your home.

1. Where does the waste water in your home go? If it goes to a treatment plant, where is the plant located?

2. What body of water receives the treated waste water that leaves the plant?

Treating Waste Water

Every day, we get rid of water that we have finished using or that we no longer need. Water is emptied down the drains in our homes and businesses and flushed down the toilet. With it go substances such as soap, food residue, human waste material, rags, and anything else that can accidentally or intentionally get flushed into the system.

If we were to put this waste water directly back into our rivers and lakes, we would be contaminating our drinking water supply and the water used by other animals. We therefore treat our waste water before letting it re-enter the natural environment. Several treatment methods exist. They are described below.

Septic Systems

The rural home that gets its drinking water from a well probably disposes of its waste water in a **septic system**. A septic system is a self-contained wastewater treatment facility. Waste water from all indoor sources such as toilets, sinks, and bathtubs enters the **septic tank**. Immediately, bacteria in the tank begin to break down the waste (Figure 11.16). Solid material settles to the bottom. Lighter materials such as kitchen grease float to the surface. The liquid layer in between flows into pipes that lead out from the tank. This waste water contains organic matter and nutrients such as nitrogen.

The pipes leading from the septic tank are perforated on the bottom. This means they have small holes that allow the water to seep into the soil. Once the water is in the soil, more bacteria digest and break down the organic waste. Eventually the liquid returns to the groundwater supply.

WORDS MATTER

The word septic comes from a Greek word meaning to putrefy (decay).

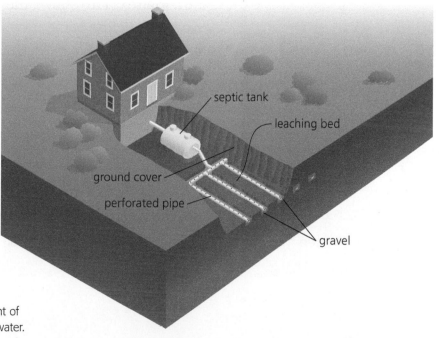

septic tank

leaching bed

ground cover

perforated pipe

gravel

Figure 11.16 A septic system. About 25 percent of Canadians use this method to treat their waste water.

Wetland Technology

A wetland, such as a marsh or swamp, is land that is saturated with water for long periods of time. Water-loving plants that grow in wetlands can filter and purify water. Scientists have combined knowledge of the filtering ability of natural wetlands with human technology to construct wetlands for wastewater treatment. Many smaller communities and businesses use this enhanced natural method. Some of these human-made wetlands even look like natural marshes (Figure 11.17). Just as they do in a natural setting, the plants and microorganisms in a human-designed wetland remove and recycle nutrients. Roots and soil filter out contaminants.

Figure 11.17 Instead of making expensive renovations to enlarge its existing treatment system, the Kortright Conservation Centre in Kleinburg, Ontario, constructed a wetland to treat its waste water.

The Wastewater Treatment Plant

If someone asked you to name the most expensive facility in your community, you might answer that it is the new sports complex and ice arena, or the performing arts centre with the up-to-date acoustics. It is unlikely that either of those answers is correct. The most expensive facility in any community is usually the wastewater treatment plant. It costs millions of dollars to construct. For example, for a city with a population of about 50 000, a wastewater treatment facility may cost over $40 million to build and maintain.

The treatment of our waste water involves the physical plant and the network of underground pipes that gets the waste to the plant. Figure 11.18 shows the route waste water takes from your home before being released back into the natural environment.

D30 *Learning Checkpoint*

Treating Waste Water

1. What is waste water?

2. Why is it not a good idea to put waste water directly back into the environment?

3. Name three methods of wastewater treatment that Canadians use.

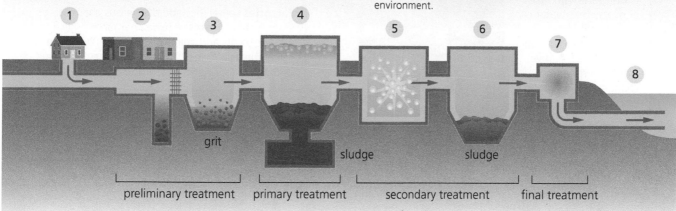

1. Waste water leaves your home through an underground system of pipes. It is pumped to the treatment plant.
2. Waste water passes through screens to remove large particles such as garbage.
3. Waste water enters the grit chamber. Small particles such as sand and coffee grounds settle to the bottom.
4. Waste water passes into a primary treatment tank. Heavy solids settle to the bottom, forming sludge. Material that floats gets skimmed off the top.
5. The grey effluent enters the aeration tank. It contains micro-organisms such as bacteria and protozoa that digest the organic wastes. Oxygen is added to supply the microorganisms with the environment they need.
6. The waste water passes into another settling tank. This time, the microorganisms settle to the bottom as sludge. Some of this sludge is returned to the aeration tank for reuse.
7. Harmful microorganisms can still be in the waste water, so the final treatment is usually disinfection with chlorine. Most of the chlorine is allowed to get used up before Stage 8.
8. Cleaned and treated water is discharged back into the environment.

grit

sludge

sludge

preliminary treatment   primary treatment   secondary treatment   final treatment

Figure 11.18 The basic stages in the wastewater treatment process

Protecting Drinking Water Sources

It costs a lot of money to treat our water so that it is safe to drink and use for other purposes. Therefore, it makes sense to prevent our rivers and lakes from becoming contaminated in the first place. The less contaminated they are, the less they need to be treated to become drinking water. Also, because not all chemical contaminants can be removed from water, it makes sense to avoid putting them there to begin with (Figure 11.19).

Protecting our drinking water sources is not only better for us, but healthier for other animals and the plants that also depend on them.

All human activities that affect our water systems affect the sources that supply our drinking water (Figure 11.20). The combined effects of these actions can make a body of water so polluted that it is unsuitable for human use.

Figure 11.19 Read product labels to find out whether special disposal is needed. Many cleaning products should not simply be poured down the drain.

Air pollution affects water systems through the water cycle. Contaminants in the air collect in precipitation, which then falls to Earth's surface.

Power stations sometimes discharge warm water into lakes or rivers. That water can harm or kill some aquatic animals. It can also lead to excessive plant growth and changes in the whole ecosystem.

Factories sometimes add dangerous chemicals or warm water to lakes or rivers, harming or killing aquatic plants and animals. Some chemicals can cause tumours or birth defects in some organisms or make them unable to reproduce.

Run-off from farmland contains fertilizers that can cause excessive plant growth. Run-off can also contain herbicides or pesticides that can kill aquatic animals and plants.

Run-off from city streets contains large amounts of oil and other chemicals, including salt. These substances can harm aquatic plants and animals.

Habitat destruction removes the places that animals can live and plants can grow.

Waste water can contain excess nutrients that promote the growth of aquatic animals and plants. These animals and plants can start using up the oxygen in lakes and rivers, leaving less available for the native fish populations.

Oil spills from ships can harm animals in, on, and near the water.

Figure 11.20 Human activities and their effects on water systems

The Yellow Fish Road Program™

If you see storm drains near your home or school marked with yellow fish symbols, you will know that the Yellow Fish Road Program™ has been to your neighbourhood. The program reminds people of the connection between our storm drains and our water systems (Figure 11.21).

As Figure 11.20 notes, city run-off may pick up many contaminants. People have even intentionally disposed of chemical products by pouring them down storm drains.

Since the Yellow Fish Road Program™ began, thousands of students have helped paint yellow fish symbols next to storm drains. Volunteers also distribute brochures to homes, educating people about the dangers that aquatic animals, plants, and our drinking water face when materials are dumped down our storm drains.

Figure 11.21 A storm drain with the Yellow Fish Road symbol

Who Manages Our Water?

All levels of government — federal, provincial, territorial, and municipal — help to manage Canada's water systems (Figure 11.22). Responsibility for a water body depends on many factors, such as where the water flows. Managing our water systems is a shared responsibility.

Your community has bylaws that manage the local water supply. An example of this is restricting lawn watering in the summer. The Ontario Water Resources Act sets out rules that apply to many water-related activities, such as the transfer of water from the Great Lakes, the construction of wells, and the operation of wastewater treatment plants.

Ontario also has laws to protect our province's drinking water specifically. These laws, made under the Clean Water Act, require communities to identify how the quality of their drinking water might be threatened and to make an action plan to reduce or remove those threats.

Suggested Activity • • • • • • • • •
D33 Decision-Making Analysis on page 331

Figure 11.22 The Canadian Coast Guard has an oil spill clean-up program that can be put into action even in remote parts of Canada's offshore areas.

The Question-Answer Relationship

The Question-Answer Relationship strategy helps a reader identify four types of questions to ask about a text and to identify where the answers might be found. The first two types of questions are "Right There Questions" and "Here and There Questions." Answers to these are likely to be in one or more places in the text. The other two types of questions are "Author and Me Questions" and "Just Me Questions." Answers to these require the reader to use prior knowledge and to look at other details in the text. Not all answers to a reader's questions will be found in the text.

Think of questions based on the title of the Quick Lab below. Identify the type of question you have created and where you expect to find the answer. Confirm this Question-Answer Relationship by reading the lab. What kinds of questions are included at the end of the lab? Where will you find these answers?

How Phosphates Affect Our Water Supply

You might have seen the words "phosphate free" on detergent boxes. Detergents and soaps that contain phosphates upset the natural balance of our lakes and rivers. Removing phosphates from these products protects our water supply.

Purpose

To investigate why phosphates contribute to pollution

Materials & Equipment

- 1 L pond water
- 2 transparent 500-mL containers
- small beaker
- tap water
- 2 measuring spoons, 5 mL and 15 mL
- 1-mL dropper pipette
- 5 mL detergent containing phosphates
- stirring spoon

Procedure

1. Fill each of the 500-mL containers two-thirds full with pond water.

2. Fill the beaker with 45 mL of tap water and add 5 mL of detergent. Stir.

3. With the pipette, add 1 mL of the detergent solution to one of the pond water samples.

4. Set both containers of pond water on a windowsill.

5. In your notebook, record what you observe about the two samples every day for five days.

Questions

6. Why did you add the detergent solution to only one pond water sample?

7. Describe the difference you observed between the two samples.

8. By preventing phospate contamination of our water supply, how could we benefit the environment?

Managing Small Sound's Water Supply

Issue

The town of Small Sound, where you live, is proposing to install a very expensive storm sewer pipe to handle an increase in storm water run-off from its streets. In addition to being very costly, the pipe will extend into the bay that is the source of the town's drinking water. You have gathered a group of friends to propose an alternative plan because you know that storm waters contain many contaminants. You do not want more of this entering your drinking water supply and the waters where you swim and kayak.

Background Information

Your community has noticed an increase in the number of extreme weather events in the past five years. Two major storms produced above-average rainfall, and in one of those storms, flooding occurred because the storm drains could not handle the run-off from the streets. They backed up and overflowed. This cost more than $1 million in property damage.

Figure 11.23 Think of Small Sound as looking something like this.

Analyze and Evaluate

Your task is to come up with a plan that will reduce the amount of run-off on Small Sound's streets. You will present your plan to town council. Part of your plan involves educating residents about the contaminants present in surface run-off.

Begin developing your plan, using the following information to guide you.

1. Go to ScienceSource to search for information on using native plants instead of paved boulevards to reduce surface run-off.

2. Look in print materials such as newspapers and books for information on how plants can protect water supplies.

3. Investigate ways in which individual homeowners can reduce surface run-off from their roofs and driveways.

4. Summarize the information you find in a short report for presentation to town council. Include only information that supports your viewpoint or refutes the proposed pipe plan.

5. Prepare a flyer for local residents that includes:

   (a) information on the kind of contaminants that can be present in surface run-off that enters a drinking water supply

   (b) an explanation of ways to reduce surface run-off on their own property

Key Concept Review

1. What methods are used for the treatment of waste water?

2. What is added to waste water during the aeration part of its treatment?

3. Give two reasons why it is necessary to protect our drinking water sources.

Connect Your Understanding

4. Why is the chlorine that is added to final, treated waste water allowed to get used up before it is discharged into a river or lake?

Practise Your Skills

5. Several of the main stages in how our bodies digest food are listed in the next column. Copy the diagram shown here into your notebook. Using the diagram, compare the stages in food digestion with the stages in wastewater treatment.

Stages in Food Digestion

- The stomach provides a site for temporary food storage.

- The stomach mechanically breaks down food.

- The stomach chemically breaks down some foods, such as protein.

- Stomach contents are transferred into the small intestine, which is the main site for food digestion.

- The intestines contain bacteria that work to break down food further.

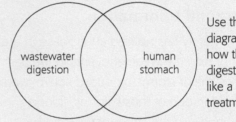

Use this Venn diagram to show how the human digestive system is like a wastewater treatment plant.

For more questions, go to ScienceSource.

D34 Thinking about Science, Society, and the Environment

Educating the Community

You read about the Yellow Fish Road Program™ in this section. This is one way to raise awareness about the risk of run-off contaminating local lakes, rivers, and streams.

What to Do

1. As a class, think of a project you could do together to educate your community about the harmful effects that run-off can have on local water systems. Participating in the Yellow Fish Road Program™ is one option, but there are many others as well.

2. Develop a plan and schedule to carry out your project and then take action.

Consider This

3. Think of ways to evaluate how effective your project has been. How could you find out, for example, how many people heard or read your message? How could you learn whether your project influenced them to change their behaviour?

Career: Public Health Inspector

Figure 11.24 Becky Hester taking a water sample for testing

When you turn on your taps to fill a glass with drinking water, you can thank people such as Becky Hester for their role in keeping it safe. Hester is a senior public health inspector (Figure 11.24). Her job is to prevent water-borne illnesses in our community. Her work is guided by the provincial standards.

On the wall in Hester's office is her framed certificate indicating that she is well qualified to help manage our water. After studying environmental health at university, Hester passed oral and written exams and a 12-week practical session to become a certified public health inspector.

"My job has a lot of variety," says Hester. "I am never bored. I deal with numerous aspects of public health, including monitoring drinking water test results, promoting well water safety, sampling beach water, and investigating the effects of a water main break."

Hester is also an educator and promoter of public health programs. "I enjoy presenting at community events," she explains. "I have spoken on such topics as how to maintain, disinfect, and treat wells, and even on how our beaches get polluted. I have also had the opportunity to work on a lot of exciting projects, such as the York Children's Water Festival" (Figure 11.25).

Questions

1. How is a public health inspector involved with people who obtain their drinking water from underground sources?

2. Why would regular tests be taken on beach water in the summer?

3. Describe three ways in which you can show respect for our water and the people like Becky Hester who help manage it.

Figure 11.25 These children are at a water festival. Learning about water systems helps children make wise choices about using them.

Key Concept Review

1. Explain the statement, "The water that flows into your sink or bathtub has flowed through your local watershed." **k**

2. (a) Explain the importance of the chlorination step in drinking water treatment. **k**

   (b) Why is chlorination usually also a final treatment step in the treatment of waste water? **k**

3. Give an example of each type of drinking water contaminant: biological, chemical, or physical. **t**

4. The waste water that enters a treatment plant is 98 percent water. The other 2 percent is removed during preliminary treatment. What might the other 2 percent contain? **t**

5. Describe four threats to our drinking water sources. **k**

Connect Your Understanding

6. A company wanting to extract ground water for use in a bottled water plant must first obtain a licence from the province. Explain why this licence helps to manage our freshwater supplies. **t**

7. In desert areas, such as the Los Angeles region of California, hot, dry summers have led to a lot of water being pumped from underground aquifers for use by the large population.

   (a) If annual rainfall is not enough to recharge these aquifers, how would the water table be affected? **t**

   (b) Describe two ways in which the government of California could manage the drinking water supply. **k**

8. When water is withdrawn from natural water systems to irrigate crops, much of it is returned to the environment in a more contaminated state.

   (a) Explain what this statement means. **t**

   (b) What kind of contaminants might be of concern? **k**

After Reading Thinking Literacy

Reflect and Evaluate

Science is about inquiry and asking questions. Have all your original questions from the beginning of the chapter been answered? Use the following organizer to summarize what you have learned about the value of asking questions as you read:

3-2-1 Review

3 things I learned about the strategy of "asking questions."

2 ways this strategy helps me as a reader.

1 question I still have.

ACHIEVEMENT CHART CATEGORIES
k Knowledge and understanding   **t** Thinking and investigation   **c** Communication   **a** Application

Practise Your Skills

9. Each circle below represents a step in the treatment of drinking water in a typical water treatment plant. Copy the diagram into your notebook.

(a) Label each step in the correct order, choosing from the list provided. ⓚ

(b) Describe what happens after step 4. ⓚ

filtration through a membrane or sand and gravel

addition of chlorine to kill microorganisms

screening out of large solids

addition of chemical so solids clump and settle out

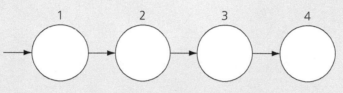

Unit Task Link

If you lived in the African country of Sierra Leone, your supply of water would be limited. What personal behaviours would you need to change immediately?

D35 *Thinking about Science, Society, and the Environment* Ⓢ Ⓔ

Lessons Learned

At the beginning of this chapter, you read about how, even in a country such as Canada, we cannot take having clean, safe water for granted. Maintaining water quality is a responsibility we all share.

What to Do

Working with a small group, reread the Walkerton story at the beginning of the unit. Then discuss the following points.

1. What three things happened at the same time that led to the tragic outcome?

2. Identify two ways in which the outcome could have been prevented.

Consider This

The events at Walkerton, Ontario, led to a public inquiry. An inquiry is a formal and detailed examination by government of what went wrong in a situation and why. At the Walkerton inquiry, many scientists were asked to give their expert opinion about water contamination and water treatment methods.

3. Can knowledge of science alone prevent a similar event like Walkerton from happening in another town or city? Discuss your answer to this question with your group.

Water is a precious resource that we all have a role in caring for. As an old proverb says, "We never know the worth of water until the well is dry."

What You Will Learn

In this chapter, you will:

- compare your personal water consumption with that of others in the world
- use critical thinking to assess how issues related to water systems are reported by media sources
- analyze the impact of some scientific discoveries and technological innovations on water systems

Skills You Will Use

In this chapter, you will:

- use a variety of forms to communicate with different audiences for a variety of purposes
- test a method of desalinating water
- use appropriate science and technology vocabulary in oral communication

Why This Is Important

Understanding how valuable water is enables us to better understand the importance of working individually and together to protect and manage our water systems for current and future needs.

Before Writing

Thinking Literacy

Descriptive Writing Tells Us...

This chapter describes what stewardship and sustainability mean in relation to water systems. Predict one thing that you will learn about these terms. Scan the next page to check your prediction. Why are stewardship and sustainability "hot topics" for writers these days?

Key Terms

- stewardship
- sustainability
- bias
- bioremediation
- desalination
- impartial

Figure 12.1 In Canada, where we have so much fresh water, it is easy to think that our water supply is limitless.

We are fortunate to live in one of the most water-rich countries on Earth (Figure 12.1). You have learned, however, that there are many reasons for us to be concerned about both our supply of water and our water quality. Natural events such as droughts and human activities such as farming and industrial development remind us that the supply of water is not endless. At the same time, the Walkerton story reminds us of how critical it is to safeguard the quality of our water.

For these reasons, taking action to protect our water systems is something we should all care about. We can do this by practising **environmental stewardship**. This means taking action to manage and maintain the environment to protect its well-being for current and future generations. At the same time, we need to use our water systems in a way that keeps them sustainable.

Sustainability is the ability of something to exist or be used at the same level for a long period of time without being damaged, harmed, or reduced for future use. Therefore, when we develop our water systems to meet today's needs, we must do so in a way that protects the quality and supply of water for generations to come.

Niagara Falls is a good example of this. When the rushing water of the falls started being used to produce electricity, Canada and the United States realized that regulations were needed to protect this natural resource (Figure 12.2). Without such protection and concern for sustainable development, the supply of water for electricity production in the future could be affected.

Figure 12.2 Canada and the United States must share the resources of Niagara Falls.

D36 *Quick Lab*

What Does Stewardship of Water Systems Look Like?

The schools and communities that take part in the Yellow Fish Road Program™ are helping to maintain a healthy watershed. They are practising environmental stewardship.

Purpose

To identify ways in which we can be stewards of our water systems.

Procedure

1. Working with a partner, look at the three photographs in Figure 12.3.

2. Consider how each photograph involves our water systems.

Questions

3. You are part of a stewardship group.
   (a) Does your group identify any concerns for water systems in the photographs? Explain.
   (b) Suggest one corrective action that your group recommends for any concern identified.

(a)

(b)

(c)

Figure 12.3 Watching out for our water systems

Here is a summary of what you will learn in this section:

- Canadians are large consumers of water, on average, compared to people in other developed countries.
- Actions taken today to conserve water will protect our future supply.
- Individual actions add up, so what you do matters.

Researchers have estimated that Canadians each consume, on average, 335 L of water a day. This is water consumed for a variety of purposes, not just for drinking (Figure 12.4).

There are many ways in which we all use water during a day, often without really being aware of it. Try to imagine how it would be possible to shower, flush a toilet, brush your teeth, cook, and wash dishes and clothes if you did not have access to water.

Only in the United States is daily water consumption per person higher than it is in Canada. This is not something to be proud of.

Our water use per person in Canada has also changed over time. Today, each of us is consuming, on average, six times more water daily than people in this country did 100 years ago.

Figure 12.4 Almost half of the water that Canadians use in the summer is sprayed onto lawns.

D37 *Starting Point*   Skills **P** **C**

Daily Water Use in an Average Canadian Home

Table 12.1 lists typical Canadian indoor activities that use water daily. The average consumption rate of 335 L per person per day is also shown.

1. Look at each activity. Think about your own water use. Then guess how many litres of water, out of the 335 L daily total, a person in Canada consumes for that activity.

2. Compare your guesses with the figures your teacher provides. Do any surprise you?

Table 12.1 Daily Water Use in an Average Canadian Home

Activity	Amount of Water Used (L per person per day)
bathing and showering	
using the toilet	
laundry	
kitchen activities (for example, drinking and cooking)	
cleaning	
TOTAL	335

Gathering Information in a Web

When writers want to explain something, they may use a "descriptive organizational pattern" to write some of the topic's main features in chunks.

In section 12.1, you will read about water consumption and conservation. As you read, create a web to record what the writer tells you about the benefits of water conservation and how we can reduce our water consumption. Once you have gathered information from the text, add to the web your own personal reasons and ideas for conserving water. Did you find any specific "signal words" for this pattern of writing?

Comparing Water Consumption

The way water is distributed in many Canadian communities (removed from a water body, treated, stored, and sent to homes and businesses in pipes) does not happen everywhere else in the world. As Canadians, we are also fortunate to pay much less for treated water than the true cost of treating it. Compared to people living in other developed countries, we pay very little for the water that comes out of our taps. For these reasons and others, water use in other parts of the world is much lower than it is in this country (Figure 12.5).

Country	L/Day
Israel	135
France	150
Sweden	200
Italy	250
United States	380
United Kingdom	200
Mozambique	10

Figure 12.5 Comparison of water consumption rates per person in several countries

The Benefits of Water Conservation

A family that draws water from a well and disposes of waste water in a septic system knows the two main benefits of water conservation. One benefit is having enough water when they need it. The other is not contaminating their water supply with an over-used septic system. Well-users pay attention to activities that remove a lot of water from their underground source, such as doing many loads of laundry in a day or letting lawn sprinklers run for hours. They are also careful not to dispose of harmful products down their drains.

People living in communities with a municipal water distribution system often pay less attention to water usage than well-users do. The city or town water supply is often taken for granted and activities that consume a lot of water are often not given any thought. However, conserving water in these communities also offers many benefits, including the following.

Figure 12.6 As our population grows, so does our demand for water. However, our supply is limited to how much clean water treatment plants can produce.

- Ensuring water supply: Our supply of water is limited by how much our treatment plants can produce and the distribution system can store (Figure 12.6). Water conservation allows our treatment plants to work efficiently and allows our groundwater sources to recharge.

- Putting less demand on water distribution and collection systems: The pipes beneath our streets are as old as the communities themselves. Many underground pipes are in need of repair (Figure 12.7).

- Saving money: In some communities, homes and businesses are now being charged for the amount of water they use. Using less water means having a lower water bill to pay.

Reducing Water Consumption

Knowing *why* to conserve water and finding ways to inform others about the issues is the first step in reducing how much water we use. Learning *how* to conserve water is the next step. There are many ways in which individuals and communities can accomplish this.

Adopting Improved, Water-Efficient Machines and Devices

Appliances such as dishwashers and washing machines have been redesigned in recent years to operate with less water. Shower heads that reduce the rate of flow of water can save as much as 60 L of water in a typical shower. New technology in toilets uses as little as 3 L of water per flush compared to more than 13 L of water per flush in older models.

Figure 12.7 Repairs to aging water distribution pipes and wastewater collection pipes are extremely expensive and disruptive.

Most farms and golf courses use automated sprinkler systems for watering. These systems can be programmed to turn on early in the morning or late at night and will shut off after a set period. The sprinklers also often work by dripping the water onto the ground instead of spraying it overhead (Figure 12.8). As well, technology exists for automated carwashes, public laundry facilities, and industries to recycle their water by filtering and re-using it.

Figure 12.8 Drip irrigation means that less water is lost to evaporation and more goes into the soil.

Changing How We Pay for Water

In most Canadian municipalities, households and businesses pay the same amount (called a flat rate) for water use, no matter how much or how little they consume. Many other municipalities, however, have installed water meters on homes and businesses. These meters keep track of exactly how much water a household or business consumes. The users then pay for that amount. This means that what people pay for water might start being closer to what it actually costs to provide treated water.

A study of water use in Canadian homes found that when water use is monitored with meters, people use one-third less water a day than when water use is not metered (Figure 12.9).

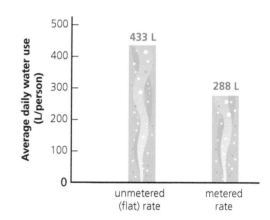

Figure 12.9 Environment Canada reports that when people know they have to pay for the volume of water they use, the consumption rate drops significantly.

Taking Direction from Government

Numerous government regulations and programs are aimed at protecting water resources. For example, many building codes (the rules for how someone builds a house or an office tower) now require that only water-efficient toilets be installed in new buildings. Some municipalities, such as the City of Toronto, also offer home-owners a rebate if they replace old toilets in already existing homes. This means that if a home-owner purchases one of the water-efficient toilets from a certain list, the city will refund the person part of the purchase cost.

As well, many municipalities have bylaws restricting water use during drought periods.

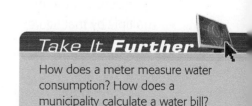

*Take It **Further***

How does a meter measure water consumption? How does a municipality calculate a water bill? Find out at ScienceSource.

DI Anchor Activity

D39 *Inquiry Activity*

Toolkit 2

SKILLS YOU WILL USE
- Recording and organizing data
- Analyzing patterns

Be a Water Watchdog

In the Starting Point activity on page 340, you examined the daily water consumption of Canadians. Now it is time to evaluate how much water you personally consume in one day.

Question

Why is it important to evaluate your personal water use?

Materials & Equipment

- observation sheet from your teacher
- 5-L bucket
- watch or clock with a second hand
- 1-L container

Procedure

1. Choose one 24-h period on a weekend, when you will be at home to carry out this investigation. On that day, you are going to record how much water you use for every activity you do that requires you to run water.

2. Showering: Holding the 5-L bucket up to the shower head, turn on the cold water for 1 min at the pressure you would normally use to shower. Turn off the water and measure how much water has filled the bucket. Multiply this amount by the number of minutes of your usual shower.

3. Toilet flushing: If your home has an older-model toilet, multiply the number of times you flush it by 13.5 L. Otherwise, if you know the actual volume of water your toilet uses, multiply by that figure.

4. Cooking: For anything that is cooked with water (for example, hot cereal, pasta, rice, soup), measure how much water is used.

5. Drinking: Measure all the water you drink in the 24-h period.

6. Dishwashing: If you wash dishes by hand, fill the 5-L bucket first before pouring the water into the sink or washbasin. Measure how much water in total you use (you may need more than 5 L or less). If you have a dishwasher, look in the operating manual to see how much water it uses per load. For either case (handwashing or using the dishwasher), divide the amount of water required by the number of people in your household to get your individual use figure. Multiply that figure by the number of times dishes are washed that day.

7. Teeth brushing: Put the 1-L container under the sink faucet when you brush your teeth. Do not let the container overflow. Measure the total amount that ran until you finished brushing.

Analyzing and Interpreting

8. Look at the data your teacher gave you in the Starting Point activity. Explain how your water use compared per activity and per day with the average Canadian's water use.

9. What other activities using water that involve you indirectly were not counted in this activity?

Skill Builder

10. List two sources of error that affected how you determined your water use.

Forming Conclusions

11. Write a sentence explaining why it is important to evaluate your personal water use.

12. Make a two-step plan of action to reduce your personal water consumption.

Key Concept Review

1. (a) How does Canada rank compared to the rest of the world in terms of daily water consumption per person?

   (b) Give two reasons why Canada has this ranking.

Connect Your Understanding

2. Give a "water-wise" alternative to each activity below.

   (a) hosing off a driveway to clean it

   (b) watering outdoor plants with a hose

   (c) letting the tap run to get cold water

Practise Your Skills

The table in the next column shows the amount of water it takes to produce 1 kg of four common products. Use the information to answer the next two questions.

Product (1 kg)	Water (L)
steel	95
paper	324
potatoes	1 000
beef	99 980

3. How much more water does it take to produce:

   (a) 1 kg of paper than 1 kg of steel?

   (b) 1 kg of potatoes than 1 kg of paper?

   (c) 1 kg of beef than 1 kg of potatoes?

4. Explain why so much more water is needed to produce beef than potatoes.

For more questions, go to ScienceSource.

D40 Thinking about Technology, Society, and the Environment

S T S E

You and Your Water Bill

How much does your water cost? It is hard to know because we do not have to pull money out of our wallets to pay every time we turn on a tap in our kitchen or bathroom.

What to Do?

1. Your teacher will give you a copy of his or her home water bill or that of the school and will show you how to read it. Your teacher will also give you a price list of bottled water products of different sizes.

2. As a class, figure out a way to compare the cost of regular municipal tap water with the cost of bottled water. Calculate the average cost of each for a standard volume.

Consider This

3. Many people feel that Canadians pay too little for municipal water. Think about how our behaviour might change if the price we had to pay for tap water doubled. Brainstorm a list of the advantages and disadvantages of such an increase in municipal water charges.

Here is a summary of what you will learn in this section:

- People hold very differing opinions about how human activities affect water systems.
- Media such as newspapers, television, radio, and the Internet often present information about water issues from a biased viewpoint.
- Thinking crtically about water issues is necessary if we are to make good decisions about managing our water systems.

Imagine that you and your classmates are asked to come up with a plan for improving your school building. Do you think you would all start with having exactly the same ideas about what is needed? It is not likely. We all bring our own unique ideas and values to any topic or issue.

This is the case with the management of water resources. Different groups have very different opinions about how water should be managed, protected, and shared so that water's sustainability is assured. They also hold different views about how human activities could affect local, national, and even international water systems.

Bottled Water vs. Tap Water

Consider the issue of removing and selling water from freshwater systems. As you learned in Chapter 11, this is what the bottled water industry does (Figure 12.10). The growing export of our water resources has created great controversy. A controversy is a disagreement that goes on for some time.

Many people against the use of bottled water point to several facts. One is that bottled water costs about $1 for a 500-mL container. Tap water costs just pennies a litre. It would take a lot of increase in the price of municipal water to reach the price of bottled water. Another fact is that the treated tap water across Canada is of good quality and can be consumed safely.

Figure 12.10 Those plastic or glass containers of water you see everywhere are part of a multibillion-dollar industry.

Those people in favour of bottling water point to other facts. One is that the industry creates many jobs. Another is that bottled water can be shipped to areas that do not have treated water supplies. Furthermore, bottled water can be life-saving in emergencies when a supply of safe drinking water is not available.

When you read or hear facts like these in a newspaper, on an Internet website or blog, or on a radio or television report, you might not be able to tell whether the media source is in favour of bottling water or not. The viewpoint or opinion of the person providing the news report may not be evident. On the other hand, that person may present the news with a clear bias. A **bias** is an obvious opinion about an issue. By knowing what biases a reporter or broadcaster might have, you can better judge the content of the information presented.

If facts about an issue are presented in a fair and unbiased way, we say that the speaker is being **impartial**.

D41 *Starting Point*

Skills Ⓐ Ⓒ

Finding Messages behind Words

When people write or speak about a subject, you can often tell a lot about whether they are for or against something by their choice of words. Read the three statements below and then answer the questions that follow.

(a) "Our town doesn't need to worry about conserving water. After all, there is a huge lake right in our backyard!"

(b) "Some people get all excited because they think a few litres of water disappearing is a big deal."

(c) "The study carried out by the government found that 6000 L more water than the standard rate is being removed from the reservoir."

1. Suppose these sentences were spoken by a news reporter. Which one or ones show that he or she:

   (a) has a bias? Explain.

   (b) is impartial? Explain.

2. (a) Which statements show that a message is implied (that is, meant but not stated) in the words?

   (b) What is the message that you think is being implied?

Bias behind the Reporting of Issues

Media sources such as newspapers, magazines, television, radio, and websites often contain biased information on an issue. It is helpful to know who wrote an article that you are reading so that you can determine whether the information discussed might be biased. For example, a report about the bottled water industry written by the president of MegaBlue Bottled Water may not tell you the same information as a report written by the president of the local "Don't Sell Our Water!" association. Each source would want to convince you that its viewpoint is the right one, and that would influence the information provided.

The same is true when you watch a television documentary or listen to a radio program about a topic (Figure 12.11). It is important that you know who is behind the information before you evaluate its meaning.

Figure 12.11 Always ask yourself if the media source you are listening to or reading might be biased in how it addresses water issues.

Figure 12.12 The damming of the Yangtze River in China is an issue because many people have different viewpoints about its benefits.

Issues Involving Water Systems

Removing and selling water from freshwater systems has become the topic of a national and international debate. However, it is just one of many issues related to the sustainable development of our water systems.

Another example is the world's largest hydroelectric dam project, Three Gorges Dam. It is built across the Yangtze River in China (Figure 12.12). It has received much global attention. If you were to read only reports by the Chinese government about the project, you might think that the benefits of the hydroelectric power generated at the dam were a good use of technology. Yet, you would be getting only part of the story. Other media sources report how the project has forced nearly 1.5 million people to move, flooded dozens of towns and villages, destroyed animal habitat, and threatened important archaeological sites.

Closer to home, the impact of human activities on the long-term health of the Great Lakes has been debated for decades (Figure 12.13). One issue is the destruction of Great Lakes coastal wetland habitats. Across southern Ontario, development for housing and agriculture has reduced or altered wetlands by approximately 70 percent. In the past, people viewed swamps and marshes as wastelands and did not understand their importance (Figure 12.14). Today, pro-development and anti-development groups continue to express their viewpoints about which activities near the Great Lakes should be permitted.

All issues relating to our water systems — whether they affect the local, national, or global community — require careful and critical thinking. We must reason through all issues by asking questions, separating facts from opinions, and examining viewpoints.

Figure 12.13 How to maintain the health of the Great Lakes and their shorelines (such as Lake Superior's, shown here) is a hotly debated issue.

Figure 12.14 When wetlands become filled up and built on, the habitat they provide for wildlife is destroyed.

Take It *Further*

There are national standards for how drinking water should be monitored and managed in First Nations communities. Learn the various viewpoints about these guidelines. Begin your research at ScienceSource.

D42 *During Writing*

Thinking Literacy

Writers Make Decisions with RAFTS

RAFTS is a writing strategy that writers use to remind themselves of several decisions they need to make as they begin the writing process. The letters stand for **R**ole of writer, **A**udience, **F**ormat, **T**opic, and **S**trong verb.

Using the information on your water consumption and conservation web, write a description of five behaviours people could change to reduce their water consumption. Use the RAFTS strategy to finish making your writing decisions. Then complete your writing piece.

Exploring a Great Lakes Issue

More and more people in Ontario are concerned about the quality and supply of water in the Great Lakes. In this activity, you will look critically at how an issue involving the Great Lakes is reported by a range of media sources.

Issue

The impacts of rising and falling water levels in the Great Lakes

Background Information

The level of water in the Great Lakes rises and falls all the time. This has been happening since the glaciers receded after the last ice age. Most changes in Great Lakes water levels occur naturally. If the water flowing into them equals the water flowing out of them, then levels remain the same. Usually, however, changes in evaporation, precipitation, and spring run-off cause the water levels to change. Human activities such as diverting water in and out of locks and canals also change water levels.

High water levels are a concern for many reasons, including increasing the chances of flooding. Concerns over low water levels include difficulty securing boats to high docks and loading and unloading a ship's cargo (Figure 12.15).

Figure 12.15 Companies that use ships to transport products such as road salt from one port to another on the Great Lakes are very concerned about water levels.

Analyze and Evaluate

1. Working with a small group, find at least five different reports, articles, or radio or television programs about the water levels in the Great Lakes–St. Lawrence River basin. Make sure that you choose a range of media types and sources.

2. As you read, listen to, or watch the information presented, make notes about the facts that are given.

3. Answer the following questions to evaluate the viewpoints or opinions of your media sources.

   (a) What is the main purpose of the piece? For example, is it to provide facts or to put blame on something?

   (b) Who is the main audience or group of readers that the piece is directed to? Examples include scientists and researchers, the general public, schoolchildren, or special interest groups.

   (c) How does the information in each of the sources compare with the others?

4. Explain why one media source would take a different position from that of another media source.

5. Think of the issue of changing water levels in the Great Lakes. Has your research found any decisions that have been made? Explain.

Key Concept Review

1. Why is it important to question what you read, watch, or listen to in the media?

2. What is the difference between a fact and an opinion?

Connect Your Understanding

3. Suppose you belong to a stewardship group looking at ways to improve the health of your local watershed. What media sources might you access for information on the subject?

Practise Your Skills

4. Many coastal communities depend on tourism to provide income and jobs to its citizens. Describe what viewpoint the following individuals might have.

   - the mayor of a coastal city
   - members of an environmental group

For more questions, go to ScienceSource.

D44 Thinking about Science, Society, and the Environment

Mini Media Analysis

Water-related topics are written about and reported on every day. Many are about controversies over who has the right to use water when, why, for how long, and in what amount. When we read, watch, or hear media stories, it can be difficult sometimes to know whether the information we are getting is based on facts, opinions, or personal interests.

What to Do

1. Choose a water-related issue that has made headlines recently. Then find at least three different media sources that have reported on the matter.

2. Read, watch, or listen to each report critically. Analyze the way that each source has presented the information. For example, ask yourself:

   - Does the information provided in the report seem accurate? If science or technology information is provided, where can I check to see if it is factual?

   - Does the source seem impartial or biased? What evidence makes it seem that way?

3. Write a summary of your media analysis, stating your conclusions about how balanced each report's presentation was.

4. Think about everything else you read, watch, and listen to in the media daily. Is it only about water issues that biased reporting might occur? Explain your answer with several examples.

Water Sustainability through Science and Technology

Here is a summary of what you will learn in this section:

- Using our water systems in a sustainable way will enable us to protect our natural ecosystems and protect the quality and supply of water for future generations.
- Science and technology offer solutions to many water-related problems, but the impact of any innovation on local and global water systems must always be assessed.

The connection between land and water reminds us that stewardship of one must involve stewardship of the other if our water systems are to be sustainable. Many organizations, government departments, businesses, farmers, waterfront owners, and individuals just like you are working together to improve water quality and protect our supply so that it is sustainable.

D45 *Starting Point*   Skills Ⓐ Ⓒ

Looking More Closely at Solutions

Scientific and technological solutions to problems often create a new set of issues. Therefore, when we are trying to solve a problem in one part of the environment and society, it is important to consider how that might affect other parts.

With a partner, think about the problem below and the two proposed solutions shown in the table. For each solution given, list in your notebook what needs to be considered for all parts of (a) the environment and (b) society.

Problem:
A company discharges wastes from manufacturing processes as smoke through a tall chimney called a stack. Chemicals in the smoke are creating acid rain, which, in turn, is killing fish in a nearby lake.

Proposed Solution	Environmental Considerations	Societal Considerations
1. Update the stack with new technology that reduces the amount of chemicals released by 75 percent. This technology is very expensive.		
2. Install a much taller stack that discharges the smoke higher into the atmosphere and lets the smoke spread out over a larger area. This technology is less expensive than Proposed Solution 1.		

One place where we can look to see examples of sustainable practices is in our farming communities. Farmers use land and water management techniques and participate in programs that protect and enhance our watersheds. For example, the Ontario Environmental Farm Plan educates farmers in using plants along streams (Figure 12.16). These plants reduce the amounts of chemicals and nutrients produced by farm practices entering the local watershed.

Ongoing research in science and technology continues to offer solutions to many problems involving our water systems. However, a solution to any problem must always be assessed in terms of how it affects the environment and society.

Figure 12.16 A strip of plants between the stream and the nearby farm helps to filter contaminants and reduce pollution in the watershed.

Sustainability Solutions Using Bioremediation

The technique of using living organisms to clean up contamination in land and water is called **bioremediation**. A subset of bioremediation is phytoremediation, which is the technique of using plants as environmental clean-up remedies (as discussed in the farm example, above). Scientists often use the term bioremediation to apply specifically to clean-up remedies involving microorganisms.

Bacteria are the microorganisms most often used in cleaning up problems with our water systems. For instance, the petroleum industry employs bacteria to clean up after oil spills and leaks have occurred. Some types of bacteria use the petroleum chemicals as food. These chemicals can harm people and animals, but oil-loving bacteria break down the chemicals into natural substances, including carbon dioxide gas, a type of alcohol, and water (Figure 12.17).

Bioremediation, while safe, relies on the natural processes of bacteria. Therefore, one disadvantage of this technology is that it takes a long time to complete. Another is that scientists who are knowledgeable about the technology are needed to carry out the remediation. This can mean hiring the services of someone to do the work. For some small companies, that can be expensive.

Figure 12.17 Bioremediation at work cleaning toxic waste in soil to protect ground and surface water

Water Supply Solutions Using Desalination Technology

Maybe you have heard the lines "Water, water everywhere, Nor any drop to drink." They are from the poem "The Rime of the Ancient Mariner" by 19th century poet Samuel Taylor Coleridge. If you can imagine being far out at sea without fresh water to drink, you will know what Coleridge's mariner meant by those words. However, many countries with a scarce supply of fresh water are today using technology to turn ocean water into drinking water. **Desalination** is the process of removing salt from water.

Desalination plants operate in many parts of the world (Figure 12.18). Ocean-going ships also have desalination equipment on board. Desalination can be accomplished in several ways. One way is illustrated in Figure 12.19.

As with any technological solution, desalination does have some disadvantages. The waste water from a desalination plant contains a heavy concentration of salt, which is discharged back into the ocean. This unusually high concentration of salt can be toxic even to saltwater organisms if they are exposed to it for long periods. The waste water that flows out of the desalination plant and into the ocean also contains chemicals that are toxic to marine life.

Figure 12.18 Africa's largest desalination plant is in Algeria. It can produce 200 000 m³ of drinking water daily from the Mediterranean Sea.

Take It *Further*

What other parts of the world use desalination technology? Begin your research at ScienceSource.

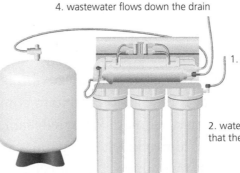

4. wastewater flows down the drain

1. salty ocean water flows in

3. tank of clean water

2. water passes through a filter that the salt cannot pass through

Figure 12.19 Reverse osmosis. In this set-up, salt water is pushed through a membrane or filter that the salt cannot get through. This is one way to desalinate water.

Changing Salt Water into Fresh Water

In this activity, you will model a simple method of desalinating water.

Question

How can fresh water be made from salt water?

Materials & Equipment

- 1-L container of salt water (35 mL of salt dissolved in 1 L of fresh water)
- 2 pans: 1 wide and flat, 1 smaller to fit inside the wide pan
- plastic wrap
- tape
- small rock
- 2 medicine droppers
- 2 glass slides

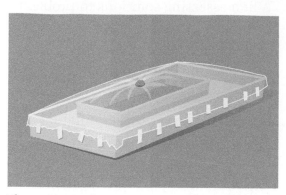

Figure 12.20 Lab set-up

Procedure

1. Set the smaller pan in the larger one. Pour the salt water into the bottom pan so that the water surrounds the smaller pan but does not spill into it.

2. Cover the whole set-up with one large piece of plastic wrap. Tape the edges to the pan. Place the small stone on the plastic over the smaller pan to make a small depression.

3. Set the pans in a sunny location in the classroom (Figure 12.20). Predict what will happen to the salt water in the large pan.

4. Make a chart and record your observations daily for the next week.

5. After one week, take samples of the water. Use one medicine dropper to place two drops of water from the large pan onto a glass slide.

Do the same for the water sample from the small pan, using the other medicine dropper and glass slide. Allow the two samples to dry and record your observations.

Analyzing and Interpreting

6. Explain how the dried samples on the slides differed.

7. How did what happened to the salt water compare with your prediction?

8. What purpose did the depression in the plastic serve?

Skill Builder

9. Why were you instructed to dissolve 35 mL of salt in 1 L of water? What did this concentration represent?

Forming Conclusions

10. Describe how fresh water was made from salt water. Use the following words in your explanation: evaporation, condensation, salinity, desalinate.

Key Concept Review

1. When assessing solutions to problems involving our water systems, what needs to be considered?

2. Give one advantage and one disadvantage of bioremediation.

3. (a) Define the word "desalination."

   (b) Describe one desalination method.

Connect Your Understanding

4. The desalination plant in Algeria shown in Figure 12.18 on page 354 cost an estimated $250 million to build. Why would the country have spent so much money to build this structure?

5. The term "brownfields" is used to describe unused properties in urban areas that have been contaminated by hazardous materials such as petroleum. What is one way in which municipalities could clean up brownfields? Explain.

Practise Your Skills

6. Bioremediation offers many possibilities for decontaminating water and land sites in a watershed. Cleaning sites contaminated with petroleum is just one use. Think about how this technology could be applied more widely. What other problems can you think of where bioremediation might offer a possible solution? Make a chart listing your ideas and the societal impacts of each.

7. You have been given two unmarked containers. In one is a sample of salt water and in the other a sample of fresh water. You are asked to identify which is which, without tasting them. Explain the procedure you would use to do this.

For more questions, go to ScienceSource.

D47 *Thinking about Technology, Society, and the Environment* **S T S E**

Fog Water

In some parts of the world, polluted ground water and little precipitation mean that potable water is in short supply. Thanks to the work of many scientists and technologists, however, ways of collecting water from the air have been developed. "Fog catchers" are large screened panels that are installed outside like big sections of fencing. When fog or mist blows against them, the water droplets in the air condense, drip down the panels into pipes, and collect in storage tanks. These systems are fairly simple and inexpensive to build and operate.

1. Consider this scenario: A community has been using 12 fog catcher panels for a year, but now decides it could get much more water by increasing the number of panels across its area to 100.

2. Think about the intended and unintended consequences that such a step might have. Make a list of both. Then explain whether you feel the advantages of expanding this technology's use outweigh the disadvantages for the community.

Making Connections

Jay Ingram

Jay Ingram is an experienced science journalist and is the host of *Daily Planet* on Discovery Channel Canada.

A Tea Cup of Storm Clouds

If you have tea-drinkers in your house, you have a good opportunity to see a fascinating display of miniature weather.

First, you need a cup of very hot tea with no milk or sugar. Sit the cup under a bright light bulb or on a table or counter in the early morning sun. Watch carefully and you will see a pattern on the surface of the tea. The pattern will be made up of irregular white patches separated by thin black lines. These patches will change their shape from moment to moment.

The whitish areas you are seeing are places where hot tea is rising to the surface. The black lines are where cooler tea is sinking beneath the surface.

Why, you might ask, would warm tea be a different colour than cold tea? In fact, there is no colour difference in the tea. The whitish areas are not tea at all, but droplets of water suspended in the air.

When hot tea rises and reaches the surface, individual particles of water from the tea evaporate, breaking away and rocketing into the air. These particles are much too small to see, but there are millions of them. They do not go far. They cool quickly, slow down, and collect together to form tiny but visible droplets of water. Normally, these droplets would be pulled right back down into the tea by gravity. However, all the other particles that are still evaporating from the surface keep the droplets suspended about a millimetre above the tea. So, what you are seeing in the whitish areas are really miniature clouds that are floating above the tea.

Eventually, as the tea cools, the clouds disappear. Imagine if you were miniaturized and floating in a nano-boat on the tea. It would be as if the storm had passed and the sky had cleared.

Unstable weather above a cup of hot tea

Key Concept Review

1. Describe one thing you can do in your home, in your school, and in your community to reduce your personal water consumption. *(k)*

2. Identify the following statements as being true or false. If a statement is false, rewrite it so that it is true. *(k)*

   (a) Ontarians live in one of the richest water areas on Earth, so our water supply is not threatened.

   (b) We pay about the same price for treated tap water as it costs to produce.

   (c) Judging the content of information on our water issues is easier when you know what biases the writer might have.

   (d) All scientific discoveries and technologies developed to help clean up our water systems are always safe.

3. For each word below, write a sentence that uses the word and shows its meaning. *(k)*

   (a) controversy

   (b) viewpoint

   (c) critical thinking

4. Explain what bioremediation is and how it works. *(k)*

Connect Your Understanding

5. Do you think that the price we pay for our water should cover the costs to produce it? Give reasons for your answer. *(a)*

6. Name five behaviours that people could change in order to reduce their personal water consumption. *(a)*

7. All kinds of cargo are transported by ship along Canadian waterways each year. Explain why a reliable water level in our Great Lakes is important to the shipping industry. *(a)*

After Writing · Thinking Literacy

Reflect and Evaluate

Exchange your writing piece on reducing water consumption with a partner. How did knowledge of the "descriptive organizational pattern" for writing help you when you were reading your partner's work? Was this pattern an easy way to organize and present your information? What other organizational pattern did you use or could you have used? Share your experiences and ideas with the class.

ACHIEVEMENT CHART CATEGORIES
(k) Knowledge and understanding · *(t)* Thinking and investigation · *(c)* Communication · *(a)* Application

8. Look back at Figure 11.17 on page 326, which shows the human-made wetland at the Kortright Conservation Centre. Explain the technology behind this solution to waste water treatment. ⓐ

9. Many groups, such as conservation authorities, provide stewardship education.

   (a) What educational messages about our water systems might they give? ⓣ

   (b) How does educating the public help to protect and preserve our water systems? ⓐ

Unit Task Link

How would acting out a part of life in an African village that is short of water help you to understand water's value?

Practise Your Skills

10. The pie chart on the right shows a breakdown of monthly household expenses for an average Canadian family. From the data in the pie chart, explain why households are more interested in saving electricity than in saving water. Use figures from the graph to support your answer. ⓣ

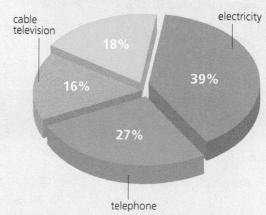

Comparison of some monthly household expenses for an average family

---

D48 *Thinking about Society and the Environment*

Group Actions

Even though many separate actions can bring about a change, it often takes the actions of individuals and groups working together to create a sustainable solution to a problem with our water systems.

Think of an example that illustrates what this statement means. Your example can be one from your local area or one that applies provincially, nationally, or internationally.

Consider This

1. Group action is necessary to bring about change. At the same time, however, the greater the number of people involved in solving an issue, the harder it can be to reach a solution that will make everyone happy. Working with a partner, discuss why you think this is the case.

2. What are some ways that people can work together to resolve differences of opinion?

UNIT D Summary

10.0 Water on Earth exists in different states and is always moving and changing.

KEY CONCEPTS

- Water on Earth exists in three states: liquid, solid, and gas.
- In a watershed, water from all sources on the land drain to one main water body.
- Activities in one part of a watershed affect all living things downstream.
- Water influences our climate and creates our weather.

CHAPTER SUMMARY

- Water in all three states covers approximately 70 percent of Earth's surface and cycles constantly between the surface and the atmosphere.
- Of the two kinds of water on Earth, salt water is more abundant, but humans can drink only fresh water.
- Large water bodies influence the climate of coastal areas.
- Glaciers and ice sheets are affected by changes in temperature and precipitation. In turn, changes to glaciers and ice sheets influence water systems.

11.0 Monitoring water systems is critical for maintaining water supply and quality.

KEY CONCEPTS

- Our supply of water on Earth is limited.
- The supply and quality of our water is threatened by natural events and human activity.
- Our sources of drinking water must be protected.

CHAPTER SUMMARY

- Proper management of our water supply is needed so that there is enough for all living things and for the future.
- Canadians obtain drinking water from below- and aboveground sources, and it must be treated and tested before it is safe to drink.
- Protecting our drinking water sources from pollution and overuse is the first step in ensuring water's sustainability.
- Treating water and waste water is expensive and does not remove all contaminants.

12.0 Stewardship of our water systems is needed to ensure their sustainability.

KEY CONCEPTS

- Sustainable water systems provide the quality and supply of water for the future.
- Through stewardship action, our water systems can be properly managed, maintained, and enhanced.
- Issues involving our water systems must be examined critically.

CHAPTER SUMMARY

- Canadians are large consumers of water, and conservation is necessary to protect our future supply and Earth's ecosystems.
- Thinking critically about water issues involves asking questions, separating facts and opinions, and examining viewpoints for biases.
- Science and technology offer solutions to problems involving our water systems, but their impact on the environment and society must be assessed.

The Worth of Water

Getting Started

The United Nations considers access to clean drinking water to be a fundamental human right. Yet this is not the reality for more than one billion people worldwide. We rarely have to think about putting a value on water. One way to do it, however, is to measure the time and effort needed to gather and store it for our use.

Your Goal

Using a simulation, you will share the experience of a student your age who lives in rural Sierra Leone, in western Africa. Your task will be to supply your family with enough water for their daily routine, collecting that water from the community well.

What You Need to Know

Your teacher will help you research (1) the volume of potable water that a family of four in a rural west African country uses in a day, and (2) how much water a young person might carry per trip to the well. You will then use appropriate sizes of containers to represent your home cistern (storage container) and the container you will carry.

Your teacher will also set a distance in your schoolyard to represent the distance between your village and the well. The well will be represented by an outdoor hose. A pathway will be laid out for you to follow as though you were travelling to and from the well.

Steps to Success

1. With a team of three or four, walk from your "home" to the well along the set path, each carrying a water container. At the well, fill your container.

2. Return home along the same path. Empty your container into the cistern and return to the well for a refill. Repeat as often as it takes to fill the cistern.

3. When finished, sit down with your team to discuss the activity. Was it physically difficult? What would it feel like if you had to do this every day?

4. On your own, compose a first-person story as though you are a student in Sierra Leone describing the responsibility of taking water to your family. Include events that might occur during the travel to and from the well and your feelings about how you view this duty.

5. With your whole class, consider the information you learned in this unit about the volume of water required for a family's use in Canada. Develop a graphic organizer to contrast the information about family water consumption in Sierra Leone to that in Canada.

How Did It Go?

6. Suppose that your family in Canada had access only to the same amount of water per day as the family in Sierra Leone. Examine your graphic organizer. What water use habits are you prepared to change?

7. Examine the length of the path set out by your teacher. How long would it take your team to get the required volume of water if the path were 1 km? What if it were 5 km?

8. International organizations such as OXFAM and UNESCO work to bring low-technology wells to villages in the developing world. What might be the effect on a community if the water supply was located only a short distance from the homes?

Key Terms Review

1. Create a concept map that illustrates your understanding of the following terms. ⓚ

- aquifer
- bias
- bioremediation
- chlorine
- contaminants
- desalination
- discharge
- groundwater zone
- heat capacity

- impartial
- polar ice-cap
- potable water
- recharge
- salinity
- septic tank
- stewardship
- sustainability
- water table

Key Concept Review

10.0

2. Match the definition in Column A with the term in Column B. ⓚ

Column A	Column B
(a) a long, hollow shaft drilled into an aquifer	(i) oceans
(b) massive bodies of surface water that are referred to as Earth's water reservoirs	(ii) water table
(c) natural, underground freshwater reservoirs	(iii) river
(d) a large body of flowing fresh water that usually leads to a lake or ocean	(iv) aquifer
(e) the upper surface of the groundwater zone	(v) well
(f) land that is permanently or seasonally covered by shallow water	(vi) groundwater zone
(g) the underground water storage zone	(vii) wetland

3. Draw a diagram of the water cycle and label it with the following words. ⓚ

- evaporation
- transpiration
- precipitation
- condensation
- surface run-off
- ocean

- lake
- river
- ground water
- clouds
- atmosphere

4. Complete the following sentences by filling in the blanks with a word or words from this unit. ⓚ

(a) The line created by the Rocky Mountains in North America that separates the direction of water flow is known as the _____.

(b) An area with a small, localized climate is called a _____.

(c) The _____ of a substance describes its ability to absorb heat.

5. Write down whether each of the following statements is true or false. Give one piece of evidence from this unit to support your answer. ⓚ

(a) Large bodies of water have a moderating effect on the climate of a nearby region.

(b) Water takes the same amount of time to absorb heat as soil does.

(c) Rising temperatures and an increase in precipitation over a long period of time have a minimal effect on massive ice formations.

6. Describe three natural events that can affect the depth of the water table. ⓚ

7. (a) Explain how overuse of water threatens drinking water supplies. ⓚ

(b) Describe two human activities that contribute to overuse. ⓚ

8. What three tests are regularly carried out on drinking water to ensure that it is safe? ⓚ

9. The following steps are part of the treatment process for municipal waste water. Place them in the sequence in which they occur. ⓣ

(a)   Clean water is returned to the river or lake.

(b)   Waste water from homes and businesses is sent to the treatment plant through underground pipes.

(c)   In the aeration tanks, micro-organisms digest the organic wastes.

(d)   A coarse screen removes large debris such as toys, false teeth, and rags.

(e)   Settling tanks separate the floaters and the sinkers. The remaining liquid is sent to the aeration tanks.

(f)   Liquid from the secondary tanks can contain harmful microorganisms, so it is usually disinfected with chlorine.

10. Which of the following statements about wetlands are true and which are false? Rewrite the false statements to make them true. ⓚ

(a) Wetlands have no impact on our drinking water.

(b) Marshes and swamps are both types of wetlands.

(c) Wetlands are not important ecosystems.

11 Explain the term "sustainable development" as it applies to our water systems. ⓚ

12. Give one example of a biased statement and one of an impartial statement. ⓐ

13. Copy the following table into your notebook. In the Positive column, list benefits of the technology. In the Negative column, list drawbacks to the technology. In the third column, note interesting facts or comments about each technology. ⓣ

Examining Technological Innovations Using Water Systems

Technology	Positive	Negative	Interesting Fact
1. bioremediation			
2. desalination			

Connect Your Understanding

14. The large amount of snowfall in areas near the Great Lakes is often referred to as "lake effect snow." Explain why that term is used. ⓐ

15. The owners of a small hotel that draws water from a well submit a water sample for testing. The test result indicates the presence of *E. coli*, so the public health department issues a Boil Water Advisory. This tells the hotel owners to boil their water before consuming it. Answer the following questions about this situation.

(a) Why is drinking water tested for bacteria such as *E. coli*? *k*

(b) What is the purpose of boiling the water? *t*

(c) What could an unsatisfactory test result indicate? *t*

(d) What further investigations are necessary? *a*

16. Swimming pool water contains chlorine. Why should backyard swimming pools not be emptied down storm drains? *t*

17. Some bottled water companies remove water from municipally treated supplies. They are required to have a permit to remove the water. Do you think they should also pay for the treatment that the water received? Explain your answer. *t*

18. In the washrooms of some facilities such as airports, train stations, and shopping malls, water taps operate on sensors. Putting your hands under them starts the water flow. When you remove your hands, the water shuts off. Explain the benefit of this technology in terms of our water systems. *t*

19. Reflect back on all you have learned in this unit.

(a) List five things that you did not know before about Earth's water systems. *t*

(b) Beside each of the things you noted in (a), describe one way that this new knowledge will affect your actions and attitude from now on. *a*

Practise Your Skills

20. The map below shows the Niagara Peninsula watershed.

(a) Into which large waterfall does most of this watershed's water drain? *k*

(b) Does the rain that falls during a thunderstorm over Welland reach the ground water of Hamilton? Explain. *t*

(c) To what major ocean watershed does all water from this smaller watershed drain? *a*

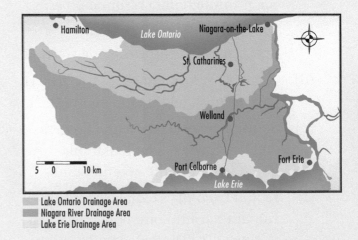

Lake Ontario Drainage Area
Niagara River Drainage Area
Lake Erie Drainage Area

21. Imagine that you are camping in the woods with friends. You brought enough drinking water with you, but you need to use lake water to wash your dirty dishes.

Write a plan for: ⓐ

(a) the safe use of lake water for washing dishes.

(b) disposal of dish water so that there is minimal impact on the environment.

Revisit the Big Ideas

22. Weather is an important part of our lives. Read the following statements about weather. Explain how water systems are involved in each one. ⓣ

(a) Weather forecasts explain how the weather will change over a short period of time.

(b) Cloud types and patterns can be used to interpret the weather.

(c) In the daytime, air rises over warmer land and cooler air moves in from the nearby water.

23. You have learned that water is an important five-letter word. For each letter, write down the name of something that depends on a sustainable use of water. ⓐ

24. How crucial is water to our lives? Write a one-page essay to answer this question. First, write down all the responses you can think of. Then organize these ideas into a logical point-form outline. Finally, develop your ideas into sentences and paragraphs that describe how crucial water is to our lives. ⓒ

D49 **Thinking about Science, Technology, Society, and the Environment** S T S E

Water for All

Each photograph in Figure 12.21 shows one or more ways that water plays a role in supporting the world around us.

1. How are human lives dependent on or improved by each use shown?

2. What competing water uses could harm or disrupt the existing uses shown in each photograph? Would the impacts be social, cultural, political, environmental, or a combination of these? Explain.

(a) (b) (c) (d)

Figure 12.21 Water everywhere

Toolkits

Contents

Safety Symbols

Safety symbols identify potential hazards. When you see any of the following symbols, either in this book or on a product, take extra care.

Safety Symbols in This Book

Some activities in this book have symbols to help you conduct the activity safely. Look for these symbols at the beginning of activities.

 When you see this symbol, wear goggles or safety glasses while doing the activity.

 This symbol tells you that you will be using glassware during the activity. Take extra care when handling it.

 When you see this symbol, wear an apron while doing the activity.

 When you see this symbol, wear gloves while doing the activity.

WHMIS Symbols

Here are symbols you might see on the materials you use in your classroom. You will see them occasionally in the Materials and Equipment lists for activities when a substance that needs a warning is used. These symbols are called Workplace

Hazardous Materials Information System (WHMIS) symbols. They are placed on hazardous materials used at job sites and in science classrooms. They may also be on other manufactured products bought for home use. A container may have one or more of the symbols shown below. Discuss with your teacher what the symbols mean.

compressed gas

biohazardous infectious material

dangerously reactive material

corrosive material

oxidizing material

flammable and combustible material

poisonous and infectious causing immediate and serious toxic effects

poisonous and infectious causing other toxic effects

Hazard Symbols for Home Products

You have probably seen some of these hazard symbols on products at home. They are a warning that the products can be harmful or dangerous if handled improperly. These hazard symbols have two shapes: a triangle (a traffic yield sign) or an octagon (a traffic stop sign). A triangle means that the container is dangerous. An octagon means that the contents of the container are dangerous. Here are four of the most common symbols.

Can you identify the symbols that are similar to the WHMIS symbols on the previous page?

 Flammable Hazard: The product could ignite (catch on fire) if exposed to flames, sparks, friction, or even heat.

 Toxic Hazard: The product is very poisonous and could have immediate and serious effects, including death, if eaten or drunk. Smelling or tasting some products can also cause serious harm.

 Corrosive Hazard: The product will corrode ("eat away at") clothing, skin, or other materials, and will burn eyes on contact.

 Explosive Hazard: The container can explode if it is heated or punctured.

The Inquiry Process of Science

Scientists are always asking a lot of questions. They are always inquiring. They want to understand why the things they observe, and wonder about, happen. Experiments are important tools scientists use to help them answer their questions.

When scientists plan experiments, they usually follow a simple set of steps.

Hints

- Answers may lead to additional questions. New questions often lead to new hypotheses and experiments. Don't be afraid to ask questions, or to rethink the ones you've already asked.

- Science grows when scientists ask questions, answer them, and are willing to question those answers. Scientific knowledge is always growing and changing.

Step 1
Ask a cause-and-effect question.

Step 2
Restate the question in the form of a hypothesis.

Step 3
Develop a procedure to test the hypothesis fairly.

Change procedure if there are flaws in the steps.

Step 4
Carry out the procedure and collect data.

Change procedure if data require it.

Step 5
Analyze and interpret the data.

Step 6
Form conclusions based on the data, and compare them with the hypothesis.

Step 7
Communicate the procedure and results of the experiment.

STEP 1 Ask a cause-and-effect question.

Asking questions is easy. Asking questions that lead to reliable answers is more challenging. That's the reason scientists usually ask cause-and-effect questions. Here are a few examples.

- How does the concentration of laundry detergent in wash water affect the cleanliness of clothing?

- How do different temperatures affect the growth of seedlings?

- How does the amount of moisture affect the growth of mould on bread?

Notice how the causes — the detergent, temperature, and moisture — are things that are changeable. For example, you can have different concentrations of detergent, different temperatures, and different amounts of moisture. Causes are manipulated or independent variables. They are factors that you change when you investigate a cause-and-effect question.

The results are changeable, too. For example, some clothes may become cleaner than others, or not clean at all. Some seedlings may grow better than others, or some might not grow at all. Some bread samples may have lots of mould, some may have less, and some might not have any. Results are responding or dependent variables. They change because of the manipulated variable.

When you ask a cause-and-effect question, you should include only one manipulated variable in your question. This allows you to see the effect of that variable on the responding variable.

STEP 2 Restate the question in the form of a hypothesis.

A hypothesis is a way of restating a cause-and-effect question so that it gives a reasonable, possible answer. Basically, a hypothesis is an intelligent guess at the solution to a problem or question. It is usually in the form of an "If ... then" statement and states the relationship between the manipulated and responding variables.

Here are hypotheses for the questions outlined in Step 1.

- If the concentration of the detergent is high, then clothing will become cleaner.

- If the temperature is decreased, then the seedlings will not grow as well.

- If the amount of moisture is increased, then the bread will get mouldier.

Hint

A hypothesis is an early step in the experiment-planning process. Your hypothesis can turn out to be "right," but it doesn't always. That's what the experiment is for — to test the hypothesis.

STEP 3 Develop a procedure to test the hypothesis fairly.

When you develop a procedure, you need to ask yourself some questions. Your answers to these questions will help you plan a fair and safe experiment. Here are some questions you should think about. These questions are answered for the seedling experiment.

- **Which manipulated variable do you want to investigate?** The manipulated variable is temperature.

- **How will you measure this variable (if it is measurable)?** You can measure temperature with a thermometer.

- **How will you keep all other variables constant (the same) so they don't affect your results?** In other words, how will you control your experiment so it is a fair test? To control the experiment, these variables should be kept constant: the amount of light the seedlings receive; the amount and temperature of water applied to the seedlings; the kind of soil the seedlings are planted in.

- **What materials and equipment will you need for the experiment?** The materials would include seedlings, soil, growing pots or containers (same size), water and a watering can, a light source, a thermometer, and a ruler or other measuring device.

- **How will you conduct the experiment safely?** What safety factors should you consider? Some of the safety factors to consider include putting the seedling pots in a place where they would not be disturbed, washing your hands after handling the materials, and making sure you don't have any allergies to the soil or seedlings you use.

- **How will you set up the procedure to get the data you need to test your hypothesis?** You could divide your seedlings into groups (e.g., three seedlings for each temperature) and grow each group at a certain temperature. You would keep track of how much each seedling in a group grew over a specified amount of time (e.g., four weeks) and calculate the average for the group.

STEP 4 Carry out the procedure and collect data.

Depending on the kind of experiment you have planned, you may choose to record the data you collect in the form of a chart or table, a labelled sketch, notes, or a combination of these. For example, a good way to record the seedling data would be in tables like the following one (one for each week of the experiment).

Week 1: Height of Seedling Grown at Different Temperatures				
Temperature seedlings grown at (°C)	Height of seedling 1 (cm)	Height of seedling 2 (cm)	Height of seedling 3 (cm)	Average height (cm)
20				
15				
10				

Hint

Analyzing the data you collect is the only way you have to assess your hypothesis. It's important that your record keeping be organized and neat.

STEP 5 Analyze and interpret the data.

Scientists look for patterns and relationships in their data. Often, making a graph can help them see patterns and relationships more easily. (Turn to Toolkit 8 for more about graphing.)

A graph of the seedling data would show you if there were a relationship between temperature and growth rate.

Hint

If you have access to a computer, find out if it has the software to help you make charts or graphs.

STEP 6 Form conclusions based on the data, and compare them with the hypothesis.

Usually, forming a conclusion is fairly straightforward. Either your data will support your hypothesis or they won't. Either way, however, you aren't finished answering your cause-and-effect question.

For example, if the seedlings did not grow as well in cooler temperatures, you can conclude that your data support your hypothesis. But you will still need to repeat your experiment several times to see if you get the same results over and over again. Doing your experiment successfully many times is the only way you and other scientists can have faith in your data and your conclusions.

If your data don't support your hypothesis, there are two possible reasons why.

- Perhaps your experimental plan was flawed and needs to be re-assessed and possibly planned again.

- Perhaps your hypothesis was incorrect and needs to be re-assessed and modified.

For example, if the seedlings grew better in the lower temperatures, you would have to re-think your hypothesis, or look at your experiment for flaws. You would need to ask questions to help you

evaluate and change either your hypothesis or plan. For example, you could ask: Do certain seedlings grow better at lower temperatures than others? Do different types of soil have more of an effect on growth than temperature?

Every experiment is different and will result in its own set of questions and conclusions.

Hint

You could also enlist the help of your classmates. If others have completed the same experiment and got the same results, the conclusions are usually reliable. If not, the hypothesis must be modified. Scientists often work this way to compare results.

STEP 7 Communicate the procedure and results of the experiment.

Scientists always share the results of their experiments with other people. They do this by summarizing how they performed the first six steps. Sometimes, they will write out a formal report stating their purpose, hypothesis, procedure, observations, and conclusions. Other times, they share their experimental results verbally, using drawings, charts, or graphs. (See Toolkits 6 and 8 for help on how to prepare your results.)

When you have finished your experiment, ask your teacher how he or she would like you to prepare your results so you can share them with the other students in your class.

The Problem-Solving Process for Technological Development

When you plan an experiment to answer a cause-and-effect question, you follow an orderly set of steps. The same is true for designing a model or prototype that solves a practical problem.

When people try to solve practical problems, they usually follow a simple set of steps.

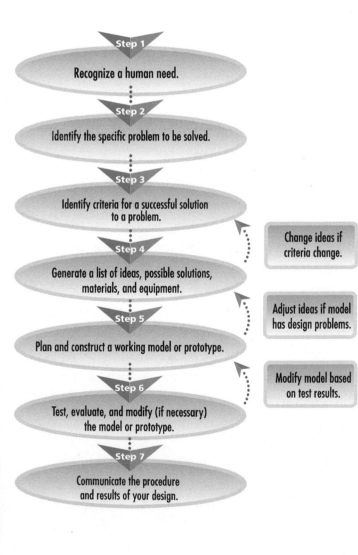

Step 1
Recognize a human need.

Step 2
Identify the specific problem to be solved.

Step 3
Identify criteria for a successful solution to a problem.

Change ideas if criteria change.

Step 4
Generate a list of ideas, possible solutions, materials, and equipment.

Adjust ideas if model has design problems.

Step 5
Plan and construct a working model or prototype.

Modify model based on test results.

Step 6
Test, evaluate, and modify (if necessary) the model or prototype.

Step 7
Communicate the procedure and results of your design.

STEP 1 Recognize a human need.

This involves recognizing what the problem is. For example, suppose you observe that a rope bridge across a ravine at a local park is very unstable and swings back and forth when crossed. This might be fine for people who want a thrill, but you find that most people are not comfortable crossing the bridge and don't get to enjoy one of the nicer areas of the park. You wish there were a way to make the bridge more stable so more people would use it. That is the situation or context of the problem.

STEP 2 Identify the specific problem to be solved.

When you understand a situation, you can then define the problem more exactly. This means identifying a specific task to carry out. In the situation with the bridge, the task might be to build a new bridge or add support to the existing bridge.

STEP 3 Identify criteria for a successful solution to a problem.

You have defined the problem and now you must look for solutions. But how will you know when you have found the best possible solution? Before you start looking for solutions, you need to establish your criteria for determining what a successful solution will be.

One of your criteria for success in the bridge example would be the completion of a stable bridge. The criteria you choose do not depend on which solution you select — whether to reinforce the old bridge or build a new bridge. In this case, whatever the solution, it must result in a stable bridge.

When you are setting your criteria for success, you must consider limits to your possible solutions.

For example, the bridge may have to be built within a certain time, so rebuilding completely may not be possible. Other limitations could include availability of materials, cost, number of workers needed, and safety.

If you are building a product or device for yourself, you may set the criteria for success and the limitations yourself. In class, your teacher will usually outline them.

Hint

Always consider safety. This includes safe handling and use of materials and equipment, as well as being aware of possible environmental impacts of your ideas. Discuss with your teacher and fellow students how your solution might affect the environment.

STEP 4 Generate a list of ideas, possible solutions, materials, and equipment.

Brainstorming, conducting research, or both, are key components of this step. When you brainstorm, remember to relax and let your imagination go. Brainstorming is all about generating as many ideas as possible without judging them. Record your ideas in the form of words, mind maps, sketches — whatever helps you best.

Conducting research may involve reading books and magazines, searching the Internet, interviewing people, or visiting stores. It all depends on what you are going to design.

One idea for the rope bridge would be to anchor the bridge with strong rope or thick metal wire to large rocks or to the hillside at either end of the

bridge. Sketches and diagrams would help to generate different ideas for the bridge design.

Hint

Humans have been inventors for tens of thousands of years — so take advantage of what has already been developed. When you're solving a problem, you don't have to "reinvent the wheel." See how others have solved the same problem before and use their efforts as inspiration. You can also look for ways to "build upon" or improve on their ideas.

STEP 5 Plan and construct a working model or prototype.

Choose one possible solution to develop. Start by making a list of the materials and equipment you will use. Then make a working diagram, or series of diagrams, on paper. This lets you explore and troubleshoot your ideas early on. Your labels should be detailed enough so that other people could build your design. Show your plans to your teacher before you begin construction work.

A simple model of the bridge could be made to show how and where components such as stabilizing wires could be added.

Hint

If things aren't working as you planned or imagined, be prepared to modify your plans as you construct your model or prototype.

STEP 6 Test, evaluate, and modify (if necessary) the model or prototype.

Testing lets you see how well your solution works. Testing also lets you know if you need to make modifications. Does your model or prototype meet all the established criteria? Does it solve the problem you designed it for?

Invite your classmates to try your product. Their feedback can help you decide what is and isn't working, and how to fix anything that needs fixing. Perhaps the stabilizing wires on the bridge model could be anchored elsewhere. Maybe more wires could be added.

Hints

- For every successful invention or product, there are thousands of unsuccessful ones. Sometimes it's better to start over from scratch than to follow a design that doesn't meet its performance criteria.

- Here's an old saying you've probably heard: "If at first you don't succeed, try, try again." Remember, there can be many possible solutions to a practical problem.

STEP 7 Communicate the procedure and results of your design.

Inventors and engineers create things to meet people's needs. When they make something new, they like to show it to other people and explain to them how it works. Sometimes they will use a carefully drawn diagram of the new device and write about how they performed the first six steps. Other times, they will show the device to people and explain verbally how it works and how they built it. Your teacher will tell you how to prepare your results so you can exhibit the new device you make.

The Decision-Making Process for Social and Environmental Issues

People can have many different viewpoints or perspectives about social and environmental issues. This usually means that an issue has more than one possible solution. Scientific and technological information can be used to increase our understanding of an issue and help resolve it.

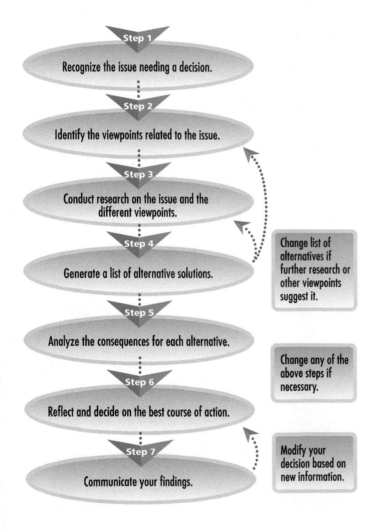

When people try to make a decision or reach a consensus about an issue, they need to use a decision-making process. Here are the steps in one possible process.

STEP 1 Recognize the issue needing a decision.

This involves recognizing that an issue exists. An issue is a controversy that needs to be resolved. It may have more than one possible solution, but the chosen one is usually the one that satisfies the most people. For example, suppose you and your friends want to have some trees in a public park cut down in order to make space for a playing field. Some members of your community feel that the trees should be preserved for the birds that nest there. The local environmental specialist says that when it rains, the trees protect a nearby stream by reducing run-off, so they should be left standing. Other people say that your idea of building a playing field is too expensive.

STEP 2 Identify the viewpoints related to the issue.

The viewpoints expressed in the example in step 1 are recreational (you and your friends), ecological (people who wish to leave the trees as they are), and economic (people who think that the cost would be too high).

People often evaluate issues using one or more viewpoints. Some of these viewpoints are:

- Cultural: interest in the customs and practices of a particular group of people

- Ecological: interest in the protection of the natural environment

- Economic: interest in the financial aspects of the situation

- Educational: interest in acquiring and sharing knowledge and skills

- Esthetic: interest in the beauty in art and nature

- Ethical: interest in beliefs about what is right and wrong

- Health and safety: interest in physical and mental well-being

- Historical: interest in knowledge dealing with past events

- Political: interest in the effect of the issue on governments, politicians, and political parties

- Recreational: interest in leisure activities

- Scientific: interest in knowledge based on the inquiry process of science (Toolkit 2)

- Social: interest in human relationships, public welfare, or society

- Technological: interest in the design and use of tools and processes that solve practical problems to satisfy peoples' wants and needs (Toolkit 3)

STEP 3 Conduct research on the issue and the different viewpoints.

You will be able to suggest an appropriate solution to an issue only if you understand the issue and the different viewpoints. It's important to gather unbiased information about the issue itself and then consider the information provided by people with different viewpoints.

Develop specific questions that will help to guide your research. Questions for the playing field issue might be:

- How many people will use the playing field?

- Is there another more suitable site for the playing field?

- What kind of birds nest in these trees? Could they nest elsewhere in the area?

- What is run-off and why is it a problem?

- What would be the full cost of building the playing field (including the cost of removing the trees)?

Conducting research may involve interviewing people, reading books and magazines, searching the Internet, or making a field trip. It is important to evaluate your sources of information to determine if there is a bias and to separate fact from opinion. In this step, you are trying to gain a better understanding of the background of the issue, the viewpoints of different groups, the alternative solutions, and the consequences of each alternative. You will find tips on how to conduct research in the following section on researching topics.

STEP 4 Generate a list of alternative solutions.

Examine the background of the issue and the viewpoints in order to generate a list of alternative solutions. Brainstorming can be a useful component of this step. Use your research to help guide your thinking.

Examples of possible alternatives for the issue in step 1 might be as follows:

- Cut the trees and build the playing field.

- Leave the park as it is.

- Find another more suitable location.

- Modify the plan in the existing park.

STEP 5 Analyze the consequences for each alternative.

Decide how you will measure the risks and benefits for the consequences of each alternative solution. You may decide to examine the importance, likelihood, and duration of each possible consequence. The importance of the consequence and the likelihood of its occurrence can be ranked high (3), moderate (2), low (1), or none (0). Duration is considered short term (S) if it is less than 50 years or long term (L) if it is longer than 50 years. Ask how many people will benefit from the alternative and how many will be affected negatively. Make sure to consider health and safety.

For the playing field example, you could analyze the consequences of each alternative solution in a table like the one shown below.

Analysis of Consequences: Alternative 1 — Build the playing field in the park.

Consequence	Importance (3, 2, 1, 0)	Likelihood of occurrence (3, 2, 1, 0)	Duration (S, L)
Trees cut	2	3	L
Run-off	3	3	S
Birds move	2 to 1	3	L
Playing field well used	2	2	possibly L
Development and maintenance cost	2 to 1	3	L

STEP 6 Reflect and decide on the best course of action.

Evaluate your decision-making process to ensure that each step is completed as fully as possible. Consider the consequences of the alternative solutions and how people will respond to each one. Then decide on what you think is the best course of action.

STEP 7 Communicate your findings.

Communicate your findings in an appropriate way. For example, you may prepare a written report, a verbal presentation, or a position for a debate or a public hearing role-play. Defend your position by clearly stating your case and presenting supporting evidence from a variety of sources.

Researching Topics

Research involves finding out something about a topic or subject. That means going to certain resources that will give you accurate information. Information can be found just about anywhere: from your home bookshelves to the public library, from asking experts to looking on the Internet. Here is the process you should follow when you do your research.

Choosing a Topic

In some situations, your teacher may give you the topic to research. Other times, you will select one of your own, such as the issue described above. If you have trouble coming up with a topic, try brainstorming ideas either by yourself or with a group. Remember, when you brainstorm, there are no right or wrong answers, just "ideas." Here are some brainstorming suggestions to get you started:

- List two or three general topics about science that interest you.

- For each topic, spend a few minutes writing down as many words or ideas that relate to that topic. They don't have to be directly connected to science.

- Share your list with others and ask them to suggest other possibilities.

- Now you have to "filter" your idea list to find a topic to research. In other words, go through your ideas until you find two or three that interest you. To help you narrow your idea list, try grouping similar words or ideas, modifying what you've written, or even writing down a new idea. Sometimes, too, working with other people will help to focus your thoughts.

- When you settle on an idea for your topic, write it down. Try to explain it in a couple of sentences or a short paragraph. Do that for each of your two or three topic ideas.

- Have your teacher approve your topics. Now you're ready to go!

Which Topic Should I Choose?

How does product design help sell a product?

How do gears improve the performance of a bicycle?

The next thing you have to do is settle on one topic. (Remember, you should start your research with two or three topic ideas.) One way to help you decide is to determine how easy it will be to find information on your topic.

- Use some of the resources listed under "Finding Information" to do your preliminary research.

- If you can't easily find at least four good references for a topic, consider dropping it and going on to the next idea.

Hint

Sometimes topics are too broad in scope or too general to make good research reports (for example, "transportation" instead of just "bicycles"). Try rewriting your topic to narrow its focus.

If all the topics are easy to research, then you'll need some other criteria to help you decide. Think about

- which topic interests you the most

- which topic is not being researched by many students in your class

- which topic interests you the least

How Hard Will It Be to Find Information?

How Camera Lenses Are Manufactured

How Mirrors Are Used in Some Optical Devices

Once you've finally chosen your topic, you might want to work with other students and your teacher to:

- finalize its wording

- make sure it matches the project or assignment you are doing

Finding Information

There are many resources that you can use to look up information. You'll find some of these resources:

- in your school

- in your community (such as your public library)

- on the Internet

- in CD-ROM encyclopedias and databases

Here is a suggested list of resources.

Resource	✓	Details
Books		
CD-ROMs		
Community Professionals or Experts		
Encyclopedias		
Films		
Government Agencies (local, provincial, and federal)		
Internet Sites		
Journals		
Library Catalogue		
Newspapers		
Non-profit Organizations		
Posters		
DVDs and Videos		

Searching Tips

Finding Information at Your Library

Library computer catalogues are a fast way to find books on the subjects you are researching. Most of these electronic catalogues have four ways to search: *subject*, *author*, *title*, and *key words*. If you know the *author* or *title* of a book, just type it in. Otherwise, use the *subject* and *key words* searches to find books on your topic.

- If you're doing a *subject* search, type in the main topic you are researching. For example, if you're searching for information on solar energy, type in "solar energy." If there are no books on that topic, try again using a more general category, like "renewable resources," or just "energy."

- If you're doing a *key words* search, type in any combination of words that have to do with your topic. For the solar energy example, you could type in

words such as: "renewable energy sun solar panels." Using several key words will give you a more specific search. Using only one or two key words, like "sun" and "energy," will give you a more general search.

Hints

- The library may also have a way to search for magazine articles. This is called a *periodical search*. It's especially useful for searching for information on events and/or discoveries that have taken place recently. Ask your librarian how to do a periodical search.

- Your library will probably have a reference section where all the encyclopedias are kept. There you may find science and technology, environmental, or even animal encyclopedias, as well as other reference books.

Finding Information on the Internet

On the Internet, you can use searching programs, called *search engines*, to search the Internet on just about any subject. To find a search engine, ask your teacher or click on the search icon found at the top of your Internet browser. Here are some suggestions on how to search the Internet:

- Once you reach a search engine Web page, type in key words or phrases that have to do with your topic. For solar energy, you could type in "solar energy," "solar panels," "renewable resources," or any combination of these and other similar words.

- The search engine will display a list of Web pages it has found that have these words or phrases somewhere in them. Click on any Web page on the list that looks interesting.

- Quite often you will get a long list of possible Web pages to look at. You may need to make your search more specific. This can be done by adding other key words to your search. For example, if you were looking for solar energy examples in Canada and used the key word "solar energy," you may want to do a second search of these results with the key word "Canada" added.

- Don't forget to record the addresses of any interesting Web pages you find. Why not work with a friend? One person can record the addresses of Web pages while the other person searches on the computer. Or you can

save any Web page as a *bookmark* for easy future access. Check with your teacher or librarian to find out how to save and organize your bookmarks.

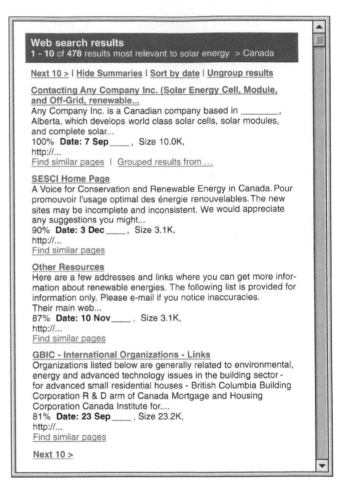

BEFORE YOU START!

Check with your teacher to find out what your school's policy is about acceptable use of the Internet. Remember to follow this policy whenever you use the Internet at school. Be aware as you use the Internet that some websites may be strongly biased toward a specific point of view. If you are looking for scientific or technical information, educational or government websites are generally reliable.

Recording Your Information Sources

An important part of researching a topic is keeping track of where you obtain information. As you do your research, you are reading through or viewing a variety of different sources. Some may be in print, such as magazines and books. Others may be electronic, such as websites and CD-ROMs. And others may be visual, such as videos and photos. No matter what sources you use, you should keep track of them.

With this information, you can easily go back and check details. You can also use it to help you respond to any questions about the accuracy or completeness of your information. Your record of sources should include at least the following basic information:

- title or name of the source (e.g., if you read a chapter of a book, you would write down the book's title; for a website, you would include the address)

- author's name, if known

- publisher (e.g., for a website, this would be the name of the person or the organization that has put up the site)

- date of publication

- pages consulted

Your teacher may want you to list your information sources in a specific format. Check what this format will be before you begin your research so that you can collect the details you need to complete your reference list later. You may want to do your own research on formats for such reference lists or bibliographies.

Reading in Science

You use different skills and strategies when reading different materials such as a novel or a textbook. In a novel, you are mainly reading to enjoy the story. In a science textbook you are reading for information. A science textbook has terms and concepts that you need to understand.

Investigating Science and Technology 8 helps you with your non-fiction reading by giving you opportunities to use different reading strategies. You will find these reading strategies in the following literacy activities:

- Getting Ready to Read at the beginning of each unit

- Before Reading at the beginning of each chapter

- During Reading or Writing Checkpoints in each section

- After Reading at the end of each chapter

Using Reading Strategies

You can use the following strategies to help better understand the information presented in this book.

Before Reading

- Skim the section you are going to read. Look at the headings, subheadings, visuals, and boldfaced words to determine the topic.

- Look at how the information is organized. Ask yourself: Is it a cause-and-effect passage? Is it a contrast and compare passage? Think about how the organization can help you access the information.

- Think about what you already know about the topic.

- Predict what you will learn.

- List questions that you have about the topic. This will help you to set a purpose for reading.

As You Read

- Rewrite the section headings and subheadings as questions. Look for the answers to the questions as you read.

- Use your answers to the questions to decide on the main idea in each section or subsection.

- Look carefully at any visuals — photographs, illustrations, charts, or graphs. Read the captions and labels that go with the illustrations and photographs, and the titles of any charts or graphs. Think about the information the visuals give you and how this information helps you understand the ideas presented in the text.

- Notice the terms that are boldfaced (dark and heavy type). These are important words that will help you understand and write about the information in the section. Make sure you understand the terms and how they are used. Check the terms in the Glossary to confirm their meanings.

- Use different strategies to help remember what you read. For example, you can make mental pictures, make connections to what you know, or draw a sketch.

After Reading

- Find the information to answer any review questions. Use the headings and boldfaced terms to locate the information needed. Even if you are sure of the answer, reread to confirm that your answer is correct.

- Write brief notes to synthesize what you have learned, or organize the information in a graphic organizer. You will find information about graphic organizers in the following section.

- Personalize the information. Think about opinions you have on what you've read. Consider if the new information you have learned has changed any previous ideas. List questions you still have about the topic.

Using Graphic Organizers

Graphic organizers can be used to organize information that you read, and to display ideas visually. You have probably learned and used several of the techniques shown here. Try out the ones that are less familiar to you. You may find that some help you open up your thinking in new and creative ways.

Venn Diagram

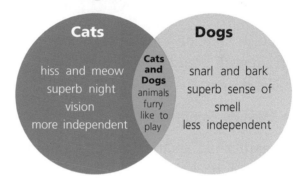

Venn diagrams are usually used to compare two things by showing their similarities and differences. To use a Venn diagram, ask yourself questions such as:

- What things do I want to compare?
- What do they have in common?
- In what ways are they different?

Hint

You can use Venn diagrams to compare more than two things. Try it and see!

Concept Map

Concept Map for Green Plants

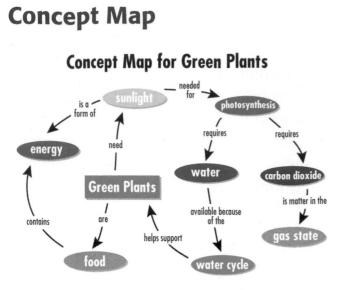

A concept map, or a mind map, is a web diagram with many uses. For example, you can use it to:

- review something you already know

- gather information about something you don't know

- explore new ways of thinking about something

- outline plans for an essay, a song, an experiment, a design challenge, a science project, and multimedia presentations

To use a concept map, ask yourself questions such as:

- What is the key idea, word, question, problem, or issue to build the map around?

- What words, ideas, objects, or questions come to mind when I think about the item at the centre of my map?

- How are the ideas, objects and concepts on my map linked or connected to each other?

Hint

If you have access to a computer, find out if it has the software to help you make your graphic organizers.

Tree Diagram

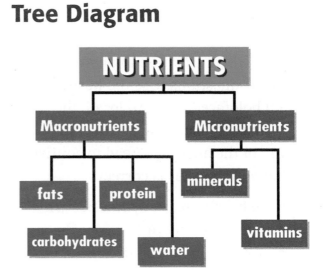

Tree diagrams allow you to see how things originate or how larger things can be broken down into their smaller components. Tree diagrams also allow you to organize or group concepts and things. Knowing about the parts of something helps you to better understand the concept or thing you are studying.

Comparison Matrix

	Characteristics			
Things to compare	walk	use food	talk	swim
goat	X	X	X	
tree		X		
rock				
person	X	X	X	X

This is often used to compare the characteristics or properties of a number of things. To use a comparison matrix, ask yourself questions such as:

- What things do I want to compare?

- What characteristics will I choose to compare?

- How are the things I'm comparing similar and how are they different?

Hint

A comparison matrix can be useful for brainstorming.

Note-Taking Chart

A note-taking chart helps you understand how the material you are reading is organized. It also helps you keep track of information as you read.

Your teacher will assign several pages for you to read. Before you begin reading, look at each heading and turn it into a question. Try to use "how," "what," or "why" to begin each question. Write your questions in the left hand column of your chart. Leave enough space between each question so that you can record information from your reading that answers your question.

For example, you may be assigned several pages about the scientific meaning of work. These pages contain the following headings:

- The Meaning of Work
- Calculating Work
- Energy and Work

You can see an example of a note-taking chart below.

Questions from Headings	Answers from Reading
What is the meaning of the word "work"?	– work is done when a force acts on an object to make the object move – If there's no movement, no work is done – just trying to push something isn't work—it's only work if the object moves
How do you calculate work?	
How are energy and work related?	

Communicating in Science

In science, you use your communication skills to clearly show your knowledge, ideas, and understanding. You can use words and visuals, such as diagrams, charts, and tables, to communicate what you know. Some communication may be short, as in answering questions, or long, as in reports.

Writing Reports

Toolkit 2 shows you how to plan a science experiment. Toolkit 3 shows you how to do technological design, and Toolkit 4 shows you how to use a decision-making process for social and environmental issues. Here you will learn how to write a report so you can communicate the procedure and results of your work.

Here is a list of things you should try to do when writing your science reports.

- Give your report or project a title.

- Tell readers why you did the work.

- State your hypothesis or describe the design challenge.

- List the materials and equipment you used.

- Describe the steps you took when you did your experiment, designed and made your product, or considered an issue.

- Show your experimental data, the results of testing your product, or the background information on the issue.

- Interpret and analyze the results of your experiment.

- Make conclusions based on the outcome of the experiment, the success of the product you designed, or the research you did on an issue.

Give your report or project a title.

Write a brief title on the top of the first page of your report. Your title can be one or two words that describe a product you designed and made, or it can be a short sentence that summarizes an experiment you performed, or it can state the topic of an issue you explored.

Tell readers why you did the work.

Use a heading such as "Introduction" or "Purpose" for this section. Here, you give your reasons for doing a particular experiment, designing and making a particular product, or considering a specific issue. If you are writing about an experiment, tell readers what your cause-and-effect question is. If you designed a product, explain why this product is needed, what it will do, who might use it, and who might benefit from its use. If you were considering an issue, state what the issue is and why you have prepared this report about it.

State your hypothesis or describe the design challenge.

If you are writing about an experiment, use a heading such as "Hypothesis." Under this heading you will state your hypothesis.

Your hypothesis is your guess at the solution to a problem or question. It makes a prediction that your experiment will test. Your hypothesis must indicate the relationship between the manipulated and responding variable.

If you are writing about a product you designed, use a heading such as "Design Challenge." Under this heading, you will describe why you decided to design your product the way you did. Explain how and why you chose your design over other possible designs.

List the materials and equipment you used.

This section can come under a heading called "Materials and Equipment." List all the materials and equipment you used for your experiment or design project. Your list can be in point form or set up as a table or chart. Remember to include the exact amounts of materials used, when possible (for example, the number of nails used in building a model or the volumes and masses of substances tested in an experiment). Include the exact measurements and proper units for all materials used.

Also include diagrams to show how you set up your equipment or how you prepared your materials. Remember to label the important features on your diagrams. (See the following section on diagrams for drawing tips.)

Describe the steps you took when you did your experiment, designed and made your product, or considered an issue.

Under a heading called "Procedure" or "Method," describe, in detail, the steps you followed when doing your experiment, designing and making your product, or considering an issue. If you made a product, describe how you tested it. If you had to alter your design, describe in detail how you did this.

Show your experimental data, the results of testing your product, or the background information on the issue.

Give this section a heading such as "Data," "Observations," or "Background Information." In this section, you should show the data or information you collected while performing the experiment, testing your product, or researching an issue. In reporting about an issue, use only a summary of the essential information needed for a reader to understand the issue and different viewpoints about it.

Use tables, diagrams, and any other visual aids that show the results of your tests. If you performed your experiment a few times, give results for each trial. If you tested different designs of your product, give results for each design.

Interpret and analyze the results of your experiment.

Interpret and analyze the data you collected in your experiment. Calculations, graphs, diagrams, charts, or other visual aids may be needed. (See Toolkit 8 for graphing tips.) Explain any calculations or graphs that you used to help explain your results.

Make conclusions based on the outcome of the experiment, the success of the product you designed, or the research you did on an issue.

This last section of your report can be called "Conclusions." In one or two paragraphs, explain what your tests and experiments showed, or what decision you made as a result of your research.

If you did an experiment, explain if your results were predicted by the hypothesis. Describe how you might adjust the hypothesis because of what you learned from doing the experiment, and how you might test this new hypothesis.

If you made a product, explain if your design did what it was supposed to do, or worked the way it was supposed to work. If you changed the design of your product, explain why one design is better than another.

Describe the practical applications your product or experiment might have for the world outside the classroom.

If you considered an issue, explain why you made your decision. Briefly summarize your supporting evidence. If necessary, explain how you have responded to different viewpoints on the issue.

Diagrams

Have you heard the saying "a picture is worth a thousand words"? In science, a picture can be worth even more. A carefully done diagram can help you express your ideas, record important information, and experiment with designs. Diagrams are an important tool in communicating what you know and your ideas.

Four types of diagrams you can use are a Simple Sketch, an Isometric Diagram, an Orthographic (Perspective) Diagram, and a Computer-Assisted Diagram. Examples of these types of diagrams are shown on the next two pages.

The photo on this page shows the set-up of an experiment. Practise drawing it using one or several of the diagram types presented on the next pages. What labels would you include? Would your labelling choices change depending on the style of diagram you make?

Tools of the Trade

You will need the following equipment for each type of diagram.

Hand-drawing tools
- a sharp pencil or mechanical pencil
- a pencil sharpener or extra leads
- an eraser
- a ruler

For simple and isometric diagrams
- blank white paper

For orthographic drawings
- blank orthographic graph paper

For computer-assisted diagrams
- access to computer and software

Remember!

- Give your diagram a title at the top of the page.

- Use the whole page for your diagram.

- Include only those details that are necessary, keep them simple, and identify them by name.

- If you need labels, use lines, not arrows. Place your labels in line with the feature being labelled, and use a ruler to keep your lines straight.

- Don't use colour or shading unless your teacher asks you to.

Hint

If you're going to use your diagram to help you design a structure, include a top, side, and front view.

A Simple Sketch (Front View)

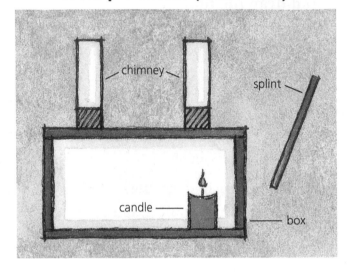

chimney

splint

candle

box

A Simple Sketch (Side View)

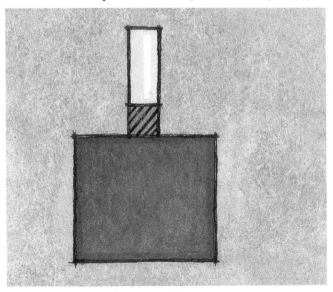

A Simple Sketch (Top View)

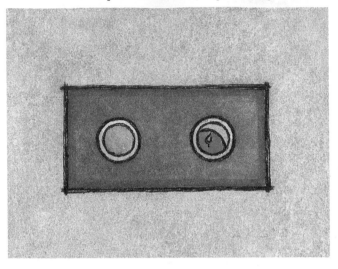

An Isometric Diagram

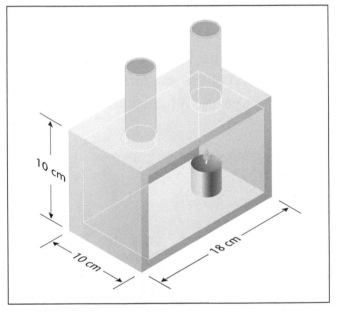

10 cm

10 cm

18 cm

Hint

You can use the squares of your graph paper to make the scale of your orthographic diagram accurate. For example, suppose that each square stood for 1 cm. If what you're drawing is 14 cm long, you would use 14 squares to represent its length.

An Orthographic (Perspective) Drawing

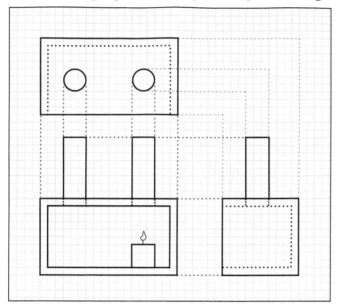

A Computer-Assisted Diagram

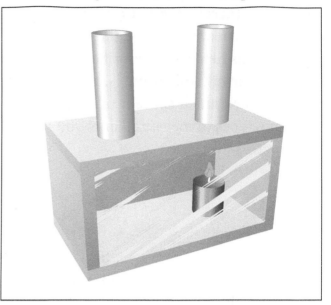

Hint

Use graph paper to help you with the details of your diagram if you don't have a ruler handy.

Hint

One advantage of using a computer is that you can easily change your work. After saving your original, practise making changes and moving the image around.

Measurement

Observations from an experiment may be qualitative (descriptive) or quantitative (physical measurements). Quantitative observations help us to describe such things as how far away something is, how massive it is, and how much space it takes up. Here are some types of measurements you might come across every day.

Length

Length tells you

- how long or short something is
- how far or near something is
- how high or low something is
- how large or small something is

Common units used to measure length include millimetres (mm), centimetres (cm), metres (m), and kilometres (km). All these units are based on a single standard: the metre.

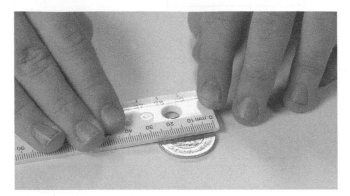

When you use a measuring tool such as a ruler, look directly in line with the measurement point, not from an angle.

Volume

The volume of something tells you the amount of space that it takes up (occupies). Common units used to measure volume include litres (L) and millilitres (mL). Remember, 1 mL equals 1 cm^3.

At home, you often use a measuring cup to determine the volume of something. At school, you usually use a graduated cylinder. Here, "graduated" means a container that has been marked with regular intervals for measuring. For example, a measuring cup, a beaker, and a thermometer are all graduated.

When you add a liquid to a graduated cylinder, the top of the liquid is curved near the sides of the cylinder. This curve is called a meniscus. To measure the liquid's volume

---

INSTANT PRACTICE

For each of the following, choose the unit of measurement that you think would be used. Explain why you chose that unit of measurement in each case.

1. the height of your best friend

2. the altitude of a satellite

3. the thickness of your textbook

4. the length of a mosquito's wing

5. the depth of the deep end of a swimming pool

6. the distance between Canada and Australia

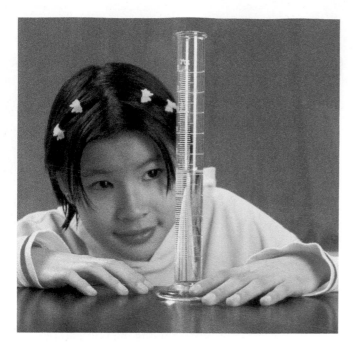

properly, you need to observe the liquid's surface from eye level so you can see the flat, bottom portion of the curve. Ignore the sides.

INSTANT PRACTICE

1. Each of the following objects takes up space. Estimate the volume of each, using appropriate units.

   (a) a basketball

   (b) a light bulb

   (c) a school locker

2. Certain ancient volume measures, such as the teaspoon, are still in use today. Write a fictional paragraph describing where the ancient Talmudic volume measure "ke'zayit" originated. One ke'zayit is approximately 6 mL.

Mass and Weight

In science, the mass of an object and its weight mean different things. The mass of something tells you the amount of matter it has. The weight of an object is the measure of the force of gravity acting on it. We use mass more often in science. Common units used to measure mass include grams (g) and kilograms (kg).

You usually measure mass with a balance. Your classroom probably has an equal arm balance or a triple beam balance like the ones shown here.

The equal arm balance and triple beam balance basically work in the same way. You compare the mass of the object you are measuring with standard or known masses (or their mass equivalent values on the triple beam).

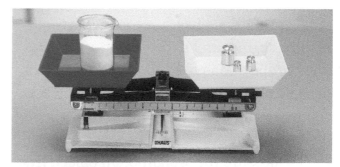

equal arm balance

An equal arm balance has two pans. You place the object whose mass you want to know on one pan. On the other pan, you place standard (known) masses until the two pans are balanced (level). Then, you just add up the values of the standard masses. The total is the mass of the object you are measuring.

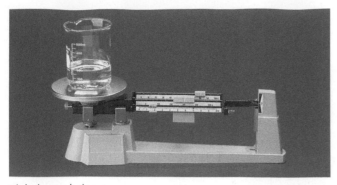

triple beam balance

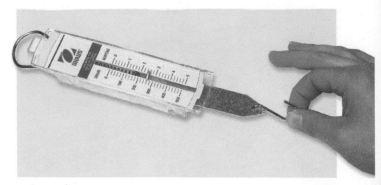

spring scale

A triple beam balance has a single pan. You place the object you are measuring on the pan. You adjust the masses on the beams until the beam assembly is level. Then, you add up the mass equivalent values of the beam masses from the scales on the beam.

You can use a spring scale to measure weight, which is the force of gravity acting on an object. A spring scale is sometimes called a force meter. A spring scale measures force in newtons.

A spring scale has three main parts: a hook, a spring, and a measuring scale. The hook at the end is used to attach the object to the scale. The spring pulls on the object. As the spring pulls, the pointer moves along the measuring scale.

To measure the weight of an object, first hang the spring scale from a clamp on a retort stand. Then hang the object from the hook of the spring scale. Once the pointer stops moving, record the measurement.

INSTANT PRACTICE

1. Describe how you would determine if a cube of ice weighs the same as the water that remains after it melts. All you can use is an ice cube, a beaker, and a triple-beam balance, and you cannot make a mess!

2. Explain why the following statement is false: "An object on the Moon has less mass than it does on Earth." Rewrite this sentence so it is true.

Estimating

When you estimate, you use your mind to guess the length, volume, or mass of an object. Sometimes, you can estimate by comparing one object with another object that has known measurements. For example, if you are asked to estimate the volume of your drink, you could estimate by comparing it with a large jar of mayonnaise that has its volume marked on the label.

Try to estimate the measurements of the items listed below. Include the measurement units that you think should go with your estimates. Then, measure them to see how close your estimates were to the real values. Did you choose the correct measurement units? If you don't have some of these items in your classroom, check at home.

Object	Length	
	estimate (cm)	actual value (cm)
pencil		
height of your teacher's desk		
length of your classroom		

For a large object or distance, you might divide it up into portions in your mind and guess the length, volume, or mass of one portion. You then multiply that guess by the number of imaginary portions to estimate the measurement of the whole.

Sometimes, it's useful to estimate the measurement of an object before you actually measure it. You might do this to help you decide which units of measurement and which measuring tool to use. In other cases, you might not be able to measure an object at all. In this case, an estimate of its length, volume, or mass might be the best you can do.

Object	Mass	
	estimate (g)	actual value (g)
this textbook		
banana from someone's lunch		
piece of chalk		

Object	Volume	
	estimate (mL)	actual value (mL)
amount of water poured into an empty jar		
marker cap		
drink thermos		

Graphing

Science and technology often involve collecting a lot of numerical data. This data may be recorded in tables or charts. Sometimes, however, it's difficult to see if there are any patterns in the numbers. That's when it's useful to reorganize the data into graphs. Graphs help to interpret data collected during an experiment by showing how numbers are related to one another. You have probably drawn a lot of graphs over the years in your studies of mathematics, geography, and, of course, science and technology.

poured hot water into a large container (Container A) and cold water into a smaller container (Container B). After recording the starting temperatures of the water in each container, they placed Container B inside Container A and took measurements every 30 s until there were no more temperature changes.

Here are the data they collected shown as a chart and as a line graph. On the graph, they put the manipulated variable — time — on the x-axis, and the responding variable — temperature — on the y-axis.

Creating Line Graphs

Line graphs are good for exploring data collected for many types of experiments. Using line graphs is a good way to analyze the data of an experiment that are continually changing. For example, here are some data collected by a group of students investigating temperature changes. They

Evidence

Temperature of Water in Container A and Container B		
Time (s)	Temperature (°C) of water in Container A	Temperature (°C) of water in Container B
0	51	0
30	45	7
60	38	14
90	33	20
120	30	22
150	29	23
180	28	24
210	27	25
240	26	26
270	26	26
300	26	26

Analysis

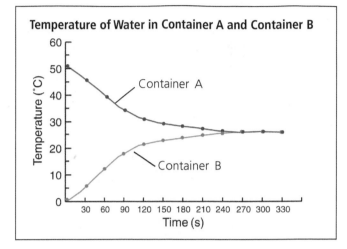

Temperature of Water in Container A and Container B

Creating Bar Graphs

Bar graphs are useful for showing relationships between separate sets of data. For example, the chart below shows the monthly average precipitation (both snow and rain) for a city in Canada. Compare the data in this chart with how they "look" when they are reorganized in the form of a bar graph. On the graph, they put the manipulated variable — month — on the x-axis, and the responding variable — precipitation — on the y-axis.

Month	Average Precipitation (mm)
January	50.4
February	46.0
March	61.1
April	70.0
May	66.0
June	67.1
July	71.4
August	76.8
September	63.5
October	61.8
November	62.7
December	64.7

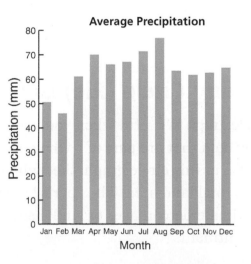

INSTANT PRACTICE

1. When their students draw graphs, most teachers prefer the graphs to be large. Why do you think it is usually better to draw a large graph instead of a smaller one?

2. The scale of an axis is the division of the axis into regular intervals. If you had a piece of graph paper with 28 squares to represent 10 min of time, suggest the scale you would use.

3. Examine the graph of the experiment shown above. Write a paragraph describing what you see happening on the graph.

4. Every 30 s, the temperature was taken. Why is the x-axis labelled "(s)" for seconds instead of "(min)" for minutes? Why is this important?

5. Why is it important to include the units on both the x- and y-axis labels?

Hint

Scales for bar graphs are often rounded off to the nearest whole number.

Percentage of Earth's Land Area

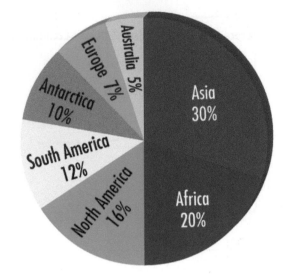

INSTANT PRACTICE

1. Each bar on a bar graph is the same width. Why?

2. Which axis is used for the responding variable? Is this always true on bar graphs? Your graph paper is 32 squares by 24 squares. August has the most precipitation of any month, with 76.8 mm. Sketch how you would create the scales to show 12 months of precipitation on a bar graph.

3. Could this data be graphed on a line graph? What is the main reason for using a bar graph instead of a line graph?

4. The next year, the data for the same city have changed. July, the wettest month, had a record amount of rainfall, 144.3 mm. How would this change in data cause the scale of your graph to change? Using the same graph paper as in question 2, sketch your new axes.

Hint

You might consider using a computer to draw your circle graphs. Some computer drawing programs allow you to use different colours for the different sections of your graph, making it easier to read.

Compare the data in this chart with how they "looked" when they were organized in the form of a circle graph on the previous page. Which can you interpret more easily and more quickly?

Creating Circle (Pie) Graphs

A circle graph is useful when you want to display data that are part of a whole. For example, in this circle graph, the "whole" is Earth's total land area. The "parts" are the approximate percentages of land made up by each continent.

Continent	Percentage of Earth's Land Area
Asia	30%
Africa	20%
North America	16%
South America	12%
Antarctica	10%
Europe	7%
Australia	5%

INSTANT PRACTICE

1. Your teacher asks the class to determine which continents, when added together, make up approximately half of Earth's land area. How many different answers could be correct? Why is the circle graph easier to use than the table of data to answer this question?

2. A survey in a class of 30 students showed the following when they were asked about their morning behaviour:

   • 10 students watched TV before school

   • 10 students listened to the radio before school

   • 5 students visited with their family before school

   • 5 students do not have time to do anything before school; they wake up too late.

   Sketch the circle graph of this data.

Using a Microscope

Classroom microscopes are compound microscopes. They are called "compound" because they have two or more lenses for viewing and magnifying objects. To view an object with a microscope, light must travel through the object. For this reason, the full name for your microscope is compound light microscope. Usually, it is shortened by leaving the word "light" out.

Before using a microscope, make sure you are familiar with its different parts and their uses. Take a look at the diagram below to remind yourself. Notice the path that light takes through a microscope to your eye.

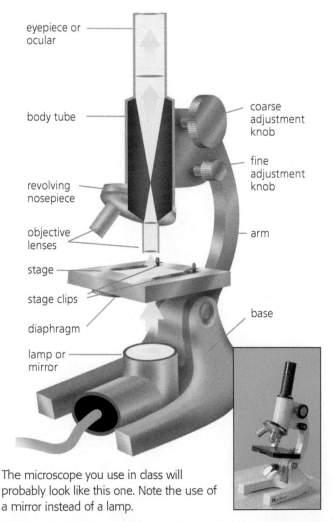

- eyepiece or ocular
- body tube
- revolving nosepiece
- objective lenses
- stage
- stage clips
- diaphragm
- lamp or mirror
- coarse adjustment knob
- fine adjustment knob
- arm
- base

The microscope you use in class will probably look like this one. Note the use of a mirror instead of a lamp.

How to Use the Microscope

1. Plug in the microscope and turn on the light source. If your microscope uses a mirror instead of a lamp, be very careful *not* to reflect direct sunlight into the microscope. You could badly damage your eyes.

2. Rotate the revolving nosepiece until the low-power objective lens (the smallest one) is pointing at the stage.

3. Place your slide on the stage. Use the stage clips to hold your slide in place.

4. Watch the stage from one side of the microscope. Carefully turn the coarse adjustment knob until the lens is as close to the slide as possible without touching it. Make sure you don't hit the slide with the lens.

5. Look through the eyepiece. Slowly turn the coarse adjustment knob to move the lens away from the stage. This will focus the image.

6. Use the fine adjustment knob to sharpen the focus of the image.

7. When your slide is in focus, try using the medium-power objective lens. Watch from the side of the microscope. Carefully rotate the nosepiece to move the medium-power lens so that it points at the stage. You should hear a "click" when it is in place. Use the fine adjustment knob to focus the image.

> **CAUTION!**
> Never use the coarse adjustment knob with the medium- and high-power objective lenses.

8. When your slide is once more in focus, try using the high-power objective lens. Repeat step 7 to change the lens from medium to high power. Make sure you watch from the side of the microscope to avoid hitting the slide with the lens.

Handling Hints

When using and handling a microscope, be sure to follow these rules:

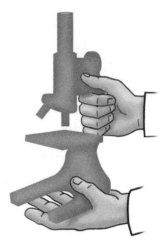

- Always use both hands to hold and carry a microscope. Support its base with one hand and hold it by the arm with your other hand.

- Place your microscope away from the edge of your desk or work area.

- Except for your notebook, writing tools, and microscope-related equipment such as glass slides, keep your desk or work area clear and neat.

- When you aren't using your microscope, always keep it in an upright position.

- Always hold glass slides by their edges, between your thumb and forefinger.

- Try keeping both eyes open when you look through the microscope. You'll be able to observe longer without tiring the muscles around your eyes.

- When you are finished using your microscope, switch back to the low-power objective, put its plastic cover on, and return it to the place where you got it.

Drawing Hints

Here are some basic guidelines for drawing what you see through the microscope. Your teacher may have other suggestions as well.

1. Start with a sharp pencil and a blank, unlined piece of paper (or a clean page in your notebook). Use the whole page for your drawing.

2. Using a mathematical compass, draw a circle with a diameter of 10 cm to 12 cm. This represents the view you see through the eyepiece. Scientists call it a *field of view*, or just *field* for short.

3. Draw only what you see. Keep your details simple and straightforward. (You don't need to add colouring or shading.)

4. Add labels that identify features by name (if you know them) or with brief notes. Always draw your label lines with a ruler. Arrange your labels and label lines clearly and neatly on the page. Record which objective lens you used to observe the image.

5. Give your drawing a title at the top of the page.

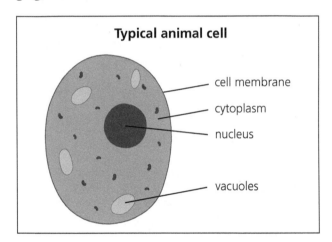

Typical animal cell

cell membrane
cytoplasm
nucleus

vacuoles

Glossary

Note: The number in parentheses at the end of each definition indicates the page number in this book where the term is defined.

A

action-at-a-distance force force that can push or pull an object without touching it; also called a non-contact force (99)

aquifer underground freshwater reservoir (282)

automated system replacement of human workers with machines that are controlled by a computer (167)

B

bias obvious opinion about an issue (347)

bioremediation technique of using living organisms to clean up contamination in land and water (353)

buoyancy tendency of an object in a fluid to rise or sink due to density differences with its surroundings (219)

buoyant force upward force exerted by a fluid (219)

C

cancer disease related to the uncontrolled and rapid reproduction of cells through cell division (73)

cell basic structural unit of an organism and the building block of life; all living things are made of cells (11)

cell division process by which a cell divides into two new cells (13)

cell membrane thin covering that holds the cytoplasm and organelles inside a cell and controls the passage of materials in or out of the cell (18)

cell theory (1) the cell is the basic unit of life; (2) all organisms are made up of one or more cells; (3) all cells come from existing cells (13)

cell wall rigid structure that surrounds the cell membrane of plant cells; provides strength and support for a plant cell (18)

cellular respiration process by which mitochondria provide energy for plant and animal cells by transforming oxygen and sugar (food) into carbon dioxide and water (51)

cellular transport movement of substances into and out of a cell; involves several different processes, such as diffusion and osmosis (25)

chlorine chemical used to disinfect water (i.e., kill organisms) (308)

chloroplast membrane-bound organelle of a plant cell that contains a green substance (pigment) called chlorophyll; chlorophyll uses the Sun's energy to convert carbon dioxide and water into sugar and oxygen in a process called photosynthesis (18)

circulatory system system made up of the heart, blood vessels, and blood; main purpose is to move nutrients, gases, and wastes throughout the body (68)

component part of a system (158)

compound light microscope microscope that uses light focussed through several different lenses, which make up the eyepiece and the objective lenses, to form a magnified image of a specimen (14)

compressibility property of being able to be compressed or made more compact (229)

compression decrease in volume caused by a force (229)

connective tissue tissue that supports and connects different parts of the body (e.g., blood, fat, cartilage, tendons, bone) (63)

consumer individual who uses the goods or services provided by a system (160)

contact force force that acts between objects that are touching (99)

contaminant content that is harmful to humans, other animals, and the environment (318)

criterion (pl. criteria) standard rule or test on which a decision or judgement can be based (169)

cytoplasm jelly-like material that fills the cell and surrounds the organelles; contains nutrients the cell needs to survive (18)

Glossary

D

density amount of mass contained in a given volume (213)

desalination process of removing salt from water (354)

diffusion movement of particles from an area of higher concentration to an area of lower concentration (26)

digestive system system made up of the mouth, salivary glands, esophagus, stomach, liver, gall bladder, pancreas, and small and large intestines; breaks food down so that nutrients can be absorbed by the blood and transported to all cells (68)

discharge release or pour out (314)

E

efficiency measurement of the useful work done by a machine compared to the work needed to operate the machine (145)

endocrine system system made up of several glands that produce hormones (69)

endoplasmic reticulum folded organelle in a cell that makes proteins (18)

energy ability to do work (107)

environmental stewardship taking action to manage, maintain, and enhance the health of the environment for current and future generations (338)

epithelial tissue tissue that covers the surface of the body and internal organs; lines the inside of some organs such as the small intestine (63)

excretory system system made up of the kidneys, ureters, bladder, and urethra; filters the blood and removes liquid waste and extra water from the body (68)

eyepiece lens of a microscope that magnifies the specimen, usually by 10 times ($10\times$) (14)

F

first-class lever lever that always has the fulcrum between the input and output forces and the output force is always in the opposite direction to the input force (e.g., pry bar) (132)

F (continued)

flow rate measure of the speed at which a fluid flows from one point to another; determined by measuring the amount of fluid that flows past a given point in a given time (213)

fluid any substance that flows (192)

fluid system group of parts, including at least one fluid, that interact with each other and function together as a whole (240)

force push or pull that acts on an object; measured in newtons (N) (98)

fresh water type of water with less than one percent dissolved salts (280)

friction force that opposes the relative motion of an object (99)

fulcrum point at which a lever is supported (132)

G

glacier mass of ice and overlying snow that moves slowly down the mountain slope under the influence of gravity (283)

Golgi apparatus folded organelle that combines proteins made by the endoplasmic reticulum and delivers them to the rest of the cell and outside the cell (18)

gravitational potential energy potential energy of an object that is able to fall (108)

gravity force of attraction between two objects because of their mass (99)

groundwater zone area where water fills all the air spaces in the soil and in the tiny cracks in the rock (282)

H

heat capacity ability of a material to absorb heat (291)

hoist fluid system that uses two pistons of different sizes to create pressure to lift a vehicle (242)

hydraulic system system that uses a liquid under pressure to transmit a force and do work (242)

I

ice sheet particularly large glacier that covers the land (284)

ideal mechanical advantage (IMA) mechanical advantage of a machine that has no friction (118)

impartial presenting facts about an issue in a fair and unbiased way (347)

impermeable that cannot be passed through (by air or water, for example) (24)

inclined plane simple machine consisting of a sloping surface on which an object can move (139)

incompressible not capable of being compressed (e.g., materials in a liquid state) (229)

input force force applied to a machine; symbolized by F_{in} (115)

integumentary system system made up of skin, hair, nails and sweat glands. The skin, hair, and nails cover and protect the body. Sweat glands are involved in maintaining normal body temperature. (68)

K

kinetic energy energy of an object in motion (108)

L

lever simple machine made up of a rigid bar that is supported at one point, the fulcrum (132)

lymphatic system system made up of lymph, lymph nodes, lymph vessels, and lymphoid tissue; protects the body and is responsible for destroying and removing any invading organisms and abnormal cells (69)

lysosome organelle that breaks down food and digests wastes (19)

M

machine any mechanical system that reduces the force required to accomplish work (113)

mass amount of matter in an object (100)

matter anything that has mass and volume (197)

mechanical advantage (MA) amount by which a machine can multiply an input force; determined by the ratio of the output force (F_{out}) to the input force (F_{in}) (116)

mechanical system group of physical parts that interact with each other and function as a whole in order to complete a task (96)

mechanism combination of simple machines working together to perform a specific function (128)

membrane thin structure that separates an interior environment from its exterior surroundings (e.g., cell membrane); organelle membranes keep different parts of the cell separate from one another (18)

microclimate area with a small localized climate variation that differs from the larger climate area around it (293)

micrograph photograph taken with a microscope (20)

microorganism organism that can only be seen under a microscope (e.g., bacteria, amoebas, and certain algae and fungi (37)

mitochondria membrane-bound organelles that break down food particles and release their stored energy into a form that the cell can use to fuel all of its activities; powerhouses of the cell (18)

multicellular describes living things made of more than one cell that rely on a variety of types of cells (specialized cells) to perform cellular functions (43)

muscle tissue tissue that allows movement (63)

muscular system system made up of skeletal muscles, including tendons and ligaments; enables movement from place to place and moves substances through the body (68)

N

nervous system system made up of the brain, spinal cord, and nerves that exist in every part of the body; sends and receives nerve messages throughout the body, and controls behaviour, movement, and processes such as digestion and circulation (68)

nervous tissue tissue that transmits and receives nerve impulses (e.g., tissue of the brain, spinal cord, nerves) (63)

non-mechanical system procedure or process designed to perform a task along with the people involved (156)

nucleus large organelle that controls all the activities in a cell, such as growth, repair, and reproduction (18)

Glossary

O

organ group of tissues in an organism that performs a specific task (62)

organ system group of two or more different organs that work together to perform one or more specific functions in the body (68)

organelle small structure (part) inside a cell that performs a specific function to meet the cell's basic needs to survive and reproduce (18)

osmosis special kind of diffusion in which a fluid (usually water) moves through a selectively permeable membrane from an area of higher concentration to an area of lower concentration (27)

output force force that a machine applies to an object; symbolized by F_{out} (115)

P

paralysis inability to move muscles (73)

particle theory of matter theory that states that all matter is made up of particles; that all particles of one substance are identical; that particles of matter are in constant motion; that temperature affects the speed at which particles move; that particles have forces of attraction between them; and that there are spaces between particles (198)

Pascal's law law that states that when force is applied to an enclosed fluid, the increase in pressure is transmitted equally to all parts of the fluid (241)

permeable that can be easily permeated or penetrated (by air or water, for example) (24)

photosynthesis process by which the chlorophyll in chloroplasts uses the Sun's energy to convert carbon dioxide and water into sugar and oxygen (51)

photosynthetic tissue tissue that transforms the Sun's energy into sugar (64)

piston disk that moves inside a cylinder (242)

Plimsoll line line painted on the hull of all cargo ships to show how heavily the ship can be safely loaded in different water conditions (221)

pneumatic system system that uses a gas, usually air, under pressure to transmit a force (244)

polar icecap sometimes used to refer to the big ice masses at the poles (284)

potential energy energy that is stored (108)

pressure amount of force applied to a given area (227)

productivity amount of output that is produced per unit of time (165)

protective tissue tissue that forms a covering on most plants to help prevent water loss and to protect the plant (64)

pulley simple machine consisting of a grooved wheel with a rope or cable looped around it; can change the direction of the force or increase the output force, depending on whether it is fixed or movable (136)

pump device that moves a fluid through or into something (245)

Q

qualitative assessment analysis made by observation (169)

quantitative assessment analysis of numerical data (169)

R

recharge refill (310)

reproductive system system made up of organs for producing offspring (69)

respiration process that involves the intake of oxygen and the discharge of carbon dioxide (68)

respiratory system system made up of the nose, trachea, and lungs, as well as the throat, larnyx, and bronchi allows oxygen from the air to enter the body and waste carbon dioxide to exit the body (68)

ribosome tiny organelle in the cell's cytoplasm that helps make proteins (18)

S

salinity amount of dissolved salts in water (280)

salt water type of water with a concentration of dissolved salts averaging 3.5% (280)

screw simple machine consisting of an inclined plane wrapped around a rod (140)

second-class lever lever that has the ouput force between the fulcrum and the input force (e.g., bottle opener) (133)

selective permeability refers to the property of a barrier, such as a cell membrane, that allows only certain substances to pass through it (24)

septic system self-contained wastewater treatment facility (325)

septic tank tank in which wastewater from all indoor sources such as toilets, sinks, and bathtubs enter (325)

simple machine machine that requires the application of a single force to do work (128)

skeletal system system made up of bones and cartilage; provides support for movement, attachment points for other tissues, and protection of other organs (e.g., the spine protects the spinal cord) (68)

slurry mixture of water and solids (193)

specialized cell cell that performs a specific function and interacts with other types of cells in the organism in order to carry out its task successfully (43)

spring scale (Newton gauge) most common force meter; consists of a spring with a hook on the end; as more force is applied to the hook, the spring stretches farther (101)

stage part of a microscope on which a slide is placed for observation (14)

sustainability ability of something to exist or be used at the same level for a long period of time without being damaged, harmed, or reduced for future use (338)

system group of individual parts or procedures that work together as a complex whole to accomplish a desired task (90)

T

thermal expansion increase in the volume of a substance in response to an increase in its temperature (200)

third-class lever lever that has the input force between the fulcrum and the output force and the input and output forces are in the same direction (e.g., garden rake) (133)

tissue group of specialized cells in an organism that have similar structure and function (62)

transport tissue tissue that contains hollow, tube-like cells that move food and water through the plant (64)

tumour mass of cells that continually reproduce but are otherwise non-functional (73)

U

unicellular describes living things made of a single cell (e.g., diatom, amoeba, paramecium) (38)

useful output work work that a machine is designed to perform (145)

V

vacuole large, membrane-bound, sac-like organelle that stores excess food, waste, and other substances required by the cell (18)

valve device that controls the flow of fluids (247)

viscosity resistance of a fluid to flow (210)

volume measure of how much space a substance takes up (197)

W

water table upper surface of the groundwater zone (282)

watershed area of land where all the water eventually drains into one main water body, such as a stream, river, wetland, lake, or ocean (286)

wedge simple machine consisting of an inclined plane that travels through an object or material (140)

weight amount of force on an object due to gravity (100)

well long, hollow shaft drilled down into an aquifer to obtain fresh water (282)

wheel and axle simple machine consisting of a shaft or axle that is attached to a larger disk called the wheel (e.g., screwdriver) (137)

work amount of effort expended when a force causes an object to move a distance and energy is transferred (106)

Index

Bold numbers indicate where the term has been defined in the text

Photo Credits and Acknowledgements

The publisher wishes to thank the following sources for photographs, illustrations, and other materials used in this book. Care has been taken to determine and locate ownership of copyright material used in this text. We will gladly receive information enabling us to rectify any errors or omissions in credits.

COVER: Warren Bolster/Getty Images

UNIT A: Pages 2-3 Grigory Dukor/Reuters/Landov; p. 4 © Roger Eritja/Alamy; p. 5 (top) © Chas/Shutterstock, (bottom) © Steve Simzer/Shutterstock; p. 6 Clive Streeter © Dorling Kindersley; p. 7 (left) © Biophoto Associates/Photo Researchers, (top right) Astrid & Hanns-Frieder Michler/Science Photo Library, (bottom right) Steve Gschmeissner/Science Photo Library; pp. 8-9 Yorgos Nikas/Stone/Getty Images; p. 10 (top) © Bettmann/Corbis, (bottom) Library of Congress/Science Photo Library; p. 11 © Vera Bogaerts/Shutterstock; p. 12 Richard Kellaway; p. 13 © Bettmann/Corbis; pp. 14-16 Ray Boudreau; p. 17 (top) © Mashe/Shutterstock, (bottom) Steve Gschmeissner/Science Photo Library; p. 18 © Biophoto Associates/Photo Researchers; p. 19 © Dr. Gopal Murti /Photo Researchers; p. 20 (left) Dr. E. Walker/Photo Science Library, (bottom) Jonathan Ashton/Science Photo Library; p. 22 Ray Boudreau; p. 24 © Workbook Stock/Jupiter Images; p. 25 (left) Eye of Science/Science Photo Library, (right) © Phototake/Alamy; p. 26 © Jaan-Martin Kuusmann/Shutterstock; p. 27 Nigel Cattlin/Photoresearchers/First Light, (insets) J.C. Revy/Science Photo Library; p. 28-29 Richard Kellaway; p. 30 © PhotoCreate/Shutterstock; p. 31 © iStockphoto, (inset left) © Image Source Black/Jupiter Images, (inset right) Steve Gschmeissner/Science Photo Library; pp. 34-35 © Photos.com/Jupiter Images; p. 36 © Jupiter Images Unlimited; p. 37 (top left) © Phototake/Alamy, (top right) © Joel Blit/Shutterstock, (bottom left) © Photos.com/Jupiter Images, (bottom right) © David Touchtone/Shutterstock; p. 38 © Emmanuel Lattes/Alamy; p. 39 (top right) John Durham/Science Photo Library. (bottom left) © Oxford Scientific/Jupiter Images, (bottom right) Hybrid Medical Animation/Science Photo Library; p. 40 (top left) Astrid & Hanns-Frieder Michler/Science Photo Library, (bottom both) © Dr. K.W. Jeon/Visuals Unlimited; p. 41 © Dennis MacDonald/Photo Edit; p. 42 Katy Williamson © Dorling Kindersley; p. 43 (top right) © Arco Images/Alamy, (bottom left to right) © Lee Torrens/Shutterstock, © Four Oaks/Shutterstock, © AbleStock/Jupiter Images; p. 44 (top) © Wolfgang Pölzer/Alamy, (bottom) © Stephen Finn/Shutterstock; p. 45 (top right) © Phototake/Alamy, (bottom left to right) Biophoto Associates/Photo Researchers/First Light, © Image Source Black/Jupiter Images, Pearson Education/PH College; p. 46 (top left to right) © Phototake/Alamy, © PureStock/Jupiter Images, © Phototake/Alamy, (bottom left to right) John Durham/Science Photo Library, © M I (Spike) Walker/Alamy, Dr. Jeremy Burgess/Science Photo Library; p. 47 Dave King © Dorling Kindersley; p. 48 Ray Boudreau; p. 50 Adam Hart-Davis/Science Photo Library; p. 51 © Oxford Scientific/Jupiter Images; p. 52 Dan Wright © Dorling Kindersley; p. 53 © Phototake/Alamy; p. 54 Will & Deni McIntyre/Science Photo Library; p. 55 (top) © Phototake/Alamy, (bottom) © Creatas/Jupiter Images; pp. 58-59 © Black Star/Alamy; p. 60 (top) CP Photo/Frank Gunn, (bottom) © Radu

Razvan/Shutterstock; p. 63 (centre) PatitucciPhoto/Aurora/Getty Images, (clockwise from top left) © Phototake/Alamy, CNRI/Science Photo Library, Eric V. Grave/Photo Researchers/First Light, © Jubal Harshaw/Shutterstock; p. 64 (all) Steve Gschmeissner/Science Photo Library; p. 65 © PeterG/Shutterstock; p. 66 (left) Simon Fraser, Royal Victoria Infirmary/Science Photo Library, (right) Dr. P. Marazzi/Science Photo Library; p. 67 Lunagrafix/Photo Researchers/First Light; p. 70 © PhotoObjects/Jupiter Images; p. 72 © Phototake/Alamy; p. 73 (top) © Phototake/Alamy, (bottom) © Image Source Pink/Jupiter Images; p. 74 Mike Cassese/Reuters/Landov; p. 75 (top) Scott Camazine/ Photo Researchers/First Light, (bottom) David Greedy/Getty Images News; p. 77 © David Olsen/Alamy; p. 79 (top left) Discovery Channel Canada © CTVglobemedia, (top right) Jay Ingram, (bottom) © Visual & Written SL/Alamy; p. 81 Peter Jones/Reuters/Landov; p. 83 © Blend Images/Jupiter Images; p. 84 (bottom left) © Dr. Gopal Murti /Photo Researchers (bottom right) © Biophoto Associates/Photo Researchers; p. 85 (both) Ray Boudreau; p. 85 (counter-clockwise from top left) © Phototake/Alamy, © Jubal Harshaw/Shutterstock, Eric V. Grave/Photo Researchers/First Light, CNRI/Science Photo Library, Steve Gschmeissner/Science Photo Library, Steve Gschmeissner/Science Photo Library, Steve Gschmeissner/Science Photo Library.

UNIT B: Pages 88-89 © AbleStock/Jupiter Images; p. 90 Peter Menzel/Science Photo Library; p. 91 (both) Courtesy of The Centre for Minimal Access Surgery; p. 93 (top) © Brand X/Jupiter Images, (centre) © Racheal Grazias/Shutterstock, (bottom) © Stephen Coburn/Shutterstock; p. 94-95 © Stefan Sollfors/Alamy; p. 96 (top) © Ponch Hawkes 2007. Circus Oz - the group bike, (bottom) © Tor Eigeland/Alamy; p. 97 © Howard Sayer/Alamy; p. 99 (top) CP Photo/Adrian Wyld, (centre) © Amoz Eckerson/Visuals Unlimited, (bottom both) © sciencephotos/Alamy; p. 100 NASA; p. 101 (top) Andrew Lambert Photography/Science Photo Library, (bottom) Ray Boudreau; p. 106 (left to right) © Larry St. Pierre/Shutterstock, © Photo Objects, © BananaStock/Jupiter Images; p. 107 © Oleksii/Shutterstock; p. 108 (left) © Comstock/Jupiter Images, (centre clockwise) © Comstock, © iStockphoto, © Corbis RF/Jupiter Images, © Comstock, © Thinkstock/Jupiter Images; p. 109 CP Photo/AP Photo/John Miller; p. 113 © Richard Griffin/Shutterstock; p. 114 (centre) © Jaimie Duplass/Shutterstock, (bottom) © Brand X/Jupiter Images; p. 115 (top) © Eric Nathan/Alamy, (bottom) Shawn Frederick/Image Bank/Getty Images; p. 117 (top) © Brian Mitchell/Photofusion Picture Library/Alamy, (bottom) Ray Boudreau; p. 119 © liquidlibrary/Jupiter Images; p. 121 © David Young-Wolff/Photo Edit; p. 123 (left) Courtesy of John Martin Rare Book Room, University of Iowa, (right) © Ed Eckstein/Corbis, (bottom) © Alessandro Di Meo/epa/Corbis; p. 124 (top) © Stephen Coburn/Shutterstock, (bottom) © liquidlibrary/Jupiter Images; pp. 126-127 Steve Mason/Photodisc/Getty Images; p. 128 © Eitan Simanor/Alamy, (bottom) Philip Gatward © Dorling Kindersley; p. 129 Susanna Price © Dorling Kindersley; p. 130 © franck camhi/Shutterstock; p. 131 Danita Delimont/ DanitaDelimont.com; p. 132 Richard Haynes/Prentice Hall School Division; p. 133 (top) Image Source/Jupiter Images, (bottom) © David Young-Wolff/Photo Edit; p. 135 (left to right) Laima Druskis/Pearson Education/PH College, © iStockphoto, Steve Gorton © Dorling Kindersley; p. 136 (top) © Tan

pp. 306-307 © Wade H. Massie/Shutterstock; p. 308 (top) Dr. Kari Lounatmaa/Science Photo Library, (bottom) CP Photo/Frank Gunn; p. 312 Saul Porto/Reuters/Landov; 314 (top) David Cooper/Toronto Star/First Light, (bottom) CP Photo/Larry MacDougal; p. 315 Richard Kellaway; p. 317 © Con Tanasiuk/Design Pics/Corbis Royalty Free; p. 318 (top) Moredun Scientific Ltd./Science Photo Library, (centre) © iStockphoto, (bottom) © Helene Rogers/Alamy; p. 319 Nora Alexander; p. 321 © Javier Larrea/maXximages.com; p. 326 Courtesy of Andrew Hellebust, P.Eng., Toronto; p. 327 Burger/Phanie/First Light; p. 329 (top) Courtesy of Trout Unlimited Canada's the Yellow Fish Road Program™, (bottom) Nora Alexander; p. 331 © Mark Romesser/Alamy; p. 333 (both) Becky Hester; pp. 336-337 © Comstock/Jupiter Images; p. 338 Georg Gerster/ Photo Researchers/First Light; p. 339 (top to bottom) © Howard Sandler/Shutterstock, © Allen Blake Sheldon/maXximages.com, © Rubberball/Jupiter Images, © Robert Brook/Alamy; p. 340 © JoLin/Shutterstock; p. 342 (top) Andrew Stawicki/Toronto Star, (bottom) Nora Alexander; p. 343 © Esseuve/maXximages.com; p. 346 Daniel Frykholm/Reuters; p. 348 (top) © David Young-Wolff/Photo Edit, (bottom) Xinhua/Landov; p. 349 (top) © SNEHIT/Shutterstock, (bottom) © photocanada.com/G. Daigle; p. 350 Nora Alexander; p. 353 (top) © Jason Lindsey/Alamy, (bottom) Paul S. Howell/Getty Images News; p. 354 GE Water & Process Technologies; p. 357 (top left) Discovery Channel Canada © CTVglobemedia, (top right) Jay Ingram, (bottom) © liquidlibrary/Jupiter Images; p. 365 (top left) © Photos.com/Jupiter Images, (top right) © Radius/Jupiter Images, (bottom left) © Photos.com/Jupiter Images, (bottom right) © Stock Image/Jupiter Images.